MATHEMATICAL METHODS
FOR THE STUDY OF
AUTOMATIC CONTROL SYSTEMS

MATHEMATICAL METHODS FOR THE STUDY OF AUTOMATIC CONTROL SYSTEMS

by

V. I. ZUBOV

TRANSLATED FROM THE RUSSIAN

by

YAAKOV SCHORR-KON

B.Sc., IRE, ACM

Translation Editor

DAVID P. GELFAND

A PERGAMON PRESS BOOK

THE MACMILLAN COMPANY
NEW YORK
1963

Distributed in the Western Hemisphere by
THE MACMILLAN COMPANY · NEW YORK
pursuant to a special agreement with
PERGAMON PRESS LIMITED
Oxford, England

Originally published under the title
Matematischeskiye metody issledovanya sistem
avtomaticheskego regulirovaniya
Sudpromgiz, Leningrad 1959

Library of Congress Card Number 62–9186

PRINTED IN ISRAEL
BY JERUSALEM ACADEMIC PRESS LTD.
JERUSALEM, ISRAEL

CONTENTS

PREFACE TO THE ENGLISH EDITION

THE present book contains an account of certain qualitative methods of investigation of automatic control systems, as also a study of methods of application of electronic computers for the solution of various problems in the analysis and design of such systems.

This is not a textbook in the usual sense of the word, but rather a scientific monograph which should prove useful to a large circle of specialists. The author will consider his object achieved if the book helps some readers to develop further mechanical and analytical methods for the study of automatic control systems and provides hints for their practical work.

I consider it a pleasant duty to express my sincere gratitude to colleagues who have prepared this English edition, and also to A. C. Lowell, V. R. Andrievskii, V. M. Yesipov, V. I. Chernetskii, V. R. Petukhov, who have rendered considerable assistance in reading the proofs.

V. I. ZUBOV

Leningrad

PREFACE TO THE RUSSIAN EDITION

WITHIN the last few years, in the theory of automatic control, problems have appeared which led to the study of the behaviour of integral curves of non-linear nonstationary systems of ordinary differential equations. These problems follow from the consideration of the behaviour of transient processes relative to the steady state. Estimate of the deviation of the transient processes from this steady state, termination time of the transient process, probabilistic characteristics of that transient process where the control system bears the influence of random forces — these are the basic indices which have an important practical value.

Beginning with the works of Vyshnegradskiy for studying the behaviour of transient processes relative to the steady state, they began making use of the theory of stability. In the event that the systems of equations under consideration are stationary, in the noncritical cases, one manages to clarify relatively simply whether the transient processes in an automatic control system are damped out or not. If the transient processes are damped out, then a question of practical importance arises as to the shape of the region of initial perturbations for which the transient processes possess the indicated property, i.e. after solving the local problem of stability of the steady state there arises the problem of finding the region of attraction. If the system of equations is non-stationary and one may not neglect the influence of time, the solution of the problems described above becomes considerably more complicated.

In the present work basic attention is given to the following problems:

1) investigation of the stability of steady motions in nonstationary systems;
2) estimation of the deviations of the transient processes from the steady motions;
3) construction of solutions of some nonstationary systems of differential equations, to the investigation of which a rather wide class of automatic control systems is reduced;
4) finding of the probabilistic characteristics of transient stochastic processes;
5) investigation of the stability of steady motions in critical cases;
6) finding the regions of stability in the space of initial conditions and in the space of admissible values of the parameters.

To facilitate the reading of the present work we shall give a short summary of the contents of each chapter.

Chapter I is concerned with the development of the second method of Lyapunov; in it theorems are proposed for the solution of the problem of stability of steady motions in the small, and also theorems which allow one to find the region of attraction of the steady motion. In the scientific literature on the theory of stability of motion for nonstationary systems, the theorems so far presented have given only the sufficient conditions for stability.

In this chapter the fundamental theorems are of a necessary and sufficient nature and, besides, in a series of cases the constraining requirements are removed from the Lyapunov function, as follows: the presence of an infinitely small upper bound, the negative definiteness of the total derivative as based on the system, and so on. In § 5 of this chapter a method is expounded allowing one, in general, to find the region of attraction up to any accuracy. This is very important since, in producing real systems, one has recourse to unjustified material investments because the dimensions of the region of attraction are not definitely known.

Chapter II is concerned with the study of linear systems of differential equations with variable coefficients. Considerable attention is given to the estimation of the deviation of the transient process from the position of equilibrium. These estimates allow one to make judgments as to stability even in the case when an infinitely small upper bound for the Lyapunov function, positive definiteness of that function, and also the constancy of sign of its derivative may all be absent.

In this chapter a method is given for representing the exact and approximate solutions of some linear systems of differential equations. In §§ 6, 7, and 9 it is shown that a series of nonstationary systems of differential equations, in studying the stability problem, may be analysed just as simply as linear systems with constant coefficients. In § 11 a method is proposed for finding the regions of stability in the space of admissible values of the system parameters. This method is new and is not connected with the construction of a characteristic polynomial. Its application allows the solution of the indicated problem by means of electronic computers, since it consists in finding the powers of some matrix.

In Chapter III a method is exposed for estimating the deviations of the transient process from the steady motion of a nonlinear system. These estimates allow one to give the condition for stability of nonlinear systems and to determine the damping time of the transient process, and also to judge the technical stability of the steady motion. Also given here is a theorem on the stability in a finite time interval, and the problem of stability in the first approximation in ordinary systems and in systems with lag is considered.

In Chapter IV a method is given for constructing the solution of a nonlinear system of equations in the neighbourhood of a regular singular point. The solutions of these systems are represented as a series, from whose form one can easily judge the behaviour of the solutions in the direct neighbourhood of the singular point. The problem, whose solution is presented here, was posed as early as 1856 in a work by the French mathematicians Briot and Bouquet. For one equation, this problem has been solved by Poincaré, and a series of special cases of systems has been analysed by Picard. In this chapter the problem solved in general form, in its classical formulation, is presented. It should be noted that a rather wide class of nonlinear nonstationary automatic control systems is reduced, with the help of a series of substitutions, to systems of this type. The problem of stability of the steady motion in this case is, with the help of the above-mentioned series, reduced to the investigation of real parts of the roots of some characteristic equation, or else to the finding of the regions of stability in the space of admissible values of the parameters, as shown in § 11.

Chapter V is devoted to the study of the influence of constantly acting perturbations upon transient processes. The theorems on stability under constantly acting perturbations, known from the theory of stability of motion, do not afford the possibility of estimating the actual deviations of the transient process from the steady motion under the action of these perturbations.

In this chapter a method allowing one to find these deviations is presented. If the constantly acting perturbations are of an accidental nature, then the transient processes become stochastic. In § 19 a method is given of constructing a complete system of correlation functions for the transient stochastic process.

The above-mentioned method consists in the finding of correlation functions of the transient stochastic process by means of infinite series containing correlation functions describing the random constantly acting perturbations. These series may be truncated, and then one obtains approximate formulae for the correlation functions suitable for use. In the last section of this chapter we present a method for estimating the correlation functions of a transient process in terms of the correlation functions of constantly acting perturbations.

Chapter VI is devoted to the problem, known for its complexity, of the stability of steady motion in the critical cases, i.e. in those cases when the linear approximation does not allow one to solve the problem of stability.

This chapter contains the development of the ideas of A. M. Lyapunov and I. G. Malkin, as well as a general method of solving the above problem. This method consists in dividing the investigated system of equations into two groups and studying these groups separately. § 23 contains a series of new assumptions allowing one to push forward the problem of investigating the stability in doubtful cases. In it the solution of the following problem is given.

Let the right-hand members of the system of equations have no linear terms in the series expansion about the steady motion, i.e. their expansion begins with homogeneous forms of an order higher than the first. Requisite are the necessary and sufficient conditions for the coefficients of these forms, for which the steady motion will be asymptotically stable. These conditions are included in the Lyapunov functions, which are constructed in finite aspect in terms of these forms.

It should be noted, however, that the problem solved in § 23 is more general than the one described above: as the first approximation one may put functions with generalized homogeneity of the class $(m_1, m_2, ..., m_n)$ of order m. These new assumptions allow one, in particular, to push forward considerably the solution of the problem of stability in the case when among the roots of the characteristic equation there are k zero roots, and to these correspond simple elementary divisors.

Chapter VII is devoted to the study of cases of the appearance of periodic motions in nonlinear systems. In § 25 the characteristic behaviour of transient processes in systems, in the presence of self-oscillations is considered. In § 26 we study the appearance of periodic oscillations under the action of an external perturbing force, and give a method of successive approximations for finding these periodic states of the system. In § 27 the cases of appearance of periodic and almost-periodic motions in nonlinear autonomous systems are investigated.

Chapter VIII is devoted to the application of electronic computers to the study of automatic control systems.

The appearance of the present work would have been impossible without the active help of Yu. O. Shternberg, V. K. Chesnokov, V. V. Khomenyuk, B. I. Korobochkin, and L. T. Tarushkina, to whom the author expresses his deep gratitude. The author will be very thankful for all critical remarks and suggestions.

CHAPTER I

GENERAL THEOREMS ON STABILITY OF MOTION

§ 1. Formulation of the problem of stability of motion — Basic definitions

LET US assume that some mechanical system is described by means of a system of ordinary n-th order differential equations of the form

$$\frac{dx_s}{dt} = f_s(t, x_1, \ldots, x_n), \tag{1.1}$$

whose right-hand members are given in the domain

$$0 \leq t < \infty,$$
$$-\infty < x_s < +\infty \quad (s = 1, \ldots, n)$$

and are continuous there.

In that case, as follows from the theory of ordinary differential equations [1], to each choice of real numbers $t_0, x_{10}, \ldots, x_{n0}$ from the above indicated domain there correspond n functions

$$x_s = x_s(t, x_{10}, \ldots, x_{n0}, t_0) \quad (s = 1, \ldots, n), \tag{1.2}$$

continuously differentiable with respect to t and satisfying system (1.1) and the conditions

$$x_s = x_{s0} \text{ for } t = t_0 \quad (s = 1, \ldots, n).$$

Let us assume that (with some choice of the quantities $t_0, x_{10}, \ldots, x_{n0}$) the mechanical system by its properties defines some motion which is described by functions (1.2) and is called free [unforced, undisturbed].

DEFINITION 1. A free motion (1.2) is called stable, in the sense of Lyapunov [2], if for any $\varepsilon > 0$ one can indicate a number $\delta(t_0, \varepsilon) > 0$ such that if

$$\sum_{i=1}^{n} (x_{i0} - x'_{i0})^2 < \delta^2$$

then

$$\sum_{i=1}^{n} [x_i(t, x_{10}, \ldots, x_{n0}, t_0) - x_i(t, x'_{10}, \ldots, x'_{n0}, t_0)]^2 < \varepsilon^2 \text{ for all } t \geq t_0.$$

5

If the property opposite to stability holds, then one says that the free motion is unstable in the sense of Lyapunov.

More precisely:

DEFINITION 2. A free motion (1.2) is called unstable in the sense of Lyapunov if there exists at least one number $\varepsilon > 0$ which, for any chosen number $\delta > 0$, implies the existence of a choice of numbers $x'_{10}, \ldots, x'_{n0}, t_0$, such that if

$$\sum_{i=1}^{n} (x_{i0} - x'_{i0})^2 < \delta^2$$

then

$$\sum_{i=1}^{n} [x_i(t, x_{10}, \ldots, x_{n0}, t_0) - x_i(t, x'_{10}, \ldots, x'_{n0}, t_0)]^2 \geq \varepsilon^2$$

for at least one value of $t > t_0$.

The direct analysis of the free motion usually leads to the investigation of the homogeneous solution of the system of ordinary differential equations. For this purpose, in system (1.1) one performs the substitution

$$x_s = y_s + x_s(t, x_{10}, \ldots, x_{n0}, t_0) \quad (s = 1, \ldots, n), \tag{1.3}$$

where the y_s are new sought functions, sometimes called the forcing or perturbing functions. As a result of this substitution, one obtains the so-called perturbed system of differential equations

$$\frac{dy_s}{dt} = g_s(t, y_1, \ldots, y_n) \quad (s = 1, \ldots, n), \tag{1.4}$$

which is obtained from system (1.1) in the following way. Taking into account that the functions x_s in equalities (1.3) satisfy system (1.1), we shall differentiate these equalities through with respect to t. Then we shall obtain

$$\frac{dx_s}{dt} = \frac{dy_s}{dt} + \frac{d}{dt} x_s(t, x_{10}, \ldots, x_{n0}, t_0)$$

or

$$f_s(t, x_1, \ldots, x_n) - f_s[t, x_1(t, x_{10}, \ldots, x_{n0}, t_0) \ldots x_n(t, x_{10}, \ldots, x_{n0}, t_0)] = \frac{dy_s}{dt},$$

whence finally we have

$$\frac{dy_s}{dt} = f_s[t, x_1(t, x_{10}, \ldots, x_{n0}, t_0) + y_1, \ldots, x_n(t, x_{10}, \ldots, x_{n0}, t_0) + y_n] -$$
$$- f_s[t, x_1(t, x_{10}, \ldots, x_{n0}, t_0), \ldots, x_n(t, x_{10}, \ldots, x_{n0}, t_0)] = g_s(t, y_1, \ldots, y_n).$$

As can be seen from the last formula, the functions $g_s(t, y_1, \ldots, y_n)$, found in the right-hand member of system (1.4), are given generally in the domain $t \geq 0$; $-\infty < y_s < +\infty$ $(s = 1, \ldots, n)$ and are continuous there.

The free motion (1.2) of system (1.1) through transforming (1.3) is reduced to the homogeneous solution of system (1.4). In what follows, the entire theory will be expounded in conformity with the investigation of the stability of the homogeneous solution of system (1.4). It is therefore worthwhile to formulate separately the definitions of stability for the homogeneous solution of system (1.4).

DEFINITION 3. The homogeneous solution of system (1.4) is called stable in the sense of Lyapunov if for any $\varepsilon > 0$ one can indicate a number $\delta(t_0, \varepsilon) > 0$ such that if

$$\sum_{i=1}^{n} y_{i0}^2 < \delta^2,$$

then

$$\sum_{i=1}^{n} y_i^2(t, y_{10}, \ldots, y_{n0}, t_0) < \varepsilon^2 \text{ for all } t \geq t_0.$$

If in addition

$$\sum_{i=1}^{n} y_i^2(t, y_{10}, \ldots, y_{n0}) \to 0 \text{ as } t \to +\infty,$$

then we shall call the homogeneous solution of system (1.4) asymptotically stable.

If in Definition 3, in the case of stability, the number $\delta(t_0, \varepsilon)$ may be chosen independent of t_0, then one says that the homogeneous solution of system (1.4) is uniformly stable with respect to $t_0 \geq 0$.

DEFINITION 4. The homogeneous solution of system (1.4) is called uniformly asymptotically stable if for any $\varepsilon > 0$ one can indicate a number $\delta(\varepsilon) > 0$ such that if

$$\sum_{i=1}^{n} y_{i0}^2 < \delta^2,$$

then

$$\sum_{i=1}^{n} y_i^2 < \varepsilon^2 \text{ for all } t \geq t_0,$$

and

$$\sum_{i=1}^{n} y_i^2 \to 0 \text{ as } t - t_0 \to +\infty,$$

uniformly relative to the quantities $t_0, y_{10}, \ldots, y_{n0}$.

In Definitions 3 and 4, and in everything that follows, we shall denote by

$$y_s = y_s(t, y_0, \ldots, y_{n0}, t_0) \quad (s = 1, \ldots, n) \tag{1.5}$$

a system of functions satisfying equations (1.4) and the conditions $y_s = y_{s0}$ at $t = t_0$.

In the case of asymptotic stability all the solutions of system (1.4) which start in a sufficiently small neighbourhood of the point $y_1 = y_2 = \ldots = y_n = 0$ tend toward a position of equilibrium as $t \to +\infty$. However, the character of this approach may depend essentially on the choice of the initial condition $t_0, y_{10}, \ldots, y_{n0}$. In the case that such a narrow dependence is not observed we shall call the homogeneous solution uniformly attracting.

More precisely:

DEFINITION 5. An asymptotically stable homogeneous solution of system (1.4) is called uniformly attracting, if for a given number $h > 0$ one can indicate numbers $\alpha > 0$, $T > 0$ such that if

$$\sum_{i=1}^{n} y_{i0}^2 > h^2,$$

then

$$\sum_{i=1}^{n} y_i^2(t, y_{10}, \ldots, y_{n0}, t_0) > \alpha^2 \text{ for } t_0 \leqq t \leqq t_0 + T.$$

If the homogeneous solution of system (1.4) has the property opposite to that of stability, then one says that the homogeneous solution of system (1.4) is unstable. The exact definition of this state of affairs may be easily derived from Definition 2.

We shall now carry out a preliminary analysis of the concepts of stability, asymptotic stablity, and the instability of the homogeneous solution of system (1.4) by a critique of the definitions given above, as applied to concrete examples.

In order not to encumber this preliminary analysis by calculations extraneous to the issue, we shall consider one linear equation of the form

$$\frac{dy}{dt} = g(t)\, y, \tag{1.6}$$

where $g(t)$ is a function given for $t \geqq 0$ and piecewise-continuous in the interval $[0, \infty]$. (More precisely, in every finite interval it may have only a finite number of discontinuities of the first kind.)

The general solution of equation (1.6) has the form

$$y = e^{\int_{t_0}^{t} g(\tau)d\tau} \, y_0. \tag{1.7}$$

The homogeneous solution of system (1.6) is stable if and only if the function $\int_{t_0}^{t} g(\tau)d\tau$ is bounded for $t \geqq 0$. The case of stability may be clarified by Fig 1.

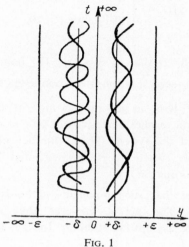

FIG. 1

In fact, we shall show that the boundedness of $\int_{t_0}^{t} g(\tau)d\tau$ implies stability. If the function is bounded, then

$$e^{\int_{t_0}^{t} g(\tau)d\tau} < k < +\infty.$$

We shall take $\varepsilon > 0$ and $\delta \leqq \varepsilon/k$. Then for $|y_0| \leqq \delta$ we shall have

$$|y| \leqq e^{\int_{t_0}^{t} g(\tau)d\tau} \delta < k\delta < \varepsilon_1.$$

Hence, it follows that the homogeneous solution of system (1.6) is stable.

If in some real system the presence of stability of the free motion has been established, then this in itself still need not denote the well-behaved nature of the chosen system. We shall demonstrate this by a numerical example.

Let

$$g(t) = \begin{cases} \ln 10 & \text{for } 0 \leqq t \leqq 10; \\ 0 & \text{for } t > 10. \end{cases}$$

Then the solution of system (1.6) satisfying the condition $y = y_0$ for $t = 0$ has the form

$$y(t) = \begin{cases} 10^t y_0 \text{ for } 0 \leq t \leq 10, \\ 10^{10} y_0 \text{ for } t > 10. \end{cases}$$

From the above it follows that in this case the homogeneous solution of equation (1.6) is stable, since $\int_{t_0}^{t} g(\tau)d(\tau)$ is bounded. However, for initial deviations in y_0 of 10^{-5}, lying in general beyond the limits of accuracy of measurement, the motion reaches deviations of 10^5, going beyond the bounds of the possible states of the system. Thus, the fact of stability may have a technical value only when it is supplemented by estimates limiting quantity ε in relation to quantity δ.

At first it may seem that such a conclusion holds only in relation to nonasymptotic stability. The fact is, however, that analogous conclusions hold also in the case of asymptotic stability. Indeed, let us assume

$$g(t) = \begin{cases} \ln 10 \text{ for } 0 \leq t \leq 10, \\ -1 \text{ for } t > 10. \end{cases}$$

Then the solution of equation (1.6) with the initial conditions $y = y_0$ for $t = t_0$ has the form

$$y(t) = \begin{cases} 10^t y_0 \text{ for } 0 \leq t \leq 10, \\ 10^{10} e^{(10-t)} y_0 \text{ for } t > 10. \end{cases}$$

It is clear that $y(t) \to 0$ as $t \to +\infty$ according to the exponential law. Nevertheless, with initial deviations in $|y_0| < 10^{-5}$, even at the instant $t = 20$, deviations in $|y|$ of $10^5 e^{-10} \approx 3$ are reached, which may also turn out to be inadmissible.

We shall now illustrate the concept of asymptotic stability by example (1.6). In order for the homogeneous solution of system (1.6) to be asymptotically stable, it is necessary and sufficient that $\int_{t_0}^{t} g(\tau)d\tau \to -\infty$ as $t \to +\infty$, and this is demonstrated, just as above without difficulty.

The behaviour of the solution is given in Fig. 2.

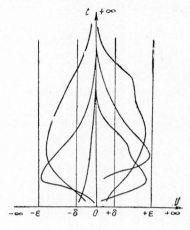

FIG. 2

In the case of uniform asymptotic stability, the behaviour of the solution is conventionally represented in Fig. 3. This Figure illustrates the fact that in the

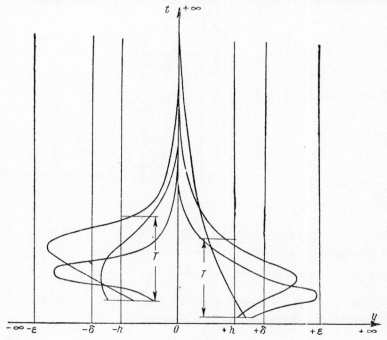

FIG. 3

case of uniform asymptotic stability, for any number $0 < h < \delta$ one can indicate a number $T > 0$ such that if

$$\sum_{i=1}^{n} y_{i0}^2 < \delta^2$$

then

$$\sum_{i=1}^{n} y_i^2(t, y_{10}, \ldots, y_{n0}, t_0) < h^2 \text{ for } t \geqq t_0 + T.$$

Fig. 4 shows the case when the homogeneous solution of system (1.6) is uniformly attracting.

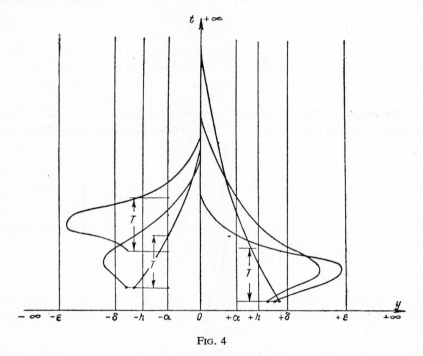

FIG. 4

We shall now turn to the analysis of the concept of instability.

The homogeneous solution of system (1.6) is unstable if, and only if, the function $\int_{t_0} g(\tau)d\tau$ is not bounded from above as $t \to +\infty$.

If it turns out that the free motion in a real system is unstable, this still does not mean that that system is unserviceable.

We shall clarify this with the help of our example.

Let

$$g(t) = \begin{cases} -1 \text{ for } 0 \le t \le 100, \\ 10 \text{ for } t > 100. \end{cases}$$

Then the solution $y(t)$ of system (1.6) with the initial conditions $y = y_0$ for $t = 0$ has the form

$$y(t) = \begin{cases} e^{-t}y_0 \text{ for } 0 \le t \le 100, \\ e^{-100+10(t-100)} \text{ for } t > 100. \end{cases}$$

If the time of action T of the real system under consideration is limited to 20 seconds, then despite the manifest instability, within the time interval under consideration the system performs very satisfactorily.

Thus the fact of instability taken by itself, as well as the fact of stability, cannot serve as the final criterion of serviceability of a given real system.

The analysis carried out above of the mathematical concepts of stability and instability refers, in general, to the case when the right-hand part of system (1.4) contain an explicitly independent variable t.

In real systems described by equations (1.4), whose right-hand parts explicitly depend on time, the character of the process behaviour is usually considered in a finite time interval $[0, T]$.

In addition, the right-hand parts of system (1.4) depend on some structural parameters $\lambda_1, ..., \lambda_m$.

DEFINITION 6. The homogeneous solution of system (1.4) is called technically stable if the following conditions are fulfilled:

1) there exist two sets G^{t_0} and G^t in the n-dimensional space $y_1, ..., y_n$, $t \in (t_0, t_0 + T)$;

2) there exists a region Φ in the space of admissible values of the parameters $\lambda_1, ..., \lambda_m$, such that the integral curves of system (1.4) which start at $t = t_0$ in the set G^{t_0} fall within the set G^t for $t \in (t_0, t_0 + T)$.

The set Φ is determined by the choice of the sets G^{t_0} and G^t. This dependence may be expressed in one of the following ways.

1. Given are sets G^t and Φ. It is required to find set G^{t_0}. This case includes the classical concept of stability (see Def. 3) and is encountered in the analysis of real systems.

2. Given are sets G^{t_0} and Φ. It is required to find set G^t. This case may occur when from a given set of initial deviations in the analysis of a given system one wishes to determine the state of that system at the instant T.

3. Given are sets G^{t_0} and G^t. It is required to determine set Φ. This problem is encountered in the synthesis of real systems. The set G^t is defined by the nature of the system being synthesized and the set G^{t_0}—by the technical conditions of its functioning.

The problem before us consists in finding the conditions for stability in the sense of Lyapunov and of the conditions for technical stability, as well as in est'mating the deviations of the perturbed motion from the free (unperturbed) one. In what follows, it is also necessary to clarify the influence of constantly acting factors upon stable systems, such as the influence of random processes upon the functioning of real systems.

§ 2. Two methods in the solution of the stability problem—Lyapunov functions

A. M. Lyapunov has proposed two methods for the solution of the problem of stability of the homogeneous solution of a system of form (1.4). These are the so-called first and second methods of Lyapunov.

The essence of the first method consists in the constructing of the general solution of system (1.4) in the form of series and in the investigation of the problem of stability of the homogeneous solution of system (1.4) directly from its outer form. We shall give a more detailed characterization of that method.

Let us assume that system (1.4) has the form

$$\frac{dy_s}{dt} = \sum_{i=1}^{n} p_{si}(t)y_i + \sum_{m_1+m_2+\ldots+m_n > 1} p_s^{(m_1,\ldots,m_n)}(t)y_1^{m_1},\ldots,y_n^{m_n}$$

$$(s = 1,\ldots,n), \tag{2.1}$$

where $p_{si}(t)$ and $p_s^{(m_1,\ldots,m_n)}(t)$ are real continuous bounded functions given for $t \geqq 0$. However, these functions may be piecewise-continuous, having in every finite time interval a finite number of discontinuities of the first kind, just as the right-hand members in system (1.4). In that case, at the point of discontinuity of the coefficients, the derivatives dy_s/dt are understood to be one-sided.

We shall consider that the series in the right-hand members of system (2.1) converge in the region $t \geqq 0$; $|y_s| \leqq \delta \leqq$ const; $0 < \delta$.

A. M. Lyapunov has proposed to construct the general solution of this system in the form of a series

$$y_s = \sum_{m_1+m_2+\ldots+m_n \geq 1} L_s^{(m_1, m_2, \ldots, m_n)}(t) e^{-\sum_{i=1}^{n} m_i \lambda_i t} c_1^{m_1} c_2^{m_2} \ldots c_n^{m_n}$$

$$(s = 1, \ldots, n), \tag{2.2}$$

where the λ_i $(i = 1, \ldots, n)$ are the characteristic numbers of the linear system

$$\frac{dy_s}{dt} = \sum_{i=1}^{n} p_{si}(t) y_i \quad (s = 1, \ldots, n), \tag{2.3}$$

which forms the first approximation of system (2.1).

The functions $L_s^{(m_1, \ldots, m_n)}(t)$ in series (2.2) are continuous, given for $t \geq 0$ and satisfy the conditions

$$L_s^{(m_1, \ldots, m_n)}(t) e^{-\alpha t} \to 0 \text{ as } t \to +\infty \text{ for any number } \alpha > 0.$$

If the characteristic numbers of system (2.3) are positive and system (2.3) is correct, then series (2.2) converge for $t \geq 0$ and $|c_s| < \gamma$ $(s = 1, \ldots, n)$, where γ is a positive constant.

In that case from the outer form of these series it is easy to establish that the homogeneous solution of system (2.1) is asymptotically stable.

If even one characteristic number, for example λ_1, is negative, then to it corresponds a solution represented in the form of the series

$$y_s = \sum_{m_1=1} L_s^{m_1}(t) e^{-\lambda_1 m_1 t} c_1^{m_1} \quad (s = 1, \ldots, n), \ \lambda_1 < 0, \tag{2.4}$$

converging when $|c_1| < \gamma, \gamma > 0$.

From the outer form of the series it follows that the homogeneous solution of system (2.1), which in this case we consider as independent of t, is unstable.

Thus the problem of stability according to the first method will be solved if one manages to find the characteristic numbers [2] of system (2.3). In the general case, however, there exist no recommendations allowing one to find them even approximately. An exception is formed by the case when all the functions p_{si} are constant. As is known, in that case the numbers $\lambda_1, \ldots, \lambda_n$ coincide with the real parts of the roots of the characteristic equation, taken with the opposite sign.

From the above it can be seen that the first method in the form which had been proposed by Lyapunov may be applied only in the case when system (1.4) is presented in form (2.1), and then one can determine the characteristic numbers of system (2.3). Whereas the first requirement

imposed by this method upon system (1.4) may be satisfied in a large number of cases, the second requirement is equivalent to the solution of the problem of the stability of the homogeneous solution of system (1.4), and therefore causes considerable difficulties in the application of this method.

If, however, the general solution is sought not in the form of series (2.2), then one manages to get around the difficulties associated with the finding of the characteristic numbers of the first approximation. This modification of the first method will be expounded in what follows.

We shall now briefly expound the essence of the second method of Lyapunov, and also dwell upon those mathematical tools which are principally used in its application.

For greater clarity of the exposition we shall consider a simple example. Given (say) is the system of equations

$$\left. \begin{array}{l} \dfrac{dx}{dt} = a_{11}(t)\,x + a_{12}(t)y, \\[2mm] \dfrac{dy}{dt} = a_{21}(t)\,x + a_{22}(t)y. \end{array} \right\} \tag{2.5}$$

One wishes to establish the conditions imposed upon functions $a_{jk}(t)$ $(i, k = 1, 2)$ under which the homogeneous solution of system (2.5) is stable, or asymptotically stable, in the sense of Definition 3. We shall consider functions $a_{ik}(t)$ as given for $t \geq 0$, and to be piecewise-continuous, having in any finite interval a finite number of discontinuities of the first kind.

To solve the proposed problem we shall take function $V(x, y) = x^2 + y^2$. We shall choose any solution $x = x(t)$; $y = y(t)$ of system (2.5) and evaluate the function chosen by us upon this solution. Then we shall obtain

$$V[x(t),\ y(t)] = x^2(t) + y^2(t) = V_1(t).$$

Thus, on the curve under consideration, function $V(x, y)$ turns into a function of the argument t. We shall evaluate the derivative of this function with respect to the variable t. Then we shall obtain

$$\frac{dV}{dt} = 2x(t)\frac{dx}{dt} + 2y(t)\frac{dy}{dt} = 2[a_{11}x^2(t) + (a_{12} + a_{21})x(t)\,y(t) +$$
$$+ a_{22}y^2(t)] = W(t).$$

The function V represents the square of the distance from the integral curve to the coordinate origin. Therefore the homogeneous solution of that system will be known to be stable if that distance decreases monotonically as $t \to +\infty$.

In order to ensure this monotonic decrease, it is sufficient to require the fulfillment of the inequality $W(t) \leq 0$ for $t \geq 0$.

The latter inequality will be known to be satisfied, if

$$a_{11} \leq 0 \text{ and } a_{11}a_{22} - \frac{(a_{12} + a_{21})^2}{4} \geq 0, \qquad (2.6)$$

as with the fulfillment of these conditions the quadratic form W will be non-positive.

If it turns out that the above-indicated distance tends to zero as $t \to +\infty$, then the homogeneous solution will be asymptotically stable. This will be known to be the case if

$$a_{11} < -\alpha; \; a_{11}a_{22} - \frac{(a_{12} + a_{21})^2}{2} > \beta, \qquad (2.7)$$

where α and β are positive numbers.

In fact, in that case we shall have $W < -\gamma V$, where γ is a positive constant. Then integrating the inequality $\dfrac{dV}{dt} < -\gamma V$, we shall obtain

$$V[x(t), y(t)] \leq (x_0^2 + y_0^2)e^{-\gamma(t-t_0)},$$

where $x = x_0; \; y = y_0$ for $t = t_0$ is the initial condition defining the integral curve under consideration.

We shall now consider the geometric interpretation of the above argument. In the plane xoy we shall mark concentric circles corresponding to $V = \text{const.}$

Conditions (2.6) denote that all the integral curves starting on the circle $V = c$ do not exit from it, remaining within it for $t \geq t_0$ (the case of stability).

Case (2.7) denotes that the integral curves beginning on the circle $V = c$ intersect any other circle $V = c_1$ where $c_1 < c$ (the case of asymptotic stability).

The example analysed above allows one to give a general formulation of the idea behind the second method of Lyapunov. The second method of solving the problem of stability of the homogeneous solution of system (1.4) consists in finding a function $V(y_1, ..., y_n, t)$, which allows one to measure the distance from the integral curve of system (1.4) to the coordinate origin (to the equilibrium position) as the time varies from t_0 to ∞. Geometrically this method consists in finding a family of surfaces embracing the equilibrium position, with respect to each of which it can be established whether, as $t \to \infty$, all the integral curves intersect it passing from the outside inward (the case of stability) or from the inside outward (the case of instability).

DEFINITION 7. All the functions $V(y_1,\ldots, y_n, t)$ allowing one to solve the problem of stability (or instability) of the homogeneous solution of system (1.4) shall, in what follows, be called Lyapunov functions. Lyapunov functions are usually sought among the class of all the functions satisfying the conditions of sign definiteness and having an infinitely small upper bound.

DEFINITION 8. A real single-valued function $V(y_1,\ldots, y_n, t)$ given for $t \geq 0$; $|y_s| \leq r$ is called positive-definite if there exists a continuous function $V_2(y_1,\ldots, y_n)$ given for $|y_s| \leq r$ $(s = 1,\ldots, n)$; $r > 0$, such that

$$V_2(0,\ldots,0) = 0; \quad V_2 > 0 \text{ for } \sum_{i=1}^{n} y_i^2 > 0;$$

$$V(y_1,\ldots, y_n, t) \geq V_2(y_1,\ldots, y_n)$$

and $V(y_1,\ldots, y_n, t)$ is identically equal to zero for $y_1 = y_2 = \ldots = y_n = 0$.

If the relation $V(y_1,\ldots, y_n, t) \leq - V_2(y_1,\ldots, y_n)$ holds, then the function V is called negative-definite.

Positive-definite functions and negative-definite functions are called sign-definite functions.

For example, the function

$$V = x^2 + \frac{y^2}{1 + t}$$

is not positive-definite, and the function

$$V = x^2 + y^2 + \tfrac{1}{2} xy \sin t$$

is positive-definite.

DEFINITION 9. A real single-valued function $V(y_1,\ldots, y_n, t)$ given for $t \geq 0$; $|y_s| \leq r$ admits of an infinitely small upper bound if $V(y_1,\ldots, y_n, t)$ tends uniformly to zero with respect to $t \geq 0$ as $\sum_{i=1}^{n} y_i^2 \to 0$, i.e. for every number $\varepsilon_1 > 0$ one can indicate a $\delta_1 > 0$ such that

$$|V(y_1,\ldots, y_n, t)| < \delta_1 \text{ for } \sum_{i=1}^{n} y_i^2 < \varepsilon_1^2$$

or, in other words: there exists a positive-definite function $V_2(y_1,\ldots, y_n)$ such that

$$|V(y_1,\ldots, y_n, t)| \leq V_2(y_1,\ldots, y_n).$$

To simplify computations, the Lyapunov function is often sought as a quadratic form [3] of the phase variables, whose coefficients are either sought or fixed functions of time

$$V = \sum_{i\,k=1}^{n} a_{ik}(t)\, y_i y_k. \tag{2.8}$$

The quadratic form (2.8) will be nonnegative provided that the Sylvester conditions

$$\Delta_1 \geq 0; \quad \Delta_2 \geq 0; \ldots; \Delta_n \geq 0$$

are satisfied, where the Δ_i are the principal minors of the matrix

$$\begin{pmatrix} a_{11} & a_{12} & \cdot & \cdot & a_{1n} \\ a_{21} & \cdot & \cdot & \cdot & \cdot \\ \cdot & \cdot & \cdot & \cdot & \cdot \\ \cdot & \cdot & \cdot & \cdot & \cdot \\ a_{n1} & a_{n2} & \cdot & \cdot & a_{nn} \end{pmatrix}. \tag{2.9}$$

It is well known that the quadratic form (2.8) will be positive-definite if the principal minors of matrix (2.9) differ from zero by positive constants, i.e. $\Delta_i > \alpha;\ (i = 1,\ldots, n)$, where $\alpha > 0$ is a constant.

The quadratic form (2.8) will admit of an infinitely small upper bound if the moduli of its coefficients are bounded, i.e. $|a_{ik}(t)| \leq m < +\infty$.

From algebra it is known that one can indicate a linear transformation over the variables after which the quadratic form (2.8) will assume the canonical aspect. This linear transformation may be represented in the form

$$y_s = \sum_{i=1}^{n} g_{si}(t)\, x_i, \quad (s = 1,\ldots, n),$$

where

$$\sum_{i=1}^{n} g_{si}^2(t) = 1 \text{ and } \sum_{i=1}^{n} g_{si}\, g_{\sigma i} = 0 \text{ for } \sigma \neq s,$$

i.e. the indicated transformation is orthogonal.

After this transformation the quadratic form (2.8) will appear as

$$V' = \sum_{i=1}^{n} \lambda_i(t)\, x_i^2, \tag{2.10}$$

where $\lambda_1(t) \leq \lambda_2(t) \leq \ldots \leq \lambda_n(t)$ are real functions of the argument t, which for any fixed t are the characteristic values of matrix (2.9).

It is easily seen that the quadratic form admits an estimate such as

$$\lambda_1(t) \sum_{i=1}^{n} x_i^2 \leq \sum_{i=1}^{n} \lambda_i x_i^2 \leq \lambda_n(t) \sum_{i=1}^{n} x_i^2. \tag{2.11}$$

If now in inequalities (2.11) we again proceed to the variables $y_1,..., y_n$, keeping in mind that the inverse transformations from the variables $x_1,..., x_n$ to the variables $y_1,..., y_n$ are also orthogonal and, consequently, do not alter the sums of the squares of the variables, we shall obtain

$$\lambda_1(t) \sum_{i=1}^{n} y_i^2 \leq \sum_{i,k=1}^{n} a_{ik} y_i y_k \leq \lambda_n(t) \sum_{i=1}^{n} y_i^2. \qquad (2.12)$$

From formula (2.12) it follows that the quadratic form (2.8) will be positive-definite if, and only if, $\lambda_1(t) > \alpha > 0$, $\alpha = $ const. Here the quadratic form (2.8) will admit of an infinitely small upper bound if, and only if, $\lambda_n(t)$ is bounded from above as $t \to +\infty$.

The second method of investigating the stability of the homogeneous solution of system (1.4) leads to the study of the behaviour of a Lyapunov function upon any fixed integral curve of system (1.4). Therefore the function $V(y_1,..., y_n, t)$ on every integral curve is a function of just the one variable t and, consequently, may be studied by the tools of mathematical analysis.

By $V_1(t, y_{10},..., y_{n0}, t_0)$ we shall denote the function $V[y_1(t, y_{10},..., y_{n0}, t_0),$ $..., y_n(t, y_{10},..., y_{n0}, t_0), t]$.

If the derivative of the function V_1 with respect to t exists, then it can be said that the function $V(y_1,..., y_n, t)$ is differentiable on the basis of system (1.4) along a chosen integral curve.

Let us note that there exist two ways of computing this derivative. One of them is applied when the function $V(y_1,..., y_n, t)$ is continuously differentiable with respect to all its arguments. In that case, according to the formula for calculating the derivative of a complex function, we shall have

$$\frac{dV_1}{dt} = \frac{\partial V}{\partial t}(y_1',..., y_n', t) + \sum_{i=1}^{n} \frac{\partial V}{\partial y_i}(y_1',..., y_n', t) \frac{dy_i'}{dt}$$

$$= \frac{\partial V}{\partial t}(y_1',..., y_n', t) + \sum_{i=1}^{n} \frac{\partial V}{\partial y_i} g_i(y_1',..., y_n', t) = W. \qquad (2.13)$$

The functions $y',..., y_n'$ in formula (2.13) denote the chosen integral curve of system (1.4), along which one is computing the derivative of V.

The function

$$W = \frac{\partial V}{\partial t}(y_1',..., y_n', t) + \sum_{i=1}^{n} \frac{\partial V}{\partial y_i}(y_1,..., y_n, t) g_i(y_1',..., y_n', t), \qquad (2.14)$$

considered without any connection with the integral curves o f system (1.4), is called the total derivative of the function V with respect to t, calculated on the basis of system (1.4).

We shall assume that in system (1.4) there enter additively some constantly acting perturbations $\phi_s(y_1,\ldots,y_n,t)$, i.e. system (1.4) has the form

$$\frac{dy_s}{dt} = g_s(y_1,\ldots,y_n,t) + \phi_s(y_1,\ldots,y_n,t). \tag{2.15}$$

We shall set up the total derivative of the function V as based on equations (2.15)

$$\frac{dV}{dt} = \frac{\partial V}{\partial t}(y_1,\ldots,y_n,t) + \sum_{i=1}^{n}\frac{\partial V}{\partial y_i}[g_i(y_1,\ldots,y_n,t) + \phi_i(y_1,\ldots,y_n,t)] = W + W_1,$$

where

$$W_1 = \sum_{i=1}^{n}\frac{\partial V}{\partial y_i}\phi_i(y_1,\ldots,y_n,t);$$

i.e. W_1 is the total derivative of the function V, calculated on the basis of system

$$\frac{dy_s}{dt} = \phi_s(y_1,\ldots,y_n,t). \tag{2.16}$$

The second method of calculating the derivative of the function V with respect to t along the integral curves of system (1.4) relates to the case when the function $V(y_1,\ldots,y_n,t)$ does not have continuous partial derivatives of all its arguments.

In that case

$$\frac{dV}{dt} = \lim_{\Delta t \to 0}\frac{V_1(t+\Delta t, y_{10},y_{20},\ldots,y_{n0},t_0) - V_1(t,y_{10},\ldots,y_{n0},t_0)}{\Delta t}$$

$$= \lim_{\Delta t \to 0}\frac{V[y_1(t+\Delta t,y_{10},\ldots,y_{n0},t_0),\ldots,y_n(t+\Delta t,y_{10},\ldots,y_{n0},t_0),t+\Delta t] -}{\Delta t}$$

$$\frac{- V[y_1(t,y_{10},\ldots,y_{n0},t_0),\ldots,y_n(t,y_{10},\ldots,y_{n0},t_0),t]}{\Delta t}.$$

From system (1.4) we find

$$y(t+\Delta t,y_{10},\ldots,y_{n0},t_0) = y_s(t,y_{10},\ldots,y_{n0},t_0) +$$

$$+ \int_{t}^{t+\Delta t} g_-(y_1,\ldots,y_n,t)\,d\tau = \Delta t g'_s + y_s(t,y_{10},\ldots,y_{n0},t_0).$$

Thus we have

$$\frac{dV}{dt} = \lim_{\Delta t \to 0} \frac{V(y_1 + \Delta t g_1', \ldots, y_n + \Delta t g_n', t + \Delta t) - V(y_1, \ldots, y_n, t)}{\Delta t}$$

$$= \frac{d}{d\tau} V(y_1 + \tau g_1, \ldots, y_n + \tau g_n, t + \tau) = W, \text{ for } \tau = 0,$$

if one takes into account † that

$$\lim_{\Delta t \to 0} \frac{V(t + \Delta t, y_s + \Delta t g_s') - V(t + \Delta t, y_s + \Delta t g_s)}{\Delta t} = 0, \qquad (*)$$

where

$$g_s = \frac{1}{\Delta t} \int_t^{t + \Delta t} g_s' dt.$$

Function W, just as above, is called the total derivative with respect to t as based on system (1.4).

If in system (1.4) there are constantly acting perturbations, then the total derivative of the function V may be represented in the form

$$\frac{dV}{dt} = W + W_1,$$

where $\dfrac{dV}{dt}$ is the total derivative as based on system (2.15);

W is the total derivative of function V as based on system (1.4);

W_1 is the total derivative of function V as based on system (2.16).

---

† The condition (*) is known to be fulfilled if function V satisfies the Lipschitz condition with respect to the variables $y_1, \ldots, y_n$ with exponent unity, and the functions $g_s(t, y_1, \ldots, y_n)$ are continuous.

§ 3. Theorems on stability and instability

In this section we expound the theorems constituting the substance of the second method of Lyapunov. These theorems are the direct development of the theorems first formulated by Lyapunov.

THEOREM 1. In order that the homogeneous solution of system (1.4) be stable in the sense of Lyapunov, it is necessary and sufficient that there exist a function $V(y_1,\ldots,y_n,t)$ satisfying the following conditions:

1) the function $V(y_1,\ldots,y_n,t)$ is given for

$$\sum_{i=1}^{n} y_i^2 \leqq r^2, \quad t \geqq 0,$$

where r is a positive constant;

2) the function $V(y_1,\ldots,y_n,t)$ vanishes identically at $y_1 = y_2 = \ldots = y_n = 0$ and with a fixed value of t is continuous with respect to the variables $y_1,\ldots,y_n$ at the point $y_1 = \ldots = y_n = 0$;

3) the function $V(y_1,\ldots,y_n,t)$ is positive-definite;

4) the function $V(y_1,\ldots,y_n,t)$ is defined on any integral curve of system (1.4) as long as the integral curve lies in the region of assignment of functions V, and on any integral curve it is a nonincreasing function for $t \geqq t_0$, i.e.

$V_1(t, y_{10},\ldots, y_{n0}, t_0)$ does not increase with $t \geqq t_0$ and with $\sum_{i=1}^{n} y_{i0}^2 < r^2$.

PROOF: *Sufficiency.* We shall assume that there exists a function $V(y_1,\ldots,y_n,t)$, satisfying the conditions formulated in Theorem 1. It is to be shown that in this case the homogeneous solution of system (1.4) is stable in the sense of Lyapunov. For this we shall take $0 < \varepsilon < r$. For such an ε one may indicate a number $\lambda > 0$ such that

$$V(y_1 \ldots, y_n, t) > \lambda \text{ for } \sum_{i=1}^{n} y_i^2 = \varepsilon^2.$$

Such a number λ exists by virtue of the positive-definiteness of the function $V(y_1,\ldots,y_n,t)$. In fact, the function $V(y_1,\ldots,y_n,t)$ is positive-definite. Therefore there exists a continuous function $V_2(y_1,\ldots,y_n)$ such that

$$V_2 = 0 \text{ for } y_1 = \ldots = y_n = 0,$$

$$V_2 > 0 \text{ for } \sum_{i=1}^{n} y_i^2 \neq 0,$$

and

$$V_2 \leqq V(y_1,\ldots,y_n,t).$$

by m we shall denote the smallest valne of the function V_2 on the sphere $\sum_{i=1}^{n} y_i^2 = \varepsilon^2$. Then, from the continuity of V_2 it follows that $m > 0$. On the basis of the inequality $V \geqq V_2$ we shall have

$$V(y_1, \ldots, y_n, t) \geqq m \quad \text{for} \quad \sum_{i=1}^{n} y_i^2 = \varepsilon^2.$$

It is easily seen that for λ one may choose a number $\lambda \leqq m$. On the basis of the continuity of the function $V(y_1, \ldots, y_n, t)$ (condition 2) there exists a number $\delta(t_0, \varepsilon) > 0$ such that

$$V(y_1, \ldots, y_n, t_0) < \lambda \quad \text{for} \quad \sum_{i=1}^{n} y_i^2 < \delta^2(t_0, \varepsilon).$$

We shall show that the number $\delta(t_0, \varepsilon)$ found corresponds to the number ε taken according to Definition 3 (on stability).

Indeed, let

$$\sum_{i=1}^{n} y_i^2 < \delta^2(t_0, \varepsilon).$$

Then

$$V(y_{10}, \ldots, y_{n0}, t_0) < \lambda. \tag{3.1}$$

Further, on the basis of condition 4 of Theorem 1 the function $V_1(t, y_{10}, \ldots, \ldots, y_{n0}, t_0)$ is nonincreasing with $t \geqq t_0$. Therefore,

$$V_1(t, y_{10}, \ldots, y_{n0}, t_0) < V(y_{10}, \ldots, y_{n0}, t_0) \quad \text{for} \quad t \geqq t_0.$$

On the basis of inequality (3.1) we shall obtain that $V_1(t, y_{10}, \ldots, y_{n0}, t_0) < \lambda$ for $t \geqq t_0$, whence follows that the integral curve with $t \geqq t_0$ satisfies the conditions $\sum_{i=1}^{n} y_i^2 < \varepsilon^2$, as in the contrary case there has to exist an instant $T > t_0$ such that

$$\sum_{i=1}^{n} y_i^2 (T, y_{10}, \ldots, y_{n0}, t_0) = \varepsilon^2.$$

Then, because of the choice of the number λ, $V_1(T, y_{10}, \ldots, y_{n0}, t_0) > \lambda$ should hold, which is impossible since with $t \geqq t_0$ by virtue of (3.1) the opposite inequality is satisfied.

Thus if

$$\sum_{i=1}^{n} y_{i0}^2 < \delta^2(t_0, \varepsilon),$$

then

$$\sum_{i=1}^{n} y_i^2 (t, y_{10}, \ldots, y_{n0}, t_0) < \varepsilon^2 \quad \text{for} \quad t \geqq t_0.$$

This completes the proof of the sufficiency of the conditions of Theorem 1.

Necessity. This portion of the proof is, generally speaking, of academic interest only. It is very useful in view of the fact that it indicates how the Lyapunov function appears in the presence of stability and what form it takes in relation to the behaviour of the integral curves.

We shall now assume that the homogeneous solution of system (1.4) is stable. Then for $\varepsilon > 0$ one can indicate a number $\delta(t_0, \varepsilon) > 0$ such that if

$$\sum_{i=1}^{n} y_{i0}^2 < \delta^2(t_0, \varepsilon)$$

then

$$\sum_{i} y_i^2(t, y_{10}, \ldots, y_{n0}, t_0) < \varepsilon^2 \quad \text{for} \quad t \geq t_0.$$

We shall show that then there exists a function $V(y_1, \ldots, y_n, t)$ satisfying the conditions of Theorem 1. We shall consider an integral curve of system (1.4)

$$y_s = y_s(t, y_{10}, \ldots, y_{n0}, t_0) \quad (s = 1, \ldots, n) \tag{3.2}$$

$$\sum_{i=1}^{n} y_{i0}^2 < \delta^2(t_0, \varepsilon).$$

We shall define the function V at the point $(y_{10}, \ldots y_{n0}, t_0)$ in the following way:

$$V(y_{10}, \ldots, y_{n0}, t_0) = \sup_{t \geq t_0} \sqrt{\sum_{i=1}^{n} y_i^2}, \tag{3.3}$$

where $\sum_{i=1}^{n} y_i^2$ is the distance from integral curve (3.2) of system (1.4) at the instant $t \geq t_0$ to the equilibrium position of the system. If it turns out that on the same integral curve of system (1.4) the right-hand member of relation (3.3) is greater than unity, then at that point we shall set $V(y_{10}, \ldots, y_{n0}, t_0) = 1$.

Relation (3.3) together with the remark just made uniquely defines a single-valued function $V(y_1, \ldots, y_n, t)$ given in the region

$$\sum_{i=1}^{n} y_i^2 \leq r^2; \quad t \geq 0,$$

where r is some positive constant. Thus the conditions of Theorem 1 are satisfied.

We shall show that the function constructed satisfies condition 2. In fact, the function $V(y_1,\ldots,y_n,t)$ is identically equal to zero when $y_1 = \ldots = y_n = 0$, which follows from (3.3).

We shall show that, for fixed t, the function V is continuous at the point $y_1 = \ldots = y_n = 0$, for which we shall take the number $\varepsilon_1 > 0$. For it, because of existing stability there exists a number $\delta(t_0, \varepsilon)$, such that

$$\sum_{i=1}^{n} y_i^2(t, y_{10},\ldots,y_{n0},t_0) < \varepsilon_1^2 \ \text{ for } \ \sum_{i=1}^{n} y_{i0}^2 < \delta^2(t_0,\varepsilon_1).$$

Then, on the basis of (3.3), $V(y_{10},\ldots,y_{n0},t_0) \leqq \varepsilon_1$ will hold.

Thus the continuity of the function $V(y_1,\ldots,y_n,t)$ with a fixed value of t may be considered to be demonstrated. From relation (3.3) it follows that

$$V(y_{10},\ldots,y_{n0},t_0) \geqq \sqrt{\sum_{i=1}^{n} y_i^2} \ .$$

Setting

$$V_2(y_1,\ldots,y_n) = \sqrt{\sum_{i=1}^{n} y_i^2} \ ,$$

we shall obtain that $V \geqq V_2$. Thus the function V is positive-definite and consequently conditions 3 of Theorem 1 are satisfied.

In order to show that the function V satisfies condition 4, it is sufficient to establish that the value of the function $V_1(t_1, y_{10},\ldots,y_{n0},t_0)$ is no less than $V_1(t_2, y_{10},\ldots,y_{n0},t_0)$, provided only that $t_2 \geqq t_1 \geqq t_0$. For this, we shall choose two points on integral curve (3.2) corresponding to the instants t_1 and t_2, and shall compute the value of V at these points according to formula (3.3).

In the first case the exact upper bound of the quantity $\sqrt{\sum_{i=1}^{n} y_i^2}$ is calculated at $t \geqq t_1$, in the second at $t \geqq t_2$. Since $t_2 \geqq t_1$, then

$$\sup_{t \geqq t_1} \sqrt{\sum_{i=1}^{n} y_i^2} \geqq \sup_{t \geqq t_2} \sqrt{\sum_{i=1}^{n} y_i^2} \ .$$

Therefore the function defined by relation (3.3) along integral curve (3.2) is nonincreasing. This completes the proof for the necessity of the conditions of Theorem 1.

COROLLARY 1. The requirements posed by Theorem 1 upon the function V (with the exception of condition 4) are easy to verify. However, the fulfillment of condition 4 at first sight seems undecidable, as the integral curves of system (1.4) are unknown and, consequently, it does not seem possible to verify condition 4. Nevertheless on the basis of condition 4 the function V will be monotonic along any integral curve for $t \geq t_0$ and therefore is differentiable for almost all values of t for $t \geq t_0$ (according to a theorem of Lebesgue [4] on the existence almost everywhere of the derivative of a monotonic function). Then the relation $dV/dt = W \leq 0$ will hold almost everywhere.

Thus condition 4 may be verified directly by finding the total derivative of the function V as based on system (1.4).

COROLLARY 2. If in the region $\sum_{i=1}^{n} y_i^2 \leq r^2$ with $t \geq t_0$ there exists a continuous and differentiable function $V(y_1, \ldots, y_n, t)$, and its total derivative with respect to t as based on system (1.4)

$$ W = \frac{\partial V}{\partial t} + \sum_{i=1}^{n} \frac{\partial V}{\partial y_i} g_i(y_1, \ldots, y_n) $$

is nonpositive, then the homogeneous solution of system (1.4) is stable in the sense of Lyapunov.

In fact, in the presence of such a function all the conditions of Theorem 1 are fulfilled.

The assertion just formulated was first established by A. M. Lyapunov [2] and bears the name of Lyapunov's first theorem on stability.

COROLLARY 3. If the function V, which is dealt with in Theorem 1, admits of an infinitely small upper bound, then the homogeneous solution of the system (1.4) is uniformly stable with respect to $t_0 \geq 0$.

As a matter of fact [5], in the sufficiency proof the number $\delta(t_0, \varepsilon)$ was chosen from the condition

$$ V(y_1, \ldots, y_n, t_0) < \lambda \quad \text{for} \quad \sum_{i=1}^{n} y_i^2 < \delta^2(t_0, \varepsilon). $$

As the function V admits of an infinitely small upper bound, there exists a number $\delta(\varepsilon)$ such that

$$V(y_1,\ldots,y_n,t_0) < \lambda \quad \text{for} \quad \sum_{i=1}^{n} y_i^2 < \delta^2(\varepsilon)$$

for $t_0 \geqq 0$. It is clear that the number $\delta(\varepsilon)$ corresponds to the number $\varepsilon > 0$ chosen by us.

The condition of the presence of an infinitely small upper bound for the function $V(y_1,\ldots,y_n,t)$, which ensures the uniform stability with respect to t_0, was first laid down by Lyapunov and has continued to remain the only known requirement of this kind in the works of all subsequent authors.

In the practice of finding the stability criteria there sometimes appears the possibility of constructing easily a positive-definite function, not admitting an infinitely small upper bound having a nonpositive derivative as based on system (1.4). The question arises whether with the aid of such functions it is possible to derive the conditions for stability, uniform with respect to the initially given $y_{10},\ldots,y_{n0}$ for $t_0 > 0$.

Say one is given a positive-definite function $V(y_1,\ldots,y_n,t)$. We shall take a number $\varepsilon > 0$ and a number $t \geqq 0$. We shall set

$$\lambda(\varepsilon, t_0) = \inf_{t \geqq t_0} V(y_1,\ldots,y_n,t),$$

$$\sum_{i=1}^{n} y_i^2 = \varepsilon^2.$$

We shall construct a function $\gamma(t_0, \varepsilon) = \sup \delta$, where δ is determined from the condition

$$V(y_1,\ldots,y_n,t_0) < \lambda(t_0,\varepsilon) \quad \text{for} \quad \sum_{i=1}^{n} y_i^2 < \delta.$$

We shall set

$$\delta(\varepsilon) = \inf_{t_0 > 0} \gamma(t_0, \varepsilon).$$

DEFINITION 10. We shall say that a positive-definite function $V(y_1,\ldots,y_n,t)$ is given in the region $\sum_{i=1}^{n} y_i^2 \leqq r^2$; $t \geqq 0$ and belongs to the class L, if $\inf \gamma(t_0, \varepsilon) = \delta(\varepsilon) \neq 0$ for every $\varepsilon > 0$.

THEOREM 2. In order that the homogeneous solution of system (1.4) be stable uniformly with respect to $t_0 \geqq 0$, it is necessary and sufficient that there exist a function $V(y_1,\ldots,y_n,t)$ of the class L satisfying all the conditions of Theorem 1.

PROOF: *Sufficiency.* Let there be a function $V(y_1,\ldots,y_n,t)$ of the class L satisfying the conditions of Theorem 1. We shall then show that the homogeneous solution of system (1.4) is stable uniformly with respect to $t_0 \geq 0$. Indeed, for any $\varepsilon > 0$ according to the definition of the class L one may indicate a number $\delta(\varepsilon) > 0$. We shall establish that that number is the number sought.

Let $\sum\limits_{i=1}^{n} y_{i0}^2 < \delta(\varepsilon)$. Then on the basis of condition 4 of Theorem 1 the inequality

$$V_1(t, y_{10},\ldots, y_{n0}, t_0) \leq V(y_{10},\ldots, y_{n0}, t_0) \tag{3.4}$$

will hold, where, just as before, V is the value of the function $V(y_1,\ldots,y_n,t)$ on the chosen integral curve.

Let the condition

$$\sum_{i=1}^{n} y_i^2(t, y_{10},\ldots, y_{n0}, t_0) < \varepsilon^2$$

be violated at the instant T. Then

$$\sum_{i=1}^{n} y_i^2(T, y_{10},\ldots, y_{n0}, t_0) = \varepsilon^2,$$

whence follows that $V_1(T, y_{10},\ldots, y_{n0}, t_0) > \lambda(T, \varepsilon)$. From the definition of the class L it follows that $\lambda(T, \varepsilon) \geq \lambda(t_0, \varepsilon)$, and therefore the inequality

$$V_1(T, y_{10},\ldots, y_{n0}, t_0) \geq \lambda(t_0, \varepsilon)$$

will hold.

However, from (3.4) we have $V_1(T, y_{10},\ldots, y_{n0}, t_0) < \lambda(t_0, \varepsilon)$. The contradiction obtained shows that the assumption made by us on the violation of the inequality

$$\sum_{i=1}^{n} y_i^2(t, y_{10},\ldots, y_{n0}, t_0) < \varepsilon^2 \quad \text{for } t \geq t_0$$

is made incorrectly. Consequently, the homogeneous solution of system (1.4) is stable uniformly with respect to $t_0 \geq 0$.

Necessity. We shall assume that the homogeneous solution of system (1.4) is stable uniformly with respect to $t_0 \geq 0$. We shall show that then there exists a function satisfying the conditions of Theorem 2. Actually, we shall consider a function defined by equality (3.3).

We shall establish that this function belongs to the class L. Moreover, this functoin admits of an infinitely small upper bound, inasmuch as by virtue of stability, uniform with respect to t_0, for a number ε' there is a number δ' such that if $\sum\limits_{i=1}^{n} y_{i0}^2 < (\delta')^2$ then

$$\sum_{i=1}^{n} y_i^2 (t, y_{10}, ..., y_{n0}, t_0) < (\varepsilon')^2$$

for $t \geqq t_0$, and then from (3.3) $V(t, y_{10}, ..., y_{n0}, t_0) \leqq \varepsilon'$. Since ε' has been chosen arbitrarily, we shall obtain that the function defined by equality (3.3) has an infinitely small upper bound and, consequently, belongs to the class L.

THEOREM 3. In order that the homogeneous solution of system (1.4) be asymptotically stable, it is necessary and sufficient that the conditions of Theorem 1 be satisfied and, besides, that along any integral curve the function V would decrease to zero as $t \to \infty$, i.e.

$$V_1 (t, y_{10}, ..., y_{n0}, t_0) \to 0 \text{ as } t \to \infty$$

and

$$\sum_{i=1}^{n} y_{i0}^2 \leqq \gamma^2 (t_0).$$

PROOF: *Sufficiency.* We shall assume that there exists a function $V(y_1, ..., y_n, t)$ possessing the properties indicated in Theorem 3. We shall show that the homogeneous solution of system (1.4) will be asymptotically stable. In fact, the conditions of Theorem 1 are satisfied and, consequently, the homogeneous solution of system (1.4) is stable in the sense of Lyapunov.

Then for $\varepsilon > 0$ there is a number $\delta(t_0, \varepsilon) > 0$ such that if

$$\sum_{i=1}^{n} y_{i0}^2 \leqq \delta^2 (t_0, \varepsilon)$$

then

$$\sum_{i=1}^{n} y_i^2 (t, y_{10}, ..., y_{n0}, t_0) < \varepsilon^2.$$

One may consider that $\delta(t_0, \varepsilon) \leqq \gamma(t_0)$. In that event we shall show that

$$\sum_{i=1}^{n} y_i^2 \to 0 \text{ as } t \to \infty.$$

Assume that this is not the case. Then there exists at least one integral curve

$$y_s = y_s(t, y_{10}, \ldots, y_{n0}, t_0) \quad (s = 1, \ldots, n),$$

$$\sum_{i=1}^{n} y_{i0}^2 < \delta^2(t_0, \varepsilon)$$

and the sequence of instants $t_1 < t_2 < \ldots < t_k$; $t_k \to +\infty$ as $k \to +\infty$ such that

$$\sum_{i=1}^{n} y_i^2(t_k, y_{10}, \ldots, y_{n0}, t_0) > \alpha > 0.$$

And then by virtue of positive definiteness of the function $V(y_1, \ldots, y_n, t)$ we shall have $V_1(t_k, y_{10}, \ldots, y_{n0}, t_0) > \beta > 0$, which is impossible since $V_1(t, y_{10}, \ldots, y_{n0}, t_0) \to 0$ as $t \to +\infty$. This completes the proof for the sufficiency of the conditions of the Theorem.

Necessity. We shall assume that the homogeneous solution of system (1.4) is asymptotically stable. We shall show that there exists a function $V(y_1, \ldots, y_n, t)$ satisfying all the conditions of Theorem 3. For this we shall turn again to the function defined by relation (3.3) and shall show that this function, along integral curves, tends to zero as $t \to +\infty$. Indeed, we shall take any integral curve along which

$$\sum_{i=1}^{n} y_i^2(t, y_{10}, \ldots, y_{n0}, t_0) \to 0 \text{ as } t \to +\infty,$$

$$\sum_{i=1}^{n} y_{i0}^2 < \delta^2(t, \varepsilon).$$

Then for an arbitrarily small ε' there is a sufficiently large number T' such that

$$\sum_{i=1}^{n} y_i^2(t, y_{10}, \ldots, y_{n0}, t_0) < (\varepsilon')^2 \text{ for } t > T'.$$

On the basis of relation (3.3) the function V, evaluated at the point $y_1, \ldots, y_n$; $t > T'$, lying on the curve under consideration, will satisfy the inequality

$$V_1(t, y_{10}, \ldots, y_{n0}, t_0) \leq \varepsilon' \text{ for } t \geq T',$$

which indeed indicates that the function V, defined by (3.3), tends to zero along the integral curves of system (1.4).

COROLLARY 1. If the function V dealt with in Theorem 3 admits, besides, of an infinitely small upper bound or belongs to the class L, then the homogeneous solution of system (1.4) is asymptotically stable uniformly with respect to $t_0 \geq 0$.

The conditions of Theorem 3, connected with the decrease of the function to zero along the integral curves of system (1.4) as $t \to +\infty$, cannot be verified directly in view of the fact that the explicit representation of the integral curves of system (1.4) is unknown.

Of considerable value in this connection are various sufficient conditions, which are easier to verify than those indicated above.

THEOREM 4. The homogeneous solution is asymptotically stable if the right-hand members of system (1.4) are bounded in the region

$$t \geq t_0; \ \sum_{i=1}^{n} y_i^2 < r_1^2,$$

where r_1 is a positive constant, and the following conditions are satisfied:

1) there exists a function $V(y_1, \ldots, y_n, t)$ satisfying the conditions 1–3 of Theorem 1;

2) there exists a nonpositive function $W(y_1, \ldots, y_n, t)$ which is the total derivative with respect to t of the function V as based on system (1.4), such that

$$W(y_1, \ldots, y_n, t) \leq \phi_\alpha(t) \leq 0 \text{ for } \sum_{i=1}^{n} y_i^2 \geq \alpha^2;$$

3) $\int_s \phi_\alpha(t) \, dt = -\infty$, where s is any infinite system of closed nonintersecting segments lying on the interval $[t_0, \infty)$, $t_0 \geq 0$, such that the length of each of them is not less than a fixed positive constant.

We shall precede the proof of the Theorem by a lemma.

LEMMA. Let $t_1, \tau_1; \ t_2, \tau_2; \ \ldots$ be positive points of intersection of a fixed integral curve with the spheres

$$\sum_{i=1}^{n} y_i^2 = \rho_1^2 \text{ and } \sum_{i=1}^{n} y_i^2 = \rho_2^2; \ \rho_1 < \rho_2.$$

If the right-hand members of system (1.4) are bounded in the region indicated in Theorem 4, then

$$\sum_{i=1}^{k} (\tau_i - t_i) \to \infty \text{ as } k \to \infty.$$

PROOF: In the $(n+1)$–dimensional space $y_1, ..., y_n,$ t we shall consider two semicylindrical surfaces

$$\sum_{i=1}^{n} y_i^2 = \rho_1^2; \quad \sum_{i=1}^{n} y_i^2 = \rho_2^2; \quad t \geqq 0.$$

We shall assume that the integral curve $y_s = y_s(t, y_{10}, ..., y_{n0}, t_0)$ intersects these two surfaces an infinite number of times, and let $t_1, \tau_1, ..., t_k, \tau_k, ...$ be the temporal lengths of arc of that integral curve lying between these semicylindrical surfaces. We shall find the length of arc of the integral curve with

$$t \in [t_k, \tau_k]; \quad S_k = \int_{t_k}^{\tau_k} ds,$$

where ds is the differential of length of the integral curve. It is easy to note that

$$ds = \sqrt{dt^2 + dy_1^2 + ... + dy_n^2} = dt \sqrt{1 + \sum_{i=1}^{n} g_i^2(t, y_1, ..., y_n)}.$$

Because of the boundedness of the right-hand members of system (1.4) we shall have

$$S_k \leqq (\tau_k - t_k) m,$$

where

$$m = \sup_{t \geqq 0} \sqrt{1 + \sum_{i=1}^{n} g_i^2(t, y_1, ..., y_n)}, \quad \sum_{i=1}^{n} y_i^2 \leqq r^2.$$

On the other hand, the arc length S_k is not less than the distance between the semicylindrical surfaces, i.e. $S_k \geqq \rho_2 - \rho_1$. Hence we obtain that

$$\tau_k - t_k \geqq \frac{\rho_2 - \rho_1}{m}; \quad k = 1, 2, ...$$

The last inequality shows that

$$\sum_{i=1}^{k} (\tau_i - t_i) \to \infty \text{ as } k \to \infty \text{ etc.}$$

PROOF OF THEOREM 4: As W is nonpositive, the function V along the integral curves of system (1.4) does not increase. Consequently, according to

Theorem 1 the homogeneous solution of system (1.4) is stable. Therefore for an $\varepsilon > 0$ there is a $\delta > 0$ such that if $\sum_{i=1}^{n} y_{i0}^2 < \delta^2$ then

$$\sum_{i=1}^{n} y_i^2(t, y_{10}, ..., y_{n0}) < \varepsilon^2 \text{ for } t \geq t_0.$$

We shall assume the contrary, namely, that the homogeneous solution of system (1.4) is stable nonasymptotically. Then there exists an integral curve of system (1.4), originating in the region

$$\sum_{i=1}^{n} y_{i0}^2 < \rho^2, \ t_0 \geq 0,$$

for which one may indicate two numbers S_1 and S_2 such that as $t \to \infty$ that integral curve intersects the surfaces indicated in the Lemma an infinite number of times†. Along that integral curve there holds the relation

$$\frac{dV_1(t, y_{10}, ..., y_{n0}, t_0)}{dt} = W_1(t, y_{10}, ..., y_{n0}, t_0), \tag{3.5}$$

where W_1 represents $W(y_1, ..., y_n, t)$ considered along the integral curve.

By S we shall denote the union of the intervals $[t_k, \tau_k]$. With $t \in S$ the distance from the integral curve under consideration to the origin exceeds ρ_1. Therefore

$$W_1(t, y_{10}, ..., y_{n0}, t_0) \leq \phi_{\rho_1}(t) \text{ for } t \in S. \tag{3.6}$$

From (3.5) and (3.6) with $t \in S$ we have $dV_1/dt \leq \phi_{\rho_1}(t)$.

Integrating both members of the last inequality with respect to S_l, we shall obtain:

$$\int_{S_l} \frac{dV_1}{dt} dt \leq \int_{S_l} \phi_{\rho_1}(t) dt,$$

where

$$S_l = \bigcup_{i=1}^{l} [t_i, \tau_i].$$

Further, we have

$$\sum_{i=1}^{n} V_1(\tau_i, y_{10}, ..., y_{n0}, t_0) - V_1(t_1, y_{10}, ..., y_{n0}, t_0) > - V_1(t_1, y_{10}, ..., y_{n0}, t_0).$$

---

† The case $\sum_{i=1}^{n} y_i^2(t, y_{10}, ..., y_{n0}) > \alpha > 0$ is simpler.

On the other hand, that sum is less than or equal to the integral $\int_{s_1} \phi_{\rho_1}(t)\,dt$, which is impossible, since

$$\int_{s_1} \phi_{\rho_1}(t)\,dt \to -\infty.$$

The contradiction obtained shows that any integral curve of system (1.4) tends to the position of equilibrium as $t \to \infty$.

COROLLARY. By $M(t)$ we shall denote a positive function satisfying the inequality

$$M(t) \geq 1 + \sum_{i=1}^{n} g_i^2(t, y_1, \ldots, y_n) \text{ for } \sum_{i=1}^{n} y_i^2 \leq r^2 \text{ and } t \geq 0.$$

We shall consider the function $M(t)$ as continuous and given for $t \in [0, \infty]$. We shall set

$$\tau = \int_0^t M(t)\,dt$$

and in system (1.4) we shall perform the substitution of τ for t; then we shall obtain

$$\frac{dy_s}{d\tau} = \frac{g_s(t, y_1, \ldots, y_n)}{M(t)} = \bar{g}_s(\tau, y_1, \ldots, y_n) \quad (s = 1, \ldots, n). \tag{3.7}$$

The right-hand members of system (3.7) are bounded, and from the asymptotic stability of its solutions one may draw conclusions as to the asymptotic stability of the homogeneous solution of system (1.4).

Thus the assertion is correct that if there exist two functions $V(\tau, y_1, \ldots, y_n)$ and $W(\tau, y_1, \ldots, y_n)$ satisfying the conditions of Theorem 4, then the homogeneous solution of system (1.4) will be asymptotically stable.

THEOREM 5. If there exists a function $V(t, y_1, \ldots, y_n)$ satisfying the following conditions:

1) the function $V \in L$;

2) there exists a total derivative of the function V as based on system (1.4) $\frac{dV}{dt} = W$, where the function $W(t, y_1, \ldots, y_n)$ is such that if $\sum_{i=1}^{n} y_i^2 > \alpha^2$ then

$$W(t, y_1, \ldots, y_n) \leq \phi_\alpha(t) \leq 0;$$

3) the function $\phi_\alpha(t)$ is integrable in every finite interval of $[0, \infty)$ and

$$\int_{t_0}^{\infty} \phi_\alpha(t)\, dt = -\infty$$

— then the homogeneous solution of system (1.4) is asymptotically stable uniformly with respect to $t_0 \geq 0$.

PROOF: Say the functions indicated in Theorem 5 exist. We shall show then that the homogeneous solution of system (1.4) is asymptotically stable. According to Theorem 2 the homogeneous solution will be stable uniformly with respect to $t_0 \geq 0$. We shall show that asymptotic stability also holds. Say that this is not the case. Then for any $\delta > 0$ there exist numbers $y_{10}, \ldots, y_{n0}, t_0$, defining an integral curve, which do not tend to the position of equilibrium. Then, that integral curve may possess, in general, one of the two properties:

1) either

$$\inf \sum_{i=1}^{n} y_i^2(t, y_{10}, \ldots, y_{n0}, t_0) \geq \alpha^2 > 0 \text{ for } t \geq t_0, \tag{*}$$

2) or

$$\inf \sum_{i=1}^{n} y_i^2(t, y_{10}, \ldots, y_{n0}, t_0) = 0 \text{ for } t \geq t_0.$$

We shall show that in the second case the integral curve necessarily possesses the property

$$\sum_{i=1}^{n} y_i^2(t, y_{10}, \ldots, y_{n0}, t_0) \to 0 \text{ where } t \to \infty.$$

We shall take an arbitrarily small $\varepsilon' > 0$. For it, according to the existing stability, one may find $\delta' > 0$ such that with $\sum_{i=1}^{n} y_{i0}^2 < (\delta')^2$

$$\sum_{i=1}^{n} y_i^2(t, y_{10}, \ldots, y_{n0}, t_0) < (\varepsilon')^2 \tag{3.8}$$

for $t \geq t_0 \geq 0$.

With the presence of the second property, on the integral curve there exists a point whose distance from the coordinate origin exceeds δ'. Let the instant T correspond to that point. Then from (3.8) it follows that with $t \geqq T$ the distance of the integral curve from the origin will be less than ε', which also means that

$$\sum_{i=1}^{n} y_i^2(t, y_{10}, \ldots, y_{n0}, t_0) \to 0 \text{ as } t \to \infty.$$

Thus, the assertion that the integral curve does not tend to the position of equilibrium as $t \to \infty$ is equivalent to the inequality (*). With the fulfillment of the inequality (*) we shall have

$$\frac{dV_1(t, y_{10}, \ldots, y_{n0}, t_0)}{dt} \leqq \phi_\alpha(t). \tag{3.9}$$

Integrating both members of (3.9), we shall obtain

$$V_1(t, y_{10}, \ldots, y_{n0}, t_0) \leqq V(t_0, y_{10}, \ldots, y_{n0}) + \int_{t_0}^{t} \phi_\alpha(\tau)\, d\tau, \tag{3.10}$$

which is impossible, since the right-hand member of the inequality obtained tends to $-\infty$ as $t \to \infty$, and the function $V_1(t, y_{10}, \ldots, y_{n0}, t_0) \geqq 0$.

COROLLARY 1. We shall assume that there exists a function $M(t_0)$ such that

$$M(t_0) \geqq V(t_0, y_{10}, \ldots, y_{n0}) \text{ for } \sum_{i=1}^{n} y_{i0}^2 < \delta^2,$$

where $V(t, y_1 \ldots, y_n)$ is the function dealt with in Theorem 5. If

$$M(t_0) + \int_{t_0}^{\infty} \phi_\alpha(\tau)\, d\tau < 0,$$

then the homogeneous solution of system (1.4) is asymptotically stable. The proof of that assertion follows from inequality (3.10).

COROLLARY 2. If the function $V(t, y_1, \ldots y_n)$ admits of an infinitely small upper bound †, is continuously differentiable with respect to all of its arguments, and has a negative-definite total derivative with respect to t as based on system (1.4), then the homogeneous solution of system (1.4) is asymptotically stable uniformly with respect to $t_0 \geqq 0$.

---

† $V(t, y_1, \ldots, y_n)$ is assumed to be positive-definite.

This Corollary follows from Theorem 5, since in that case V belongs to the class L, and for the function $\phi_\alpha(\tau)$ one may choose a negative constant.

The proposition formulated in Corollary 2 bears the name of Lyapunov's theorem on asymptotic stability [6].

THEOREM 6. In order that the homogeneous solution of system (1.4) be uniformly-asymptotically stable, it is necessary and sufficient that all the conditions of Theorem 3 be satisfied, and that the function

$$V_1(t, y_{10}, \ldots, y_{n0}, t_0) \to 0 \text{ as } t - t_0 \to \infty$$

uniformly with respect to $t_0 \geqq 0$ and $\sum_{i=1}^{n} y_{i0}^2 < \gamma^2$, where γ is a positive constant.

PROOF: *Sufficiency.* Say the conditions of Theorem 6 are satisfied. We shall show then that the homogeneous solution of system (1.4) is uniform-asymptotically stable. In fact, on the basis of Theorem 3 the homogeneous solution of system (1.4) will be asymptotically stable. Let that stability be nonuniform. Then one may indicate numbers h and $\delta < \gamma$ such that there exists a sequence of points $y_{10k}, y_{20k}, \ldots, y_{n0k}, t_{0k}$ and a sequence of numbers t_k such that $(t_k - t_{0k}) \to +\infty$ as $k \to +\infty$, and such that

$$\sum_{i=1}^{n} y_i^2(t_k, y_{10k}, \ldots, y_{n0k}, t_{0k}) \geqq \delta^2.$$

And then, by virtue of the positive-definiteness of the function V,

$$V_1(t_k, y_{10k}, \ldots, y_{n0k}, t_{0k}) > h,$$

which is impossible, since $V_1 \to 0$ as $(t_k - t_{0k}) \to +\infty$.

The contradiction obtained shows that the assertion made is correct.

Necessity. We shall assume that the homogeneous solution of system (1.4) is uniform-asymptotically stable. We shall indicate then that there exists a function $V(y_1, \ldots, y_n, t)$ possessing all the properties indicated in Theorem 6. For this we shall return again to the considerations of the function defined by relation (3.3). That function possesses all the properties formulated in Theorem 3. We shall show that on the integral curves that function tends to zero uniformly as $(t - t_0) \to \infty$.

In fact, the function V is defined in terms of the supremum of the distance from the integral curves to the coordinate origin, which tends to zero uniformly as $(t - t_0) \to + \infty$ with respect to $t_0 \geqq 0$ and $\sum\limits_{i=1}^{n} y_{i0}^2 \leqq \gamma^2$, where γ is a sufficiently small positive quantity. Therefore this property will be possessed also by the function defined by (3.3), as was to be shown.

COROLLARY. If there exists a function V of the class L and a function W which is the total derivative of the function V with respect to t as based on system (1.4), $dV/dt = W$, such that $W \leqq \phi_\alpha(t) \leqq 0$ for $t \geqq 0$ and $\sum\limits_{i=1}^{n} y_i^2 \geqq \alpha^2 > 0$, then the homogeneous solution will be uniform-asymptotically stable provided that the integral $\int\limits_{t_0}^{t+t_0} \phi_\alpha(\tau)\, d\tau \to - \infty$ as $t \to + \infty$ and the function $V(y_1, \ldots, y_n, t)$ is bounded.

In fact, the homogeneous solution of system (1.4) in that case is asymptotically stable uniformly with respect to $t_0 \geqq 0$.

We shall assume that the integral curves tend to zero nonuniformly as $(t - t_0) \to +\infty$. Then there will exist a sequence of points $y_{10k}, \ldots, y_{n0k}, t_{0k}$, $k = 1, 2, 3\ldots$; a number $h > 0$; and numbers $t_k \geqq t_{0k}, (t_k - t_{0k}) \to \infty$ as $k \to \infty$, such that

$$\sum_{i=1}^{n} y_i^2 (t_k, y_{10k}, \ldots, y_{n0k}, t_{0k}) \geqq h^2.$$

Then the entire arc of the integral curve

$$y_s = y_s(t, y_{10k}, \ldots, y_{n0k}, t_{0k}) \quad (s = 1, \ldots, n)$$

should lie within a sphere $\sum\limits_{i=1}^{n} y_i^2 \leqq \delta^2\ (h)$, where $\delta(h)$ is a number chosen for h on the basis of stability. And then $W \leqq \phi_\delta(t)$ [here we have set $\alpha = \delta(h)$]. Integrating the relation $dV/dt = W$, we obtain

$$V_1(t_k, y_{10k}, \ldots, y_{n0k}, t_{0k}) = V(y_{10k}, \ldots, y_{n0k}, t_{0k}) + \int_{t_{0k}}^{t_k} W\, d\tau. \tag{3.11}$$

In (3.11), replacing W by $\phi_\delta(t)$, we shall obtain

$$V_1 \leqq V(y_{10k}, \ldots, y_{n0k}, t_{0k}) + \int_{t_{0k}}^{t_k} \phi_\delta(\tau)\, d\tau. \tag{3.12}$$

The right-hand member of inequality (3.12) becomes negative as $k \to + \infty$ in view of the fact that V is a bounded function and the integral tends to $- \infty$; the left-hand member of inequality (3.12) is positive. The contradiction obtained proves the Theorem.

THEOREM 7. In order that the homogeneous solution of system (1.4) be uniformly attracting, it is necessary and sufficient that there exists a positive-definite function $V(y_1, ..., y_n, t)$ admitting of an infinitely small upper bound. The function $V_1 \ (t, y_{10}, ..., y_{n0}, t_0)$ possesses the properties:

1) for every $h > 0$ there exists a $T > 0$ and $\alpha > 0$ such that

$$V_1(t, y_{10}, ..., y_{n0}, t_0) > \alpha \text{ for } t_0 \leq t \leq t_0 + T \text{ for all } t_0 \geq 0 \text{ and } \sum_{i=1}^{n} y_{i0}^2 \geq h^2;$$

2) V_1 does not increase with $t \geq t_0$ and $V_1 \to 0$ as $t \to +\infty$.

PROOF: *Sufficiency.* According to Theorem 3 the homogeneous solution of system (1.4) is asymptotically stable. We shall show that with the fulfillment of the conditions of Theorem 7, it is uniformly attracting. Assume that this is not the case. Then one can indicate a number $h > 0$ such that for some number $T > 0$ and any $\alpha_1 > 0$ there exists a point $y_{10}, ..., y_{n0}, t_0$ such that if

$$\sum_{i=1}^{n} y_{i0}^2 > h^2; \ t_0 \geq 0, \text{ then } \sum_{i=1}^{n} y_i^2 (t', y_{10}, ..., y_{n0}, t_0) < \alpha_1^2 \text{ for at least one value of}$$

t' in the interval $[t_0, t_0 + T]$. The function V admits of an infinitely small upper bound, therefore the number α_1 may be chosen so small that $V_1(t', y_{10}, ..., y_{n0}, t_0) < \alpha_1$ will hold, and this contradicts the condition of the Theorem. Thus, the sufficiency of the conditions of the Theorem is proved.

Necessity. We shall return again to that function which is defined by means of relation (3.3). That function is defined by the supremum of the distances from the integral curves to the equilibrium position. From this it follows that the function satisfies the same inequalities as the integral curves of system (1.4). Then the conditions of Theorem 7 are satisfied, which was to be shown.

COROLLARY. The homogeneous solution of system (1.4) will be uniformly attracting, provided:

1) there exists a function $V(y_1, ..., y_n, t)$ positive-definite and admitting of an infinitely small upper bound;

2) there exists a function $W(y_1, ..., y_n, t)$ which is the total derivative of function V with respect to t as based on system (1.4), $W \leq 0$;

3) there exists a function $\psi_\beta \ (t)$ such that

$$\psi_\beta \leq W \leq 0 \quad \text{for} \quad \sum_{i=1}^{n} y_i^2 \geq \beta^2$$

and

$$\int_{t_0}^{t_0+T} \psi_\beta(\tau) \, d\tau \to 0 \text{ as } T \to 0$$

uniformly with respect to $t_0 \geq 0$.

In fact, we shall take a number $h > 0$. We shall set

$$\lambda = \inf_{t \geq 0} V(y_1, \ldots, y_n, t).$$

$$\sum_i y_i^2 \geq h^2$$

We shall find a positive number T such that

$$\lambda + \int_{t_0}^{t_0+T} \psi_\beta(\tau)d\tau > \alpha > 0.$$

Now we shall assume that the numbers α and T satisfy the conditions of uniform attraction formulated in Theorem 7. Integrating the relations $dV/dt = W$ along the integral curves of system (1.4), we shall obtain

$$V_1(t, y_{10}, \ldots, y_{n0}, t_0) = V(y_{10}, \ldots, y_{n0}, t_0) + \int_{t_0}^{t} W \, d\tau, \tag{3.13}$$

where $V_1(t, y_{10}, \ldots, y_{n0}, t_0)$ represents, just as before, the value of the function $V(y_1, \ldots, y_n, t)$ on the integral curve of system (1.4).

From equality (3.13) we have

$$V_1(t, y_{10}, \ldots, y_{n0}, t_0) \geq \lambda + \int_{t_0}^{t_0+T} \psi_\beta(\tau)d\tau \quad (t_0 \leq t \leq t_0 + T), \tag{3.14}$$

whence we shall obtain

$$V_1(t, y_{10}, \ldots, y_{n0}, t_0) > \alpha \text{ for } \sum_{i=1}^{n} y_{i0}^2 \geq h^2 \text{ and } t_0 \leq t \leq t_0 + T.$$

The last inequality shows that the function V satisfies all the conditions of Theorem 7, and therefore the homogeneous solution of system (1.4) will be uniformly attracting.

Note that the function $\psi_\beta(t)$ dealt with in this Corollary is known to exist and may be chosen in the form of a negative constant if the function W does not depend on time t or admits of an infinitely small upper bound.

THEOREM 8. In order that the homogeneous solution of system (1.4) be uniform-asymptotically stable and uniformly attracting, it is necessary and sufficient that there exist two functions $V(y_1, \ldots, y_n, t)$ and $W(y_1, \ldots, y_n, t)$ possessing the following properties:

1) the function $V(y_1, \ldots, y_n, t)$ admits of an infinitely small upper bound and is positive-definite;

2) the function $W(y_1, \ldots, y_n, t)$ admits of an infinitely small upper bound and is negative-definite;

3) the function $W(y_1, \ldots, y_n, t)$ is the total derivative of the function $V(y_1, \ldots, y_n, t)$ with respect to t as based on system (1.4), $dV/dt = W$.

PROOF: *Sufficiency.* Say there exist two functions V and W satisfying all the conditions of Theorem 8. We shall show that then the homogeneous solution is uniform-asymptotically stable and uniformly attracting.

By virtue of Corollary 2 of Theorem 5 the homogeneous solution of system (1.4) is asymptotically stable uniformly with respect to $t_0 > 0$. On the basis of the Corollary to Theorem 6 it will be uniform-asymptotically stable.

From the Corollary to Theorem 7 it follows that the homogeneous solution will be uniformly attracting. This completes the proof of the sufficiency of the conditions of Theorem 8.

Necessity. We shall assume that the homogeneous solution of system (1.4) is uniform-asymptotically stable and uniformly attracting. We shall then show that there exist two functions V and W satisfying the conditions of Theorem 8.

We shall first expose the plan of action.

1. First we shall show that from uniform asymptotic stability follows the existence of a continuous function $L(t - t_0)$ given for $t > -\infty$, strictly monotonically decreasing from $+\infty$ to 0 as $t - t_0$ tends to $+\infty$, and such that

$$L(t - t_0) \geqq \sum_{i=1}^{n} y_i^2(t, y_{10}, \ldots, y_{n0}, t_0) \text{ for } t \geqq t_0 \text{ and } \sum_{i=1}^{n} y_{i0}^2 \leqq \delta^2, \quad (**)$$

where δ is some sufficiently small positive constant

2. We shall choose a function

$$W(y_1, \ldots, y_n) = -\sum_{i=1}^{n} y_i^2 e^{-K\left(\sum_{i=1}^{n} y_i^2\right)} \tag{3.15}$$

where K is a function inverse to L (i.e. $K = L^{-1}$).

3. We shall set $V(y_{10}, \ldots, y_{n0}, t_0) = -\int_{t_0}^{+\infty} W dt$ and shall show that this function admits of an infinitely small upper bound, is positive-definite, and its total derivative with respect to t, as based on system (1.4), coincides with W.

To carry out this plan we shall take $\varepsilon > 0$. According to the definition of uniform asymptotic stability we shall find a $\delta(\varepsilon) > 0$ such that if $\sum_{i=1}^{n} y_{i0}^2 < \delta^2$, then

$$\sum_{i=1}^{n} y_i^2(t, y_{10}, \ldots, y_{n0}, t_0) \to 0$$

as $t - t_0 \to \infty$ uniformly with respect to $t_0 \geq 0$ and $y_{10}, \ldots, y_{n0}$. We shall set

$$\lambda(t - t_0) = \sup_{\substack{t_0 \geq 0 \\ \sum_i y_{i0}^2 < \delta^2}} \sum_{i=1}^{n} y_i^2(t, y_{10}, \ldots, y_{n0}, t_0). \qquad (3.16)$$

It is clear that the function λ, defined by means of equality (3.16), is given for $t - t_0 \geq 0$ and possesses the properties: 1) $\lambda \to 0$ as $t - t_0 \to +\infty$; 2) $\lambda(t - t_0) \leq \varepsilon$ for $t - t_0 \geq 0$.

We shall now choose a strictly monotonic $L(\tau)$, given and continuous for $-\infty < \tau < \infty$, strictly monotonically decreasing from $+\infty$ to 0 as τ increases from $-\infty$ to $+\infty$, and such that $L(t - t_0) \geq \lambda(t - t_0)$.

It is easy to see that the function thus constructed satisfies all requirements of point 1 of our programme.

The function W is negative-definite and admits of an infinitely small upper bound, therefore it remains to be shown that the function

$$V(y_{10}, \ldots, y_{n0}, t_0) = -\int_{t_0}^{+\infty} W \, d\tau$$

exists and possesses the indicated properties.

For a number $\varepsilon' > 0$ we shall find, just as above, a $\delta(\varepsilon') > 0$ such that, if $\sum_{i=1}^{n} y_{i0}^2 < \delta^2(\varepsilon')$, then

$$\sum_{i=1}^{n} y_i^2(t, y_{10}, \ldots, y_{n0}, t_0) < (\varepsilon')^2 \ .$$

For all the integral curves with such initial conditions, the inequality

$$e^{-(t-t_0)} \geq e^{-K\left(\sum_{i=1}^{n} y_i^2\right)} \qquad (3.17)$$

will hold. It is obtained from the inequality (**) by applying the inverse function K to both of its members.

From inequality (3.17) and equality (3.15) we obtain

$$V(y_{10},\ldots,y_{n0},t_0) < \int_{t_0}^{+\infty} \sum_{i=1}^{n} y_i^2(\tau,y_{10},\ldots,y_{n0},t_0) e^{-(\tau-t_0)} d\tau \leq (\varepsilon')^2.$$

From this inequality it follows, first of all, that the integral in the right-hand member of (3.15) converges and indeed defines the function V and, secondly, that this function admits of an infinitely small upper bound, since the number ε' may be considered as arbitrarily small.

We shall now show that the function V is positive-definite. From (3.15) it follows that

$$V(y_{10},\ldots,y_{n0},t_0) \geq \int_{t_0}^{t_0+T} \sum_{i=1}^{n} y_i^2 e^{-K\left(\sum_{i=1}^{n} y_i^2\right)} d\tau, \qquad (3.18)$$

which is obtained from (3.15) by discarding the positive term, that is $-\int_{t_0+T}^{\infty} W d\tau$.

Because of the uniform attractingness of the homogeneous solution of the system (1.4), to the number $h > 0$ there corresponds a $T > 0$ and $\alpha > 0$ such that $\sum_{i=1}^{n} y_i^2(t,y_{10},\ldots,y_{n0},t_0) > \alpha^2$ for $\sum_{i=1}^{n} y_{i0}^2 \geq h^2$ and $t_0 \leq t \leq t_0+T$.

Then the expression under the integral sign in inequality (3.18) remains not smaller than a positive number $\gamma(\alpha)$, as the function W is negative-definite.

Therefore, we have

$$V(y_{10},\ldots,y_{n0},t_0) \geq \gamma T \text{ for } \sum_{i=1}^{n} y_{i0}^2 > h^2,$$

which precisely denotes the positive-definiteness of the function V.

It remains to be shown that $dV/dt = W$. For this we shall take a point $y_1',\ldots,y_n'$ on some integral curve, corresponding to the instant $t_0+\Delta t$. Then, according to (3.15),

$$V(y_1',\ldots,y_n',t_0+\Delta t) = -\int_{t_0+\Delta t}^{\infty} W d\tau. \qquad (3.19)$$

Subtracting (3.15) from (3.19) term by term and dividing both members by Δt, we shall obtain

$$\frac{\Delta V}{\Delta t} = \frac{1}{\Delta t} \int_{t_0}^{t_0+\Delta t} W d\tau, \qquad (3.20)$$

where ΔV denotes the increment of the function V along the integral curve. Letting Δt tend to 0, we shall obtain from (3.20) that $dV/dt = W$ along the integral curve.

This completes the proof of Theorem 8.

COROLLARY. Say the homogeneous solution of system (1.4) is asymptotically stable. In that system one may always perform a transformation of the independent variable t in such a way that the homogeneous solution of the newly obtained system be uniformly attracting.

In fact, as the new time in system (1.4) we shall introduce the length of the integral curve in the $(n+1)$–dimensional space $y_1, \ldots, y_n, t$:

$$ds = \sqrt{dt^2 + dy_1^2 + \ldots + dy_n^2} = dt \sqrt{1 + \sum_{i=1}^{n} g_i^2(t, y_1, \ldots, y_n)} . \quad (3.21)$$

Then system (1.4) will become a system of the form

$$\left. \begin{array}{l} \dfrac{dy_k}{ds} = \dfrac{g_k(t, y_1, \ldots, y_n)}{\sqrt{1 + \sum\limits_{i=1}^{n} g_i^2(t, y_1, \ldots, y_n)}} \\[2em] \dfrac{dt}{ds} = \dfrac{1}{\sqrt{1 + \sum\limits_{i=1}^{n} g_i^2(t, y_1, \ldots, y_n)}} \end{array} \right\} \quad (k = 1, \ldots, n). \quad (3.22)$$

If the homogeneous solution of system (1.4) is asymptotically stable, then the homogeneous solution of system (3.22) is uniformly attracting, as may be established in the same way as was done in the Lemma.

Theorem 8 will give the necessary and sufficient conditions for uniform asymptotic stability for system (3.22) without additional requirement for uniform attractingness.

We shall now turn to the symptoms of instability of the homogenous solution of system (1.4).

THEOREM 9. The homogeneous solution of system (1.4) is unstable if there exist two functions $V(y_1, \ldots, y_n, t)$ and $W(y_1, \ldots, y_n, t)$ possessing the following properties:

1) the function V admits of an infinitely small upper bound and takes negative values in an arbitrarily small neighbourhood of the semiaxis (for any fixed $t > T$) $y_1 = \ldots = y_n = 0$ and $t \geq 0$;

2) the function W is the total derivative with respect to t of the function V as based on system (1.4), i.e. $W = dV/dt$;

3) for $\sum\limits_{i=1}^{n} y_i^2 \geq \alpha^2$, $W(y_1,\ldots, y_n, t) \leq \phi_\alpha(t) \leq 0$, where $\phi_\alpha(t)$ is an integrable function and such that $\int\limits_{0}^{t}\phi_\alpha(\tau)d\tau \to -\infty$ as $t \to +\infty$.

PROOF: We shall assume that there exist two functions V and W satisfying conditions 1, 2, and 3 of Theorem 9. We shall then show that the homogeneous solution of system (1.4) is unstable. We shall construct an indirect proof.

We shall assume that the homogeneous solution of system (1.4) is stable. Then, for any $\varepsilon > 0$ there exists a number $\delta > 0$ such that if $\sum\limits_{i=1}^{n} y_{i0}^2 < \delta^2$ then

$$\sum\limits_{i=1}^{n} y_i^2 (t, y_{10},\ldots, y_{n0}, t_0) < \varepsilon^2 \text{ for } t \geq t_0.$$

We shall take a positive number $\varepsilon' < \varepsilon$. Then, one may indicate a number such that if $\sum\limits_{i=1}^{n} y_i^2 < \delta'$ then $|V(y_1, \ldots, y_n, t)| < \varepsilon'$ (because of the presence of an infinitely small upper bound).

We shall choose the points $y_{10}, \ldots, y_{n0}, t_0$ so that $V(y_{10}, \ldots, y_{n0}, t_0) < 0$ and $\sum\limits_{i=1}^{n} y_{i0}^2 < \delta^2$.

If the integral curve of system (1.4) starts at $\sum\limits_{i=1}^{n} y_{i0}^2 < \delta^2$ and with some $t \geq t_0$ is distant from the coordinate origin by less than δ', then for these t $|V_1(t, y_{10}, \ldots, y_{n0}, t_0)| < \varepsilon'$ will hold.

Along the integral curves of system (1.4) there holds the relation $dV/dt = W$, whence

$$V_1(t, y_{10},\ldots, y_{n0}, t_0) = V(y_{10},\ldots, y_{n0}, t_0) + \int\limits_{t_0}^{t} W d\tau. \qquad (3.23)$$

We shall set $\varepsilon' = -V(y_{10}, \ldots, y_{n0}, t_0)$. Then, from relation (3.23) it follows that $V_1(t, y_{10}, \ldots, y_{n0}, t_0) \leq -\varepsilon'$ for $t \geq t_0$ and consequently, with the same values of the independent variable, the inequality

$$\sum\limits_{i=1}^{n} y_i^2(t, y_{10},\ldots, y_{n0}, t_0) \geq (\delta')^2 \qquad (3.24)$$

will hold.

From inequality (3.24) it follows that $W(y_1, \ldots, y_n, t) \leqq \phi'_\delta(t)$ for $t \geqq t_0$ on the indicated integral curve. Applying the latter inequality to (3.23) we shall obtain

$$V_1(t, y_{10}, \ldots, y_{n0}, t_0) \leqq V(y_{10}, \ldots, y_{n0}, t_0) + \int_{t_0}^{t} \phi'_\delta(\tau) d\tau. \qquad (3.25)$$

From (3.25) it follows that $V_1 \to -\infty$ as $t \to +\infty$, and this is impossible, as the function V admits of an infinitely small upper bound.

The contradiction obtained shows that Theorem 9 is true, which was to be shown.

COROLLARY. If the function $V(y_1, \ldots, y_n, t)$ satisfies the first and the second conditions of Theorem 9, and the function W is negative-definite, then the homogeneous solution of system (1.4) will be unstable, as instead of the function $\phi_\delta(t)$ one may take a negative constant. The assertion formulated in this Corollary bears the name of the first theorem of Lyapunov on instability.

THEOREM 10. In order that the homogeneous solution of system (1.4) be unstable, it is necessary and sufficient that there exist two functions $V(y_1, \ldots, y_n, t)$ and $W(y_1, \ldots, y_n, t)$ possessing the following properties:

1) the function V has a total derivative with respect to t as based on system (1.4), continuous on every integral curve, satisfying the relation

$$\frac{dV}{dt} = \lambda V + W, \text{ where } \lambda = \lambda(t, y_1, y_2, \ldots, y_n); \qquad (3.26)$$

2) the function $W(y_1, \ldots, y_n, t)$ is nonnegative;

3) in any sufficiently small neighbourhood of the semiaxis $y_1 = y_2 = \ldots = y_n = 0$; $t \geqq 0$ there exist points at which the function V takes positive values for any fixed $t > T$;

4) there exists a number $\varepsilon > 0$ such that for any $\delta > 0$ $(\delta < \varepsilon)$ the inequality

$$|V[y_1(t), \ldots, y_n(t), t]| \geqq V(y_{10}, \ldots, y_{n0}, t_0) e^{\int_{t_0}^{t} \lambda(\tau) d\tau} \qquad (3.27)$$

is not maintained for all $t \geqq t_0$ for every choice of continuous functions $y_1(t), \ldots, y_n(t)$ such that

$$\sum_{i=1}^{n} y_i^2(t) < \varepsilon^2 \text{ and } y_i(t_0) = y_{i0},$$

where

$$\sum_{i=1}^{n} y_{i0}^2 < \delta^2 \text{ and } V(y_{10}, \ldots, y_{n0}, t_0) > 0.$$

PROOF: *Sufficiency.* Say there exist two functions V and W satisfying the conditions of Theorem 10. We shall then show that the homogeneous solution of system (1.4) is unstable.

Say this is not the case. Then for a number $\varepsilon > 0$ there exists a number $\delta > 0$ such that if $\sum_{i=1}^{n} y_{i0}^2 < \delta^2$ then

$$\sum_{i=1}^{n} y_i^2 (t, y_{10}, \ldots, y_{n0}, t_0) < \varepsilon^2 \tag{3.28}$$

for $t \geq t_0$.

We shall choose $y_{10}, \ldots, y_{n0}, t_0$ in such a way, that the quantity $V(y_{10}, \ldots, y_{n0}, t_0)$ be positive. We shall evaluate the function V on the integral curves satisfying conditions (3.28).

Then from (3.26) we shall obtain a linear differential equation for the function $V_1(t, y_{10}, \ldots, y_{n0}, t_0)$

$$\frac{dV_1}{dt} = \lambda V_1 + W_1, \tag{3.29}$$

where W_1 denotes the function W evaluated on the same integral curve as V. Discarding the nonnegative term of W_1 in (3.29) and integrating the resulting inequality between the limits t_0 and t, we shall obtain

$$V_1(t, y_{10}, \ldots, y_{n0}, t_0) \geq V(y_{10}, \ldots, y_{n0}, t_0) \, e^{\int_{t_0}^{t} \lambda(\tau) d\tau} \qquad \text{for } t \geq t_0,$$

which contradicts relation (3.27), since as the functions $y_i(t)$ one may here consider the integral curve satisfying condition (3.28).

Thus, the homogeneous solution of system (1.4) is unstable.

Necessity. Say the homogeneous solution of system (1.4) is unstable. We shall then show that there exist two functions V and W satisfying the conditions of Theorem 10.

If the homogeneous solution of system (1.4) is unstable, then there exists a positive number ε' such that for any $\delta > 0$, there is a point $y_{10}, \ldots, y_{n0}, t_0$ such that $\sum_{i=1}^{n} y_{i0}^2 < \delta^2$; $t_0 \geq 0$, and such that the inequality $\sum_{i=1}^{n} y_{i0}^2 (t, y_{10}, \ldots, y_{n0}, t_0) < (\varepsilon')^2$ is not fulfilled for all $t \geq t_0$.

Let $t(y_{10}, \ldots, y_{n0}, t_0)$ be the first instant after t_0 when the above-indicated inequality is violated. We shall divide the set of points in the halfcylinder

$\sum\limits_{i=1}^{n} y_i^2 < (\varepsilon')^2; t \geq 0$ into two sets, referring to the first set those points from which issue the integral curves remaining in that cylinder with unlimited increase in time. At this set of points we shall assume $V(y_1, ..., y_n, t) \equiv 0$.

To the other set of points we shall refer all those from which issue integral curves intersecting the surface of the cylinder as time increases.

If $y_{10}, ..., y_{n0}, t_0$ is such a point, then we shall assume

$$V(y_{10}, ..., y_{n0}, t_0) = e^{t_0 - t(y_{10}, ..., y_{n0}, t_0)}.$$

It is clear that in the first case $V_1(t, y_{10}, ..., y_{n0}, t_0)$ is identically equal to zero for $t \geq t_0$.

In the second case

$$V_1(t, y_{10}, ..., y_{n0}, t_0) = e^{t_0 - t(y_{10}, ..., y_{n0}, t_0)},$$

whence follows that $dV/dt = V$, i.e. in that case $\lambda(t) = 1$ and $W = 0$. The function V is nonnegative and bounded, and $\int_{t_0}^{t} \lambda(\tau) d\tau$ diverges as $t - t_0 \to \infty$ since $\lambda(\tau) \equiv 1$.

Consequently, conditions 1–3 of Theorem 10 are satisfied, which was to be shown.

COROLLARY 1. The homogeneous solution of system (1.4) is unstable provided:

1) there exist two functions V and W satisfying the first two conditions of Theorem 10;

2) the function V is bounded;

3) $\int_{t_0}^{t} \lambda(\tau) d\tau \to +\infty$ as $t \to +\infty$.

If the function λ depends on the variables $y_1, y_2, ..., y_n$, then the integral is evaluated along the bounded solutions.

In fact all the conditions of Theorem 10, with the exception of condition 3, are satisfied automatically; but condition 3 is also satisfied in view of the fact that its left-hand member is bounded when the function V is bounded, whereas its right-hand member is unbounded. Nevertheless, one may require merely that

$$\overline{\lim} \int_{t_0}^{t} \lambda(\tau) d\tau = +\infty \text{ as } t \to \infty.$$

COROLLARY 2. If conditions 1 and 2 of Theorem 10 are fulfilled, the function V is bounded, and the function λ is a positive constant, then the homogeneous solution of system (1.4) will be unstable.

The proof of this assertion follows from Corollary 1. The assertion formulated in Corollary 2 bears the name of the second theorem of Lyapunov on instability.

COROLLARY 3. The homogeneous solution of system (1.4) is unstable if there exist two functions V and W satisfying the following conditions:

1) V and W satisfy condition 3 of Theorem 10;

2) the function V is continuously differentiable along the integral curves of the system and $dV/dt = W$;

3) for every number $\varepsilon > 0$ there exists a number $\delta > 0$ such that $V > \varepsilon$ implies $W > \delta$.

In fact, we shall set $\lambda = W/V$; then

$$\frac{dV}{dt} = \lambda V.$$

If $V_0 > 0$ then $V > V_0$, and therefore

$$\int_{t_0}^{t} \lambda(\tau)d\tau \to \infty \text{ as } t \to +\infty.$$

Hence by virtue of Corollary 1 the correctness of the assertion follows. This proposition bears the name of the theorem of N. G. Chetaev on instability.

Remark 1. In §1 we have been considering systems of differential equations but did not formulate those conditions imposed on the right-hand members of the equations for which the theorems formulated are correct. All the theorems of the present section may be applied to the investigation of stability and instability of the free motion of only those systems for which continuous solutions exist, i.e. the condition of uniqueness of these solutions is not a mandatory requirement. We shall note that for the existence of continuous solutions it is sufficient that the right-hand members of the system of differential equations be continuous in the region under consideration, or admit discontinuities of the first kind with respect to t, finite in number in every finite time interval. At the points of discontinuity the right-hand members of the system are assumed to be continuous from the right.

Remark 2. In this section all the theorems referred to the case when the right-hand members of the system of differential equations are given in the region $t \geqq 0$ and $\sum_{i=1}^{n} y_i^2 < r^2$.

However, in real systems processes may be given only for $t \geqq T$ and, correspondingly, the systems of differential equations will be given for $t \geqq T$.

Then, by introducing a new time $\tau = t - T$ we may reduce the investigation to a system of form (1.4).

Remark 3. The theory considered here may also be applied to the investigation of the stability of motion in the case when the right-hand members of the system of differential equations are given only on a finite interval of time of duration T.

This investigation may be carried out by replacing the finite interval by an infinite one in another time reference.

Indeed, let the right-hand members of system (1.4) be given only for $0 \leq t < T$. We shall set $t = \phi(\tau)$, where $\phi(\tau)$ is a continuously differentiable function such that as the argument τ varies monotonically from 0 to $+\infty$, $\phi(\tau)$ varies monotonically from 0 to T.

Then, system (1.4) will take the form

$$\frac{dy_s}{d\tau} = \phi'(\tau)g_s[\phi(\tau), y_1, \ldots, y_n], \quad (s = 1, \ldots, n).$$

We shall note that for a detailed acquaintance with the theory of the second method of Lyapunov it is necessary to study works [7], [8].

§ 4. Investigation of the problem of stability of the homogeneous solution relative to separately given coordinates

In solving engineering problems one is frequently faced with the task of investigating transient processes (other than those of steady state) relative to some given coordinates.

In book [15] an example is given which illustrates the situation mentioned above.

This example shows that it is very important to know the general methods of investigating transient processes relative to separately given coordinates For a more definite formulation of the problem we shall introduce a series of definitions.

DEFINITION 11. The homogeneous solution of system (1.4) we shall call stable with respect to the coordinates $y_1, \ldots, y_k$; $k < n$ if for every $\varepsilon > 0$ there exist two numbers $\delta_1 > 0$ and $\delta_2 > 0$, $\delta_1 < \varepsilon$, such that if

$$\sum_{i=1}^{k} y_{i0}^2 < \delta_1^2 \quad \text{and} \quad \sum_{i=k+1}^{n} y_{i0}^2 < \delta_2^2 \qquad (4.1)$$

then

$$\sum_{i=1}^{k} y_i^2(t, y_{10}, \ldots, y_{n0}, t_0) < \varepsilon^2; \quad t \geq t_0 \qquad (4.2)$$

for any $t_0 \geq 0$.

DEFINITION 12. The homogeneous solution of system (1.4) is called asymptotically stable with respect to the coordinates $y_1, \ldots, y_k$ if for any $\varepsilon > 0$ there exist numbers $\delta_1 > 0$ and $\delta_2 > 0$ such that if (4.1) is satisfied then (4.2) holds and, besides,

$$\sum_{i=1}^{k} y_i^2 (t, y_{10}, \ldots, y_{n0}, t_0) \to 0 \text{ as } t \to + \infty. \tag{4.3}$$

If system (1.4) exhibits a property opposed to the property of stability with respect to the coordinates $y_1, \ldots, y_k$, then it is called unstable with respect to those coordinates.

To clarify these definitions we shall consider a system of two linear differential equations

$$\left. \begin{array}{l} \dfrac{dx}{dt} = g(t)x, \\[2mm] \dfrac{dy}{dt} = f(t)x + h(t)\,y, \end{array} \right\} \tag{4.4}$$

where $g(t)$, $f(t)$, and $h(t)$ are functions given for $t \geq 0$ and are piecewise continuous.

If $\int_{t_0}^{t} g(\tau)\, d\tau$ is bounded from above for $t \geq t_0$, then the homogeneous solution of system (4.4) will be stable with respect to the x coordinate. In fact, system (4.4) has the solution

$$\left. \begin{array}{l} x = x_0 e^{\int_{t_0}^{t} g(\tau) d\tau} \quad ; \\[6mm] y = e^{\int_{t_0}^{t} h(\tau)d\tau} \left[y_0 + \int_{t}^{t} f(\tau) e^{\int_{t_0}^{t} [g(\theta) - h(\theta)] d\theta} x_0 d\tau \right]. \end{array} \right\} \tag{4.5}$$

From the form of that solution follows our assertion, since $|x| < k\,|x_0|$, where

$$k \geq e^{\int_{t_0}^{t} g(\tau) d\tau} \quad .$$

If here in system (4.4) $\int_{t_0}^{t} h(\tau) d\tau$ is not bounded from above, then the homogeneous solution of system (4.4) will not be stable with respect to both x and y coordinates (in the sense of Lyapunov), as the system has the solution $x = 0$, $y = y_0 \exp \int_{t_0}^{\tau} h(\tau)dt$ which takes values lying arbitrarily far from the position of equilibrium.

If $\int_{t_0}^{t} g(\tau)d\tau \to -\infty$ as $t \to +\infty$, then the homogeneous solution of system (4.4) will be asymptotically stable with respect to the coordinate x, while stability with respect to both coordinates in the sense of Lyapunov may even not exist.

As the first equation of system (4.4) coincides with that equation which was considered in §1, the analysis performed there may be carried over to the case of stability with respect to the given coordinates, namely with respect to the x coordinate in system (4.4). This will allow one to analyse the concept of stability and asymptotic stability with respect to given coordinates. Just as in §1, one may arrive at the following conclusions. The fact of stability or asymptotic stability in itself cannot serve as a criterion of the adequacy of the system under consideration, as sufficiently small deviations at the initial instant, in the case of stability (even asymptotic), can lead to inadmissible deviations of the transient process from the free motion followed.

The fact of instability with respect to given coordinates of interest to us also cannot serve as a criterion of inadequacy since to small deflections, in the case of instability on a finite interval T, there may correspond small deviations of the transient process from the free motion followed. Here it is considered that the transient processes which arise in the system interest us for $t \le T$.

This preliminary analysis of the definitions of stability and instability with respect to given coordinates leads us again to the necessity of introducing the concept of technical stability. This concept was formulated in §1 and in view of its generality may be applied in investigating stability with respect to given coordinates.

We shall give the conditions of stability and asymptotic stability with respect to given coordinates $y_1, \ldots, y_k$ of the homogeneous solution of system (1.4). Say that on the basis of some mechanical or physical considerations one knows the estimates (they may be arbitrarily gross) of the behaviour of the transient processes in system (1.4) with respect to the last $n - k$ coordinates

$$|y_i(t, y_{10}, \ldots, y_{n0}, t_0)| \le \eta_i(t, y_{10}, \ldots, y_{n0}, t_0) A_i(t) \quad (i = k + 1, \ldots, n), \quad (4.6)$$

where $\eta_i(t, y_{10}, \ldots, y_{n0}, t_0) \to 0$ with $\sum\limits_{i=1}^{n} y_{i0}^2 \to 0$ uniformly with respect to $t \geq t_0$, and the functions $A_i(t)$, given for $t \geq 0$, are positive and continuously differentiable.

THEOREM 11. In order that the homogeneous solution of system (1.4) be stable with respect to the coordinates $y_1, \ldots, y_k$ it is necessary and sufficient that there exist a function $V(y_1, \ldots, y_n, t)$ satisfying the following conditions:

1) the function $V(y_1, \ldots, y_n, t)$ is given for $t \geq 0$ and $\sum\limits_{i=1}^{n} y_i^2 \leq r^2$;

2) for every number $C_1 > 0$ there is a number $C_2 > 0$ such that if

$$\sum_{i=1}^{k} y_i^2 > C_1^2 \text{ and } \sum_{i=k+1}^{n} y_i^2 A_i^{-2}(t) > C_1^2$$

then

$$V(y_1, \ldots, y_n, t) > C_2;$$

3) for every number $\gamma_1 > 0$ there exists a number $\gamma_2 > 0$ such that if

$$\sum_{i=1}^{k} y_i^2 < \gamma_1^2 \text{ and } \sum_{i=k+1}^{n} y_i^2 A_i^{-2}(t) < \gamma_1^2$$

then

$$V(y_1, \ldots, y_n, t) < \gamma_2;$$

4) the function V (see below) does not increase along the integral curves of system (4.8) on which it is defined.

PROOF: *Sufficiency.* We shall assume that the conditions of Theorem 11 are fulfilled. We shall then show that the homogeneous solution of system (1.4) is stable with respect to the coordinates $y_1, \ldots, y_k$.

In sy.tem (1.4) we shall perform a substitution of the functions sought according to the formulae

$$\left.\begin{array}{l} x_i = y_i, \quad i = 1, \ldots, k; \\ x_i A_i = y_i, \quad i = k+1, \ldots, n. \end{array}\right\} \tag{4.7}$$

Then the newly introduced functions $x_1, \ldots, x_n$ will satisfy the following system of differential equations

$$\left.\begin{array}{l} \dfrac{dx_i}{dt} = g_i(t, x_1, \ldots, x_k, x_{k+1}A_{k+1}, \ldots, x_n A_n); \quad i = 1, \ldots, k; \\[2mm] \dfrac{dx_i}{dt} = \left[-\dfrac{dA_i}{dt}x_i + g_i(t, x_1, \ldots, x_k, x_{k+1}A_{k+1}, \ldots, x_n A_n)\right]\dfrac{1}{A_i} \end{array}\right\} \tag{4.8}$$

We shall perform the substitution of the arguments in the function V. Then we shall obtain a new function $V(x_1, ..., x_n, t)$, which on the basis of condition 2 of Theorem 11 will be positive-definite, and on the basis of condition 3 will admit of an infinitely small upper bound. From that, it follows that the function V satisfies all the conditions of Theorem 2, and therefore the homogeneous solution of system (4.8) is stable. From this fact and from (4.7) it follows that the homogeneous solution of system (1.4) is stable with respect to the coordinates $y_1, ..., y_k$.

Necessity. We shall assume that the homogeneous solution of system (1.4) is stable with respect to the coordinates $y_1, ..., y_n$. Then the homogeneous solution of system (4.8) will be stable in the sense of Lyapunov. Consequently, according to Theorem 2 there exists a function $V(x_1, ..., x_n, t)$ satisfying the following conditions:

1) $V(x_1, ..., x_n, t)$ is positive-definite;

2) $V(x_1, ..., x_n, t)$ admits of an infinitely small upper bound;

3) $V_1(t, x_{10}, ..., x_{n0}, t_0)$ does not increase along the integral curves as based on system (4.8).

We shall replace the arguments of that function according to formulae (4.7); then we shall obtain a function that will satisfy all the conditions of Theorem 11, which was requisite.

COROLLARY. If estimates (4.6) are not initially known, but there exists a function $V(y_1, ..., y_n, t)$ satisfying all the conditions of Theorem 11, then the homogeneous solution of system (1.4) will be stable with respect to the coordinates $y_1, ..., y_k$ $(k < n)$, and for the remaining coordinates estimates (4.6) hold.

Actually, the homogeneous solution of system (4.8) is stable; consequently, the homogeneous solution of system (1.4) will be stable with respect to the coordinates $y_1, ..., y_k$, as has been demonstrated in the proof of Theorem 11. By virtue of stability there exist functions η_i $(i = k + 1, ..., n)$ such that

$$x(t, x_{10}, ..., x_{n0}, t_0) \leq \eta_i(t, x_{10}, ..., x_{n0}, t_0),$$

where η_i possesses the same properties as in (4.6). From that inequality and from formula (4.7) we shall obtain that the estimates

$$|y_i(t, y_{10}, ..., y_{n0}, t_0)| \leq \eta_i(t, y_{10}, ..., y_{n0}, t_0) A_i(t)$$

should hold.

THEOREM 12. In order that the homogeneous solution of system (1.4) be asymptotically stable with respect to the coordinates $y_1, \ldots, y_k$, it is necessary and sufficient that there exist functions $V(y_1, \ldots, y_n, t)$ satisfying all the conditions of Theorem 11 and, besides, that the function V decrease to zero along the integral curves of system (4.8) as $t \to \infty$.

The proof of Theorem 12 is analogous to the one which was given for Theorem 11.

Conclusion. From the proof of Theorem 11 it can be seen that, when conditions (4.6) are satisfied, the investigation of the problem of stability of the homogeneous solution of system (1.4) with respect to the coordinates $y_1, \ldots, y_k$ may be reduced to the investigation of the problem of stability of system (4.8) in the sense of Lyapunov. If relation (4.6) is not established, then the exact reduction is impossible. In that case one has to make use of Theorems 11 and 12. We shall note that the results of this section are connected with work [10].

§ 5. Concept of the region of asymptotic stability

The functions $g_i(y_1, \ldots, y_n, t)$ $(i = 1, \ldots, n)$, appearing in the right-hand members of the equations of system (1.4), may because of continuity be additionally defined in such a way that they be given for

$$-\infty < t < \infty; \quad -\infty < y_i < +\infty \quad (i = 1, \ldots, n).$$

Thus we shall arrive at a system of equations whose right-hand members are defined in the entire $(n+1)$-dimensional space.

For the sake of clarity of the following exposition we shall give a series of definitions applied to the following system of equations.

We shall consider a system of n differential equations

$$\frac{dy_i}{dt} = Y_i(y_1, \ldots, y_n, t) \quad (i = 1, \ldots, n), \tag{5.1}$$

where $Y_i(y_1, \ldots, y_n, t)$ are given as $y_i \in (-\infty, +\infty)$ for $t \in (-\infty, +\infty)$ $(i = 1, \ldots, n)$ and satisfy the conditions guaranteeing the existence of a unique solution $y_i = y_i(t, y_{10}, \ldots, y_{n0}, t_0)$, $(i = 1, \ldots, n)$, which becomes y_{i0} at $t = t_0$, where y_{i0}, t_0 are any finite quantities.

DEFINITION 4*. An asymptotically stable homogeneous solution of system (5.1) is called uniform-asymptotically stable in the sense of Lyapunov if there exist a continuous function $L(z)$, strictly monotonically decreasing from infinity to zero, where $z \in (-\infty, +\infty)$, $L(z) \to 0$ as $z \to \infty$, and an $\varepsilon > 0$ such that if

$$\sqrt{\sum_{i=1}^{n} y_{i0}^2} < \varepsilon \text{ then } \sum_{i=1}^{n} y_i^2(t, y_{10}, ..., y_{n0}, t_0) < L(t - t_0).$$

DEFINITION 5*. An asymptotically stable homogeneous solution we shall call uniformly attracting if for any quantity $h > 0$ there exist quantities τ and $\alpha(h, \tau) > 0$ such that for every solution the inequality

$$\sum_{i=1}^{n} y_i^2(t, y_{10}, ..., y_{n0}, t_0) > \alpha(h, \tau) > 0 \text{ for } \sum_{i=1}^{n} y_{i0}^2 > h^2$$

will be satisfied for all $t_0 > 0$ and for all $t \in [t_0, t_0 + \tau]$; $\tau > 0$.

DEFINITION 13. Let the asymptotic solution of system (5.1) be asymptotically stable. Then the set of all values of $(y_{10}, ..., y_{n0}, t_0)$ for which

$$\sum_{i=1}^{n} y_i^2(t, y_{10}, ..., y_{n0}, t_0) \to 0 \text{ as } t \to \infty,$$

we shall call the region of asymptotic stability. We shall denote that region by A. The boundary of the region A consists of whole trajectories [11].

Below we shall denote by δ_1 an arbitrarily small positive number.

THEOREM 13. In order that the region A, containing together with the axis $y_1 = ... = y_n = 0$ the set $\sum_{i=1}^{n} y_i^2 < \delta_1^2$ and $t \geq 0$, be a region of asymptotic stability of a uniform-asymptotically stable and uniformly attracting homogeneous solution of system (5.1), it is necessary and sufficient that there exist two functions $V(y_1, ..., y_n, t)$ and $W(y_1, ..., y_n)$ possessing the properties:

1) $V(y_1, ..., y_n, t)$ is given in A and continuous there, $W(x_1, ..., x_n)$ is given and continuous for all $y_1, ..., y_n$;
2) $V(y_1, ..., y_n, t)$ is positive-definite,

$$W(y_1, ..., y_n) > \alpha_1(\beta) > 0 \text{ for } \sum_{i=1}^{n} y_i^2 > \beta > 0;$$

3) $V(y_1, ..., y_n, t) \to 0$ as $\sum\limits_{i=1}^{n} y_i^2 \to 0$ uniformly with respect to t, $t \geq 0$, $V(0, ..., 0, t) \equiv 0$;

4) $\lim\limits_{t-t_0 \to 0} \dfrac{\{V[y_1(t, y_{10}, ..., y_{n0}, t_0), ..., y_n(t, y_{10}, ..., y_{n0}, t_0)] - V(y_{10}, ..., y_{n0}, t_0)\}}{t - t_0}$

$$= \frac{dV}{dt} = W(y_{10}, ..., y_{n0});$$

5) $\lim V(y_1, ..., y_n) = -\infty$ as $\sum\limits_{i=1}^{n} (y_i - \bar{y}_i)^2 + (t - \bar{t})^2 \to 0$, where

$(\bar{y}_1, \bar{y}_2, ..., \bar{y}_n, t) \in \bar{A} \subset A$ and is a finite point of the boundary of the region A.

PROOF: *Necessity.* According to Definition 4* there exists a function $L(z)$ continuous and strictly monotonically decreasing to zero. Consequently, there exists also an inverse function $L^{-1}(U)$.

We shall construct the function $W_1(x) = x^2 e^{-L^{-1}(x^2)}$.

$$V(y_{10}, ..., y_{n0}, t_0) = -\int\limits_{t_0}^{+\infty} W[y_1(t, y_{10}, ..., y_{n0}, t_0) ... y_n(t, y_{10}, ..., y_{n0}, t_0)]dt, \quad (5.2)$$

where $(y_{10}, ..., y_{n0}, t_0)$ is any point of the region A.

We shall assume that

$$W_1\left(\sqrt{\sum\limits_{i=1}^{n} y_i^2}\right) = W(y_1, ..., y_n).$$

From Definition 4* follows the estimate

$$W = \sum\limits_{i=1}^{n} y_i^2 e^{-(t-t_0)}$$

and convergence of integral (5.2).

The functions $W(y_1, ..., y_n)$ and $V(y_1, ..., y_n, t)$ will satisfy all the conditions of the Theorem. In fact, it is not hard to establish that the constructed functions are continuous, i.e. condition 1 is fulfilled.

We shall show that the function $V(y_1, \ldots, y_n, t)$ is negative-definite.

Let $\sum\limits_{i=1}^{n} y_{i0}^2 \geqq r_1 \geqq 0;\ r_1 < \delta_1$:

$$V(y_{10}, \ldots, y_{n0}, t_0) = -\int\limits_{0}^{+\infty} W\left[\sqrt{\sum_{i=1}^{n} y_i^2\,(t_0 + \phi, y_{10}, \ldots, y_{n0}, t_0)}\,\right] d\phi,$$

$$V(y_{10}, \ldots, y_{n0}, t_0) < -\int\limits_{0}^{\tau} W\left[\sqrt{\sum_{i=1}^{n} y_i^2(t_0 + \phi, y_{10}, \ldots, y_{n0}, t_0)}\,\right] d\phi.$$

According to Definition 5* there exists a quantity $\alpha\,(y_{10}, \ldots, y_{n0}, \tau)$ such that

$$\sum_{i=1}^{n} y_i^2\,(t_0 + \phi, y_{10}, \ldots, y_{n0}, t_0) > \alpha\,(y_{10}, \ldots, y_{n0}, \tau)\ \text{for}\ 0 \leqq \phi \leqq \tau,$$

and then

$$W\left[\sqrt{\sum_{i=1}^{n} y_i^2\,(t_0 + \phi,\, y_{10}, \ldots, y_{n0}, t_0)}\,\right] > r_2\,(y_{10}, \ldots, y_{n0}).$$

Thus we shall obtain that the functions $V(y_{10}, \ldots, y_{n0}, t_0) < -r_2\tau$ for all $t_0 > 0$. Consequently, the function $V(y_{10}, \ldots, y_{n0}, t_0)$ is negative-definite. Thus, condition 2 is fulfilled.

The function $L(z)$ is strictly monotonic, therefore

$$W\left[\sqrt{\sum_{i=1}^{n} y_i^2\,(t_0 + \phi,\, y_{10}, \ldots, y_{n0}, t_0)}\,\right] \leqq \sum_{i=1}^{n} y_i^2 e^{-(t-t_0)},$$

whence

$$V(y_{10}, \ldots, y_{n0}, t_0) > -\int\limits_{t_0}^{+\infty} \sum_{i=1}^{n} y_i^2 e^{-(t-t_0)}\, dt.$$

Because of asymptotic stability of the homogeneous solution, for every $\varepsilon > 0$ there exists a $\delta > 0$ such that if $t \geqq t_0$ and $\sum\limits_{i=1}^{n} y_{i0}^2 < \delta^2$ then $\sum\limits_{i=1}^{n} y_i^2 < \varepsilon^2$ for every value of $t_0 \geqq 0$. For such values of $y_{10}, \ldots, y_{n0}$

$$V(y_{10}, \ldots, y_{n0}, t_0) > -\int\limits_{t_0}^{+\infty} \varepsilon e^{-(t-t_0)}\, dt \geqq -\varepsilon$$

and condition 3 will be fulfilled.

Say the point $\beta(\bar{y}_1, \ldots, \bar{y}_n, t)$ is a finite point of the boundary of the region A. Further, applying the theorem on integral continuity (here it is assumed that for system (5.1) all the conditions of the theorem on continuity with respect to the initial conditions are satisfied at least, be it only in a sufficiently small neighbourhood of the boundary of region A), we shall show that condition 5 is fulfilled.

The quantity ε may be chosen so that the set of points $y_1, y_2, \ldots, y_n, t$ defined by the inequalities

$$\varepsilon^2 \leq \sum_{i=1}^{n} y_i^2 \leq (\varepsilon + \rho)^2; \ t > 0$$

for sufficiently small $\rho > 0$, does not contain points of the boundary of the region A. For a number $t_1 > t_0$ and a number $\rho > 0$ there exists a quantity $\gamma(\rho, t_1) > 0$ such that if

$$\sum_{i=1}^{n} (\bar{y}_i - y_{i0})^2 + (\bar{t} - t_0)^2 < \gamma^2(\rho, t_1)$$

then

$$\sum_{=1}^{n} [y_i(t, \bar{y}_1, \ldots, \bar{y}_n, \bar{t}) - y_i(t, y_{10}, \ldots, y_{n0}, t_0)]^2 < \rho^2$$

for $t \in [t_0 \, t_1]$.

The integral curve $y_i(t, \bar{y}_1, \ldots, \bar{y}_n, \bar{t})$ $(i = 1, \ldots, n)$ belongs to the region A, and therefore the integral curve $y_i(t, y_{10}, \ldots, y_{n0}, t_0)$ for $t \in [t_0, t_1]$ possesses the property

$$\sum_{i=1}^{n} y_i^2 (t, y_{10}, \ldots, y_{n0}, t_0) > \delta^2(\varepsilon).$$

From this inequality it follows that

$$W[y_1 (y_{10}, \ldots, y_{n0}, t_0) \cdots y_n (t, y_{10}, \ldots, y_{n0}, t_0)] > \alpha(\delta) > 0 \qquad (5.3)$$

for $t \in [t_0, t_1]$.

Substituting (5.3) in (5.2), we shall obtain

$$V(y_{10}, \ldots, y_{n0}, t_0) = - \int_{t_0}^{t_1} W dt - \int_{t_1}^{+\infty} W dt < - \int_{t_0}^{t_1} W dt < - \alpha(\delta)(t_1 - t_0).$$

Thus, for every number $\alpha(\delta)(t_1 - t_0)$ there exists a quantity $\gamma(\rho, t_1)$ such that if

$$\sum_{i=1}^{n} (\bar{y}_i - y_{i0})^2 + (\bar{t} - t_0)^2 < \gamma^2(\rho, t_1)$$

then

$$V(y_{10}, \ldots, y_{n0}, t_0) < - \alpha(\delta)(t_1 - t_0)$$

for

$$\sum_{i=1}^{n} (y_i - \bar{y}_i)^2 + (\bar{t} - t_0)^2 \to 0.$$

Thus, the Lyapunov function allows one to determine the entire region A. It is easy to show that condition 4 is also fulfilled.

Sufficiency. If the functions V and W, satisfying the conditions 1–5, exist then the homogeneous solution of system (5.1) is asymptotically stable in the sense of Lyapunov, as follows directly from Lyapunov's theorem. It remains to be shown that the homogeneous solution is uniformly attracting and that A is the region of asymptotic stability of the homogeneous solution.

We shall show that the homogeneous solution is uniformly attracting. Assume the contrary. Then there exist values of $y_{10}, \dots, y_{n0}$ sufficiently small in absolute value and such that for any $\tau^{(k)}$ there exists a sequence $t_0^{(k)}(\tau, y_{10}, \dots, y_{n0})$ $(k = 1, 2, \dots)$, $t_0^{(k)} \to +\infty$ as $k \to +\infty$, such that

$$\sum_{i=1}^{n} y_i(t_0^{(k)} + \tau, y_{10}, \dots, y_{n0}, t_0^{(k)}) \to 0 \text{ for } k \to +\infty.$$

For such values of $y_{10}, \dots, y_{n0}$ we shall have

$$V(y_{10}, \dots, y_{n0}, t_0^{(k)}) = -\int_0^{+\infty} W\left[\sqrt{\sum_{i=1}^{n} y_i^2(t_0^{(k)} + \phi, y_{10}, \dots, y_{n0}, t_0^{(k)})}\right] d\phi$$

$$= \int_0^{\tau} W d\phi - \int_{\tau}^{T} W d\phi - \int_{T}^{+\infty} W d\phi.$$

For any number $\gamma > 0$ there exists a T and an arbitrarily small τ $(T > \tau)$ such that

$$\int_0^{\tau} W d\phi < \gamma; \quad \int_{T}^{\infty} W d\phi < \gamma.$$

As

$$\sum_{i=1}^{n} y_i^2(t_0^{(k)} + \phi, y_{10}, \dots, y_{n0}, t_0^{(k)}) \to 0$$

as $k \to +\infty$ and for any ϕ, $\tau \leq \phi \leq T$, then the quantity $\int_{\tau}^{T} W d\phi < \gamma$ for all sufficiently large values of k.

Thus for $k > k(\gamma)$ the quantity $V(y_{10}, \dots, y_{n0}, t_0^{(k)}) > -3\gamma$, which is impossible, as the functions $V(y_1, \dots, y_n, t)$ are negative-definite.

Uniform asymptotic stability is proved in work [5] and in works [12], [13].

It is easy to show that any curve beginning in the region A possesses the property

$$\sum_{i=1}^{n} y_i(t, y_{10}, \dots, y_{n0}, t_0) \to 0 \text{ as } t \to +\infty,$$

and that every integral curve possessing such a property necessarily lies in region A. Thus, region A is the region of asymptotic stability of the homogeneous solution. This completes the proof of the Theorem.

Now, in system (5.1) we shall perform the substitution

$$ds = dt \sqrt{1 + \sum_{i=1}^{n} Y_i^2}.$$

Then we shall obtain the system of $n+1$ equations

$$
\left.
\begin{array}{l}
\dfrac{dy_i}{ds} = \dfrac{Y_i(y_1, \ldots, y_n, t)}{\sqrt{1 + \sum\limits_{i=1}^{n} Y_i^2}} \; ; \\[3em]
\dfrac{dt}{ds} = \dfrac{1}{\sqrt{1 + \sum\limits_{i=1}^{n} Y_i^2}} \quad (i = 1, \ldots, n).
\end{array}
\right\}
\tag{5.4}
$$

If the homogeneous solution of system (5.1) is asymptotically stable, then the solution $y_1 = \ldots = y_n = 0; \ t = s$ of system (5.4) will be uniformly attracting.

In fact,

$$s = \int_{t_0}^{t} \sqrt{1 + \sum_{i=1}^{n} Y_i^2} \; dt$$

is the length of arc of the integral curve, and therefore

$$\sum_{i=1}^{n} y_i^2(s, y_{10}, \ldots, y_{n0}, t_0) > \alpha \sum_{i=1}^{n} y_{i0}^2$$

for any

$$s > 0; \ s < (1-\alpha) \sum_{i=1}^{n} y_{i0}^2,$$

where the quantity $\alpha \in (0, 1)$ and $y_i = y_i(s, y_{10}, \ldots, y_{n0}, t_0) \ (i = 1, \ldots, n)$ denotes the solution passing at the instant $s = 0$ through $y_{10}, \ldots, y_{n0}, t_0$.

We shall assume that the soluiton $y_1 = y_2 = \ldots = y_n = 0; \ t = s$ of system (5.4) is uniform-asymptotically stable. In that case one may give a theorem embracing the case when the homogeneous solution of system (5.1) is not uniformly attracting.

THEOREM 14. In order that the region A, containing together with the axis $y_1 = y_2 = \ldots = y_n = 0$ the set $\sum_{i=1}^{n} y_i^2 < \delta_1^2$; $t \geq 0$, be the region of asymptotic stability of the uniform-asymptotically stable homogeneous solution of system (5.1), it is sufficient that there exist two functions $W(y_1, \ldots, y_n)$ and $V(y_1, \ldots, y_n, t)$ possessing the following properties:

1) $V(y_1, \ldots, y_n, t)$ is given in the region A and is continuous there, $W(y_1, \ldots, y_n)$ is given and continuous for all $y_1, \ldots, y_n$;

2) $V(y_1, \ldots, y_n, t)$ is negative-definite and $W(y_1, \ldots, y_n) > \alpha_1(\beta) > 0$ for
$$\sum_{i=1}^{n} y_i^2 > \beta > 0;$$

3) $V(y_1, \ldots, y_n, t) \to 0$ for $\sum_{i=1}^{n} y_i^2 \to 0$ uniformly with respect to t, $t \geq 0$ and $W(0, \ldots, 0) = 0$;

4) $\dfrac{dV}{dt} = W(y_1, \ldots, y_n) \sqrt{1 + \sum_{i=1}^{n} Y_i^2}$;

5) $V(y_1, \ldots, y_n, t) \to -\infty$ as $\sum_{i=1}^{n} (y_i - \bar{y}_i)^2 + (t - \bar{t})^2 \to 0$, where $(\bar{y}_1, \ldots, \bar{y}_n, \bar{t})$ is a point of the boundary of region A.

PROOF: The proof follows from condition 1 of Theorem 5.

If from relation $\sum_{i=1}^{n} y_i^2(t, y_{10}, \ldots, y_{n0}, t_0) \to 0$ as $t - t_0 \to +\infty$ uniformly for all $\sum_{i=1}^{n} y_{i0}^2 < \delta_1^2$ and $t_0 > 0$ it follows that quantity $\sum_{i=1}^{n} y_i^2(s, y_{10}, \ldots, y_{n0}, t_0) \to 0$ as $s \to +\infty$ uniformly with respect to $(y_{10}, \ldots, y_{n0}, t_0)$ where $\sum_{i=1}^{n} y_{i0}^2 < \delta^2$ and $t_0 > 0$, then the conditions of Theorem 14 are also necessary.

In some problems of the theory of automatic control and particularly in the theory of electrical systems the following problem arises.

Let $y_1 = a_1; y_2 = a_2; \ldots; y_n = a_n$ be the steady state of the system under investigation. It is known that the parameters of the system may be chosen so that this steady state be asymptotically stable. It is necessary to determine the set of initial perturbations $y_{i0} = \tilde{y}_i(0) - a_i$ $(i = 1, \ldots, n)$, (where $\tilde{y}_1(t), \ldots, \tilde{y}_n(t)$ are functions describing the transient process of the system), for which the system under consideration returns after some time has passed to its steady state. Here it is considered that some basic part of the automatic control system is given. The control parameters should be chosen so that the set of initial deviations be in some sense the greatest possible.

Below is given one of the general methods of solution for the problem posed. We shall consider that the steady-state motion of the system is located at the coordinate origin, i.e. $y_1 = \ldots = y_n = 0$, which may always be accomplished by replacing the functions sought $\tilde{y}_i = \bar{\eta} + a_i$ $(i = 1, \ldots, n)$.

We shall assume that the transient processes of the system under consideration may be described by means of a system of differential equations

$$\frac{dy_s}{dt} = \sum_{i=1}^{n} p_{si} y_i + \sum_{m_1 + m_2 + \cdots + m_n > 1} P_s^{(m_1, \ldots, m_n)} y_1^{m_1} \ldots y_n^{m_n}, \tag{5.5}$$

whose right-hand members are holomorphic functions of $y_1, \ldots, y_n$.

We shall further assume that coefficients p_{si} and $P_s^{(m_1, \ldots, m_n)}$ are real and that the real parts of the roots of the characteristic equation $|P - \lambda E| = 0$ are negative. For this system of equations we shall construct the functions referred to in Theorem 13 in order to construct by means of them the region of asymptotic stability of the homogeneous solution (5.5) or to approximate that region from within by some enclosed regions. For this we shall consider the equation in partial derivatives †

$$\sum_{i=1}^{n} \frac{\partial V}{\partial y_i} Y_i = \phi(y_1, \ldots, y_n) \left[1 + \sum_{i=1}^{n} Y_i^2 \right] (1 + V). \tag{5.6}$$

Here the function $\phi(y_1, \ldots, y_n)$ is a positive-definite quadratic form of $y_1, \ldots, y_n$. As the function $\phi(y_1, \ldots, y_n)$ one may also take any holomorphic positive function whose smallest terms of expansion in positive integral powers of the quantity $y_1, \ldots, y_n$ form a positive-definite form of degree $2m$; $m \geq 1$.

The factor $1 + \sum_{i=1}^{n} Y_i^2$, standing in the ringt-hand member of equation (5.6), may be replaced by any other holomorphic function $G(y_1, \ldots, y_n)$ such that all the integral curves of the system of equations

$$\frac{dy_s}{d\tau} = \frac{Y_s}{G}$$

are continuable to all values of τ; $-\infty < \tau < +\infty$.

If such a property is possessed by the integral curves of system (5.5), then as the functions $G(y_1, \ldots, y_n)$ one may choose unity.

---

† Eq. (5.6) is obtained from condition 4 of Theorem 14 by replacing V by $\ln(1 + V)$.

As follows from an auxiliary theorem by Lyapunov [2], with such a choice of the function $\phi(y_1, ..., y_n)$, the function $V(y_1, ..., y_n)$ may be uniquely obtained in the form of a power series, converging with sufficiently small $|y_s|$ and which becomes zero for $y_1 = y_2 = ... = y_n = 0$.

We shall seek the solution $V(y_1, ..., y_n)$ in the form of a series

$$V(y_1, ..., y_n) = V_2(y_1, ..., y_n) + V_3(y_1, ..., y_n) + ... + V_m(y_1, ..., y_n) + ... , \quad (5.7)$$

where $V_m(y_1, ..., y_n)$ is a homogeneous form of the m-th degree in the quantities $y_1, ..., y_n$.

Substituting (5.7) in (5.6), we shall obtain for the determination of the forms $V_m(y_1, ..., y_n)$ the system of equations:

$$\sum_{i=1}^{n} \frac{\partial V_2}{\partial y_i} \left(\sum_{k=1}^{n} p_{ik} y_k \right) = \phi(y_1, ..., y_n);$$

$$\left. \sum_{i=1}^{n} \frac{\partial V_m}{\partial y_i} \left(\sum_{k=1}^{n} p_{ik} y_k \right) = R_m(y_1, ..., y_n) \ (m = 3, 4, ...), \right\} \quad (5.8)$$

where R_m is a known form of the m-th degree, if the $V_2, ..., V_{m-1}$ have already been found.

From system (5.8) we shall successively find the forms $V_2, V_3, ...$ The finding of these forms is carried out in the following way. We take an arbitrary quadratic form V_2 with the coefficients to be determined. We substitute it in system (5.8) and equate on the left and on the right the coefficients of the same products $y_i y_j$ $(i, j = 1, ..., n)$. Thereupon we obtain a linear system of algebraic equations whose determinant is necessarily different from zero, and therefore the coefficients of the form V_2 are uniquely defined in terms of the coefficients of the form ϕ and the parameters of the system. Following this, we find the function R_3.

Then we seek the function V_3 as a form of the third system with coefficients to be determined.

Substituting V_3 in (5.8) with $m = 3$ and equating on the right and left the terms with the same powers of $y_1, ..., y_n$, we shall obtain a system of linear equations with a determinant differing from zero. Continuing this procedure further, one may find all the terms of the series defining the function V.

It is known that this series will be convergent in every case in a sufficiently small neighbourhood of the coordinate origin and the quadratic form V_2 will be negative-definite. We shall note that the choice of the function $\phi(y_1, ..., y_n)$

in equation (5.6) influences the domain of convergence of series (5.7); for example, the equation

$$- \sum_{i=1}^{n} y_i \frac{\partial V}{\partial y_i} = \phi(y_1, ..., y_n)(1 + V) \text{ for } \phi = 2 \sum_{i=1}^{n} y_i^2$$

has the solution

$$V(y_1, ..., y_n) = e^{-\sum_{i=1}^{n} y_i^2} - 1,$$

and with $\phi(y_1, ..., y_n)$, equal to

$$\frac{\sum_{i=1}^{n} y_i^2}{\sqrt{\left(1 + \sum_{i=1}^{n} y_i^2\right)^3}} \, ,$$

$$V(y_1, ..., y_n) = e^{\frac{1}{\sqrt{1 + \sum_{i=1}^{n} y_i^2}} - 1} - 1$$

If one seeks in that example $V(y_1, ..., y_n)$ in the form of a series then its domain of convergence in the former case will be the entire space, whereas in the latter, only a limited portion of it.

We shall consider an equation of the first order

$$\frac{dy}{dt} = f(y),$$

where $f(y)$ is an entire function having no real roots other than $y = 0$. The equation for the function will have the form

$$f(y) \frac{\partial V}{\partial y} = \phi(y)(1 + f^2)(1 + V)$$

It is not hard to show that, with $\phi = f^2$, V is also obtained as an entire function; moreover, if $f(y)$ does not have a linear term in its expansion in integral powers of y, then by the choice of the function ϕ one may arrive at obtaining V in the form of a series.

These problems have to be solved for the case of a system of equations.

We shall now give a method of constructing a region entirely contained in the region A. We shall construct a family of surfaces $V_2(y_1, ..., y_n) = -\mu$ [see (5.7)], where $\mu \in (0, +\infty)$, $\mu = \mathrm{const}$. If the surface s is the boundary of the region A, then there will exist a value of $\mu = \bar{\mu}$ such that the surface $V_2(y_1, ..., y_n) = -\bar{\mu}$ will be tangent to the surface s at some point. In fact, as the family of the surfaces $V_2 = -\mu$ fills the whole space there will exist a value of μ such that $V_2 = -\mu$ will intersect the surface s. By $-\bar{\mu}$ we shall denote the greatest value of $V_2(y_1, ..., y_n)$ on the segment of the surface s included within the surface $V_2 = -\mu$. Then $V_2(y_1, ..., y_n) = -\bar{\mu}$ will be tangent to s.

As has been shown earlier, the surface s has the equation $1 + V(X) = 0$. Then at the point of tangency $\bar{X}$ we shall have

$$\sum_{i=1}^{n} \frac{\partial V}{\partial x_i} Y_i = 0,$$

$$\frac{\partial V/\partial x_1}{\partial V_2/\partial x_1} = \frac{\partial V/\partial x_2}{\partial V_2/\partial x_2} = ... = \frac{\partial V/\partial x_n}{\partial V_2/\partial x_n} ,$$

whence we have

$$\sum_{i=1}^{n} Y_i \frac{\partial V_2}{\partial x_i} = 0$$

(the case when s lies entirely within the region A is excluded).

We shall note that $V_2(X)$ is a Lyapunov function for system (5.5). We shall find dV_2/dt as based on system (5.5):

$$W = \frac{dV_2}{dt} = \sum_{i=1}^{n} \frac{\partial V_2}{\partial y_i} Y_i = \phi(X) +$$
$$+ \sum_{i=1}^{n} \frac{\partial V_2}{\partial x_i} \left(\sum_{m_1 + ... + m_n > 1} P_i^{(m_1, ..., m_n)} y_1^{m_1} y_2^{m_2} ... y_n^{m_n} \right).$$

The function W is positive-definite. We shall find the set of points X satisfying the equation $W(X) = 0$ and shall denote it by W_0, considering that the point $X = 0$ does not belong to the set W_0. We shall find the greatest value of the function $V_2(X)$ on the set W_0 and denote it by $-\mu_0$. The value of μ_0 is positive since $W(X)$ is a positive-definite function.

The following proposition holds: the surface $V_2(X) = -\mu_0$ is entirely contained in the region A.

Indeed, we shall assume the contrary, i.e. that the surface $V_2(X) = -\mu_0$ is partially contained in the region A. This family of surfaces represents a family of ellipsoids filling the whole space with $0 \le \mu < +\infty$. Then on the segment of the surface s there exists a point at which the function $V_2(X)$ reaches its greatest value $-\mu_0$. As has been shown, at that point $W = 0$, which is impossible, since $-\mu_0$ is the greatest value of $V_2(X)$ on the set W_0. Hence the value $-\mu_0$ is not to be considered as the greatest one for the function V_2 on the set W_0, whence follows our assertion.

We shall note that in our discussion the function ϕ is an arbitrary positive-definite quadratic form. Thus,

$$V(X) = -\mu_0 \tag{5.9}$$

is a family of curves depending on the parameters $a_{ik} = \phi''_{x_i x_k}$.

Making use of this, one may formulate a series of indications for establishing the nature of the region of stability.

In order for the region of stability to be bounded, it is necessary that the family of surfaces (5.9) be bounded; and for the unboundedness of the region of stability, it is sufficient that this family be unbounded.

For a practical application of the method indicated, one may successfully make use of the family of surfaces

$$s_n = -\mu, \tag{5.10}$$

where

$$s_n = V_2(X) + \ldots + V_n(X),$$

where we consider that $s_n = -\mu$ bounds the region $s_n > -\mu$ containing the coordinate origin $X = 0$.

Analogously we shall define for that family a function $W_n(X)$, $W_n(X) = ds_n/dt$, and a set of its zeros W_{0n}, where $X = 0$ does not belong to W_{0n}. Just as earlier, one may show that the surface $s_n = -\mu_{0n}$ is entirely contained in the region of stability, and the conclusions formulated above may be carried over to family (5.10). This is the method proposed for constructing a family of regions wholly contained in the region A.

The idea of constructing some region which belongs entirely to A, based on the application of the Lyapunov function, had been applied by Lyapunov himself, and later in different forms by other authors. In the present section this idea is used in a somewhat different form.

Generally speaking, as n increases the family $s_n = -\mu_{0n}$ represents the boundary of the region A ever more exactly.

Here it should be noted that a special role is played by those systems of automatic control in which there is a unique steady state, asymptotically stable, in the large, i.e. such a steady state that its region of attraction coincides with the entire phase space.

It is self-understood that the general theorems on stability in the large indicate only the direction for investigating such systems. Therefore, for investigating concrete classes of automatic control systems it is very important to have a well-developed mathematical apparatus taking into account the peculiarities of these systems.

In this connection one should note work [13] which was first to indicate a method of constructing special Lyapunov functions exhibiting stability in the large, and also a series of investigations carried out by E. A. Barbashin, N. N. Krasovskiy, N. P. Yerugin, V. A. Plis, and a series of other authors.

CHAPTER II

INVESTIGATION OF TRANSIENT PROCESSES IN LINEAR SYSTEMS WITH VARIABLE COEFFICIENTS

§ 6. Necessary and sufficient conditions for stability and asymptotic stability of a definite type

We shall consider a linear system of differential equations

$$\frac{dy_s}{dt} = \sum_{i=1}^{n} p_{si}(t) y_i \quad (s = 1, ..., n); \ t \in [0, + \infty), \tag{6.1}$$

where the functions $p_{si}(t)$ are real, single-valued, and piecewise-continuous with a finite number of discontinuities of the first kind in every finite interval.

System (6.1) may be considered as a linear approximation to system (1.4), and therefore the character of the solution of system (6.1) is essentially related to the behaviour of the solution of system (1.4). To be more exact, if the homogeneous solution of system (6.1) is stable or asymptotically stable, then the homogeneous solution of system (1.4) will correspondingly also be stable or asymptotically stable with arbitrarily general assumptions relative to the nonlinear terms. They will be discussed in greater detail later.

From the above follows the significance of the criteria for stability and asymptotic stability of linear systems in the solution of the general problem on stability of the homogeneous solution of system (1.4).

If in system (6.1) all the coefficients are constant, then the solution of the problem of asymptotic stability reduces to the investigation of the roots of the equation $|P - \lambda E| = 0$, where P is the matrix $P = \{p_{si}\}$, constructed from the coefficients of system (6.1).

If these roots have negative real parts, then the homogeneous solution of system (6.1), in the case of constant coefficients, will be asymptotically stable, as can be established with the aid of the Routh-Hurwitz criterion or with the aid of D-expansions. It is also known that the homogeneous solution will be stable if among the roots there are roots with zero real parts and to the latter correspond simple elementary divisors of the matrix P, while the remaining roots have negative real parts.

70

If among the roots of that equation there is at least one with a positive real part or if to the roots with a zero real part correspond non-simple elementary divisors, then the homogeneous solution (6.1) in the case of constant coefficients will be unstable. This terminates the investigatioo of the problem of stability for systems with constant coefficients.

A formal carry-over of this method to linear systems with variable coefficients is inadmissible, as is apparent from the following example [14].

We shall consider the system of two equations:

$$x'_1 = (-1 - 9\cos^2 6t + 12\sin 6t \cos 6t)x_1 + (12\cos^2 6t + 9\sin 6t \cos 6t)x_2;$$

$$x'_2 = (-12\sin^2 6t + 9\sin 6t \cos 6t)x_1 - (1 + 9\sin^2 6t + 12\sin 6t \cos 6t)x_2.$$

$\lambda_1 = -1; \lambda_2 = -10$ are the roots of the equation

$$\begin{vmatrix} (-1 - 9\cos^2 6t + 12\sin 6t \cos 6t) - \lambda & (12\cos^2 6t + 9\sin 6t \cos 6t) \\ (-12\sin^2 6t + 9\sin 6t \cos 6t) & (-1 - 9\sin^2 6t - 12\sin 6t \cos 6t) - \lambda \end{vmatrix} = 0.$$

Consequently, if one carries over formally the criterion of asymptotic stability to systems with variable coefficients, then in this case the homogeneous solution of that system should have been asymptotically stable. However this is not the case, since this system has the fundamental system of solutions:

$$x_{11} = e^{2t}(\cos 6t + 2\sin 6t); \quad x_{12} = e^{-13t}(\sin 6t - 2\cos 6t);$$

$$x_{21} = e^{2t}(\cos 6t - \sin 6t); \quad x_{22} = e^{-13t}(2\sin 6t + \cos 6t).$$

For the sake of brevity, in what follows we shall denote by r the distance from the point $y_1, ..., y_n$ to the coordinate origin:

$$r = \sqrt{y_1^2 + ... + y_n^2}.$$

The distance from the integral curve to the coordinate origin we shall denote by

$$r(t, y_{10}, ..., y_{n0}, t_0) = \sqrt{\sum_{i=1}^{n} y_i^2 (t, y_{10}, ..., y_{n0}, t_0)},$$

and the distance from the initial point to the coordinate origin by

$$r_0 = \sqrt{\sum y_{i0}^2}.$$

THEOREM 15. In order that every solution of system (6.1) satisfy the inequalities

$$r_0\phi_1^{\frac{1}{2}}(t_0)\phi_2^{-\frac{1}{2}}(t)e^{-\frac{1}{2}\int_{t_0}^{t}\frac{\psi_1}{\phi_1}dt} \leq r(t, y_{10}, \ldots, y_{n0}, t_0) \leq r_0\phi_2^{\frac{1}{2}}(t_0)\phi_1^{-\frac{1}{2}}(t)e^{-\frac{1}{2}\int_{t_0}^{t}\frac{\psi_2}{\phi_2}dt}$$

for $t \geq t_0$,   (6.2)

it is sufficient that there exist two quadratic formulae

$$V = \sum_{i,j=1}^{n} a_{ij}(t)\, y_i y_j,$$

$$W = \sum_{i,j=1}^{n} b_{ij}(t)\, y_i y_j,$$

satisfying the following conditions:

1) the function V is nonnegative and satisfies the inequalities

$$\phi_1(t)\, r^2 \leq V \leq \phi_2(t)\, r^2;$$ (6.3)

2) the function W satisfies the inequalities

$$-\psi_1(t)\, r^2 \leq W \leq -\psi_2(t)\, r^2;$$ (6.4)

3) the functions $\phi_i(t) > 0$; $\psi_i(t) \geq 0$ for $t \geq 0$ and the functions ψ_i/ϕ_i are integrable;

4) the function W is the total derivative with respect to t of the function V as based on system (6.1)

$$\frac{dV}{dt} = W.$$ (6.5)

PROOF: We shall assume that there exist functions V and W satisfying all the conditions of Theorem 15. We shall then show that every integral curve of system (6.1) satisfies inequalities (6.2).

Indeed, we shall divide both members of the inequality (6.5) by, V and integrate, between the limits from t_0 to t. Then we shall obtain

$$\int_{t_0}^{t} \frac{dV}{V} = \int_{t_0}^{t} \frac{W}{V}\, dt,$$

whence

$$V_1(t, y_{10}, \ldots, y_{n0}, t_0) = V(y_{10}, \ldots, y_{n0}, t_0)e^{\int_{t_0}^{t}\frac{W}{V}dt}.$$ (6.6)

The function V_1, standing in the left-hand member of equality (6.6), is the value of the function V on the chosen integral curve of system (6.1).

We shall estimate the integral entering in the right-hand member of (6.6). For this we shall consider the expression under the integral sign

$$\frac{W}{V} = \frac{\sum\limits_{i,j=1}^{n} b_{ij}(t)\, y_i y_j}{\sum\limits_{i,j=1}^{n} a_{ij}(t) y_i y_j}.$$

If we now replace the numerator and the denominator of that fraction with the larger values from formulae (6.3) and (6.4), we shall obtain

$$\frac{W}{V} \leqq - \frac{\psi_2}{\phi_2}.$$

If the numerator of the fraction W/V is replaced by the smallest value from equality (6.4) and the denominator, by the smallest value from (6.3), then we shall obtain

$$\frac{W}{V} \geqq - \frac{\psi_1}{\phi_1}.$$

Combining the two inequalities obtained, we shall have

$$- \frac{\psi_1}{\phi_1} \leqq \frac{W}{V} \leqq - \frac{\psi_2}{\phi_2}. \tag{6.7}$$

Applying inequalities (6.7) to relation (6.6), we shall obtain

$$V(y_{10}, \ldots, y_{n0}, t_0) \cdot e^{-\int\limits_{t_0}^{t} \frac{\psi_1}{\phi_1} dt} \leqq V_1(t, y_{10}, \ldots, y_{n0}, t_0) \leqq$$

$$\leqq V(y_{10}, \ldots, y_{n0}, t_0) \cdot e^{-\int\limits_{t_0}^{t} \frac{\psi_2}{\phi_2} dt}. \tag{6.8}$$

We shall replace the function $V(y_{10}, \ldots, y_{n0}, t_0)$ by its smallest value from the inequality (6.3), and the function $V_1(t, y_{10}, \ldots, y_{n0}, t_0)$, by its greatest value from the same inequality. Then we shall obtain

$$\phi_1(t_0) r_0^2 e^{-\int\limits_{t_0}^{t} \frac{\psi_1}{\phi_1} dt} \leqq r^2(t, y_{10}, \ldots, y_{n0}, t_0)\, \phi_2(t).$$

Analogously we shall obtain

$$r^2(t, y_{10}, \ldots, y_{n0}, t_0)\, \phi_1(t) \leqq \phi_2(t_0) r_0^2 e^{-\int\limits_{t_0}^{t} \frac{\psi_2}{\phi_2} dt}.$$

Extracting the square root of both members of the last inequalities and combining them, we shall obtain (6.2), which was to be shown.

COROLLARY 1.   If the function

$$\phi_1^{-\frac{1}{2}}(t)\phi_2^{\frac{1}{2}}(t_0)e^{-\frac{1}{2}\int_{t_0}^{t}\frac{\psi_2}{\phi_2}dt}$$

is bounded from above for all $t \geq t_0 \geq 0$, then the homogeneous solution of system (6.1) is stable.

Indeed from the estimate (6.2) it is apparent that if

$$\phi_1^{-\frac{1}{2}}(t)\phi_2^{\frac{1}{2}}(t_0)e^{-\frac{1}{2}\int_{t_0}^{t}\frac{\psi_2}{\phi_2}dt} < k < +\infty$$

and

$$\sum_{i=1}^{n} y_{i0}^2 < \delta^2; \quad \delta = \frac{\varepsilon}{k},$$

then any solution of system (6.1) will satisfy the inequality

$$r(t, y_{10}, ..., y_{n0}, t_0) < \varepsilon \text{ for } t \geq t_0,$$

which proves the stability of the homogeneous solution of system (6.1).

COROLLARY 2.   If the functions

$$\phi_2^{-\frac{1}{2}}(t)\phi_2^{\frac{1}{2}}(t_0)e^{-\frac{1}{2}\int_{t_0}^{t}\frac{\psi_2}{\phi_2}dt}$$

are bounded and, besides, tend to 0 as $t \to +\infty$, then the homogeneous solution of system (6.1) is asymptotically stable.

It is obvious that in the formulation of Corollaries 1 and 2 one assumes the presence of the quadratic forms V and W satisfying the conditions of Theorem 15.

THEOREM 16.   In order that every solution of system (6.1) satisfy inequalities of the form

$$p_1 r_0 \phi^{\frac{1}{2}}(t_0)\phi^{-\frac{1}{2}}(t)e^{-p_2\int_{t_0}^{t}\frac{\psi}{\phi}dt} \leq r(t, y_{10}, ..., y_{n0}, t_0) \leq$$

$$\leq q_1 r_0 \phi^{\frac{1}{2}}(t_0)\phi^{-\frac{1}{2}}(t)e^{-q_2\int_{t_0}^{t}\frac{\psi}{\phi}dt} \qquad \text{for } t \geq t_0 , \qquad (6.9)$$

it is necessary and sufficient that there exist two quadratic forms

$$V = \sum_{i,j=1}^{n} a_{ij}(t)y_i y_j,$$

$$W = \sum_{i,j=1}^{n} b_{ij}(t)y_i y_j,$$

satisfying the conditions:

1)   the function V is nonnegative and satisfies the inequalities

$$a_1\phi(t)r^2 \le V \le a_2\phi(t)r^2; \quad a_i > 0, \ i = 1,2; \tag{6.10}$$

2)   the function W satisfies the inequalities

$$-b_1\psi(t)r^2 \le W \le -b_2\psi(t)r^2; \ b_i > 0, \ i = 1,2; \tag{6.11}$$

3)   the function $\phi(t) > 0$; $\psi(t) \ge 0$ for $t \ge 0$; the function ψ/ϕ is integrable;

4)   the function W is the total derivative of the function V with respect to t as based on system (6.1)

$$\frac{dV}{dt} = W. \tag{6.12}$$

PROOF: *Necessity.* We shall assume that any integrable curve of system (6.1) satisfies inequality (6.9). We shall take the quadratic form W in the form

$$W = -\psi(t)r^2.$$

We   shall   set

$$V(y_{10}, \ldots, y_{n0}, t_0) = -\int_{t_0}^{+\infty} W\,dt. \tag{6.13}$$

To estimate the integral standing in the right-hand member of (6.13), we shall apply inequality (6.9). Then we shall obtain

$$\psi\, p_1^2\, r_0^2\, \phi(t_0)\phi^{-1}(t)\, e^{-2p_2\int_{t_0}^{t}\frac{\psi}{\phi}dt} \le -W \le \psi\, q_1^2\, r_0^2\, \phi(t_0)\phi^{-1}(t)\, e^{-2q_2\int_{t_0}^{t}\frac{\psi}{\phi}dt}.$$

Integrating between the limits from t_0 to $+\infty$, we shall have

$$\int_{t_0}^{\infty} \psi p_1^2 r_0^2 \phi^{-1}(t)\phi(t_0)\, e^{-2p_2\int_{t_0}^{t}\frac{\psi}{\phi}dt}\, dt \le V(y_{10}, \ldots, y_{n0}, t_0) \le$$

$$\le \int_{t_0}^{\infty} \psi q_1^2 r_0^2 \phi(t_0)\phi^{-1}(t)e^{-2q_2\int_{t_0}^{t}\frac{\psi}{\phi}dt}\, dt. \tag{6.14}$$

Setting in (6.14) $\theta = \int_{t_0}^{t} (\psi/\phi)\ dt$, we shall obtain

$$p_1^2 r_0^2 \phi(t_0) \int_0^{\theta(\infty)} e^{-2p_2\theta}\ d\theta \leq V(y_{10}, \ldots, y_{n0}, t_0) \leq q_1^2 r_0^2 \phi(t_0) \int_0^{\theta(\infty)} e^{-2q_2\theta} d\theta, \quad (6.15)$$

where

$$\theta\ (\infty)\ =\ \int_{t_0}^{\infty} \frac{\psi}{\phi}\ dt.$$

System (6.1) is linear, therefore its solution is linearly dependent on the initial conditions $y_{10}, \ldots, y_{n0}$ (see [1]). Therefore the function V satisfying inequalities (6.15), will be a quadratic form. The integrals standing in both members of (6.15) converge, and therefore (6.15) becomes an inequality of the form (6.10).

The function V may be differentiated as based on system (6.1), $dV\,dt = W$.

The proof of this fact has already been given in chapter I.

Sufficiency. The sufficiency of the conditions of Theorem 16 follows from Theorem 15.

COROLLARY 1.   If $\phi(t) = \psi(t) = 1$, then every solution of system (6.1) satisfies the inequalities

$$p_1 r_0 e^{-p_2(t-t_0)} \leq r(t, y_{10}, \ldots, y_{n0}, t_0) \leq q_1 r_0 e^{-q_2(t-t_0)}. \quad (6.16)$$

Also conversely, if any solution of system (6.1) satisfies conditions (6.16), then there exist two quadratic forms V and W satisfying the inequalities

$$a_1 r^2 \leq V \leq a_2 r^2; \quad (6.17)$$

$$- b_1 r^2 \leq W \leq - b_2 r^2. \quad (6.18)$$

COROLLARY 2.   If all the coefficients of system (6.1) are bounded in absolute value for $t \geq 0$, then in order that the homogeneous solution of system (6.1) be asymptotically stable and that every solution satisfy an estimate of the form

$$r(t, y_{10}, \ldots, y_{n0}, t_0) \leq \alpha_1 r_0 e^{-\beta_1(t-t_0)}, \quad (6.19)$$

where $\alpha_1, \beta_1 \geq 0$ for $t \geq t_0$, it is necessary and sufficient that there exist two quadratic forms V and W satisfying conditions (6.17) and (6.18).

In fact, as has been shown by A. M. Lyapunov, every solution of system (6.1) with bounded coefficients satisfies the inequality

$$r(t, y_{10}, \ldots, y_{n0}, t_0) \geqq L_1 r_0 e^{-\beta_1(t-t_0)} \text{ for } t \geqq t_0 , \tag{6.20}$$

where $\alpha_1, \beta_1 \geqq 0$.

From inequalities (6.19) and (6.20) it follows that an inequality of the form (6.16) is satisfied, and then from Corollary 2 follows the evidence for the existence of two quadratic forms V and W satisfying (6.17) and (6.18).

The converse assertion is contained in Corollary 1.

The proposition formulated in Corollary 2 is contained in I. G. Malkin's book [6].

EXAMPLES

As an example we shall consider the following system:

$$\frac{dy_s}{dt} = \sum_{i=1}^{n} \sum_{k=1}^{m} p_{si}^{(k)} t^k y_i , \tag{A}$$

where $s = 1, \ldots, n$; $p_{si}^{(k)}$ are constants.

We shall seek the function $V(y_1, \ldots, y_n, t)$ in the following form

$$V(y_1, \ldots, y_n, t) = \sum_{k=0}^{m} V_k(y_1, \ldots, y_n) t^k,$$

where $V_k(y_1, \ldots, y_n)$ is a quadratic form in the variables $y_1, \ldots, y_n$ with the coefficients to be determined.

We shall construct the total derivative of the function $V(y_1, \ldots, y_n, t)$ with respect to t as based on system (A).

$$\frac{dV}{dt} = \sum_{k=0}^{m} \frac{dV_k}{dt} t^k + \sum_{k=1}^{m} k V_k t^{k-1} = \sum_{k=0}^{m} \sum_{s=1}^{n} \frac{\partial V_k}{\partial y_s} \sum_{i=1}^{n} p_{si}(t) y_i t^k + \sum_{k=1}^{m} k t^{k-1} V_k ,$$

where $p_{si}(t) = \sum_{k=0}^{m} p_{si}^{(k)} t^k$,

whence

$$\frac{dV}{dt} = \sum_{k=0}^{m} \sum_{s=1}^{n} \frac{\partial V_k}{\partial y_s} \sum_{i=1}^{n} p_{si}^{(m)} y_i t^{k+m} + \ldots .$$

We shall set

$$\frac{dV}{dt} = W = \sum_{k=0}^{2m} t^k W_k ,$$

where W_{2m} is a negative-definite quadratic form in the variables $y_1, \ldots, y_n$.

If the matrix P_m has characteristic values with negative real parts, then from equation $dV/dt = W$ one will be able to determine all the forms V_k, whatever the quadratic forms W_k $(k = 0, ..., 2m-1)$, where $V_m(y_1, ..., y_n)$ is determined as a positive-definite form.

Setting

$$V(y_1, ..., y_n, t) = t^m \sum_{i,j=1}^{n} a_{ij}(t) y_i y_j ,$$

$$W(y_1, ..., y_n, t) = t^{2m} \sum_{i,j=1}^{n} b_{ij}(t) y_i y_j ,$$

for $t > T$ we shall have

$$- b_1 \sum_{i=1}^{n} y_i^2 \leq \sum_{i,j=1}^{n} b_{ij}(t) y_i y_j \leq - b_2 \sum_{i=1}^{n} y_i^2 ,$$

$$a_1 \sum_{i=1}^{n} y_i^2 \leq \sum_{i. j=1}^{n} a_{ij}(t) y_i y_j \leq a_2 \sum_{i=1}^{n} y_i^2 ,$$

where a_1, a_2, b_1, b_2 are positive constants.

On the basis of Theorem 16

$$l_1 \sum_{i=1}^{n} y_{i0}^2 \left(\frac{t_0}{t}\right)^m e^{-\dfrac{k_1\left(t^{m+1}-t_0^{m+1}\right)}{m+1}} \leq \sum_{i=1}^{n} y_i^2(t, y_{10}, ..., y_{n0}, t_0) \leq$$

$$\leq l_2 \sum_{i=1}^{n} y_{i0}^2 \left(\frac{t_0}{t}\right)^m e^{-\dfrac{k_2\left(t^{m+1}-t_0^{m+1}\right)}{m+1}} \qquad (B)$$

for $t_0 > T$ and any $y_{10}, ..., y_{n0}$.

We shall consider the system

$$\frac{dy_s}{dt} = \sum_{i=1}^{n} a_{si}^{(k)}(t) y_i \quad (s = 1, ..., n) , \qquad (C)$$

where $a_{si}^{(k)}(t)$ are continuous functions given for $t \geq 0$.

The following assertion holds: if for a function $a_{si}^{(k)}(t)$ there exist polynomials

$$\sum_{k=0}^{n} p_{si}^{(k)} t^k,$$

where $p_{si}^{(k)}$ are real constant numbers such that

$$\frac{a_{si}^{(k)} - \displaystyle\sum_{k=0}^{n} p_{si}^{(k)} t^k}{t^m} \to 0 \text{ as } t \to +\infty$$

and the characteristic values of the matrix $P_m = \{p_{si}^{(m)}\}$ have negative real parts, then the homogeneous solution of system (C) will be asymptotically stable. Then every solution of the system will satisfy the estimates of form (B).

Indeed, system (C) may be written in the form

$$\frac{dy_s}{dt} = \sum_{i=1}^{n} \sum_{k=0}^{m} p_{si}^{(k)} t^k y_i + \sum_{i=1}^{n} R_{si}(t) y_i .$$

Thus system (B) may be investigated with the aid of these functions which had been used in system (A).

For system (A) functions $V(y_1, \ldots, y_n, t)$, $W(y_1, \ldots, y_n, t)$ are constructed above. We shall evaluate dV/dt as based on system (C):

$$U = \frac{dV}{dt} = W + \sum_{s=1}^{n} \frac{\partial V}{\partial y_s} \sum_{i=1}^{n} R_{si} y_i$$

$$= t^{2m} \left[W_{2m} + t^{-1} W_{2m-1} + \ldots + t^{-2m} W_0 + t^{-2m} \sum_{s=1}^{n} \frac{\partial V}{\partial y_s} \sum_{i=1}^{n} R_{si} y_i \right] .$$

In the last equality

$$t^{-2m} \sum_{s=1}^{n} \frac{\partial V}{\partial y_s} \sum_{i=1}^{n} R_{si} y_i \to 0$$

as $t \to +\infty$, since the highest power of the variable t entering in the function $\partial V/\partial y_s$ is equal to m.

Thus, the functions $V(y_1, \ldots, y_n, t)$ and $U(y_1, \ldots, y_n, t)$ have the form

$$V(y_1, \ldots, y_n, t) = t^m V_1(y_1, \ldots, y_n, t),$$

$$U(y_1, \ldots, y_n, t) = t^{2m} U_1(y_1, \ldots, y_n, t),$$

where $U_1(y_1, \ldots, y_n, t)$, $V_1(y_1, \ldots, y_n, t)$ are positive-definite quadratic forms for $t \geq T$.

Consequently, every solution of system (C) satisfies inequality (B) for $t_0 \geq T$, in which the constants l_1, l_2, k_1, k_2 may be different.

As a generalization of this example we shall consider the system of nonlinear equations

$$\frac{dy_s}{dt} = \sum_{i=1}^{n} \sum_{k=1}^{m} a_{si}^{(k)} t^k y_s + z_s \quad (s = 1, \ldots, n). \tag{D}$$

If the functions $z_s(y_1, \ldots, y_n, t)$ $(s = 1, \ldots, n)$ entering in the right-hand member of the system possess the properties:

1) $z(y_1, \ldots, y_n, t)$ is of the second order of magnitude relative to $y_1, \ldots, y_n$;

2) the functions $t^{-m} z(y_1, \ldots, y_n, t)$ are bounded for $t \geqq T$ and $\sum\limits_{i=1}^{n} y_i^2 \leqq r^2$ —

then the homogeneous solution $y_1 = \ldots = y_n = 0$ of system (D) is asymptotically stable and every solution of that system satisfies an inequality of form (B).

Estimates from below give the possibility of indicating the smallest possible deviation of the transient process from the steady-state motion for a given system (6.1).

The estimates from above for the distance from the integral curves of the system (6.1) to the coordinate origin, depend on the parameters of the system and may change in dependence on the variation of these parameters.

However, the preceding theorems have an essential insufficiency in that, as a rule, it is difficult to choose the function V in such a way that the function W corresponding to it be nonpositive; to be more precise, the conditions $\psi_1 \geqq 0, \psi_2 \geqq 0$ are the hardest to satisfy. Below we shall give a theorem free of the disadvantage indicated above. However, its application increases the volume of computational labour.

THEOREM 17. In order that every solution of system (6.1) satisfy the inequalities

$$r_0 \phi_1^{\frac{1}{2}}(t_0) \phi_2^{-\frac{1}{2}}(t) e^{-\frac{1}{2} \int\limits_{t_0}^{t} \frac{\psi_1}{\tilde{\phi}_1} dt} \leqq r(t, y_{10}, \ldots, y_{n0}, t_0) \leqq$$

$$\leqq r_0 \phi_2^{\frac{1}{2}}(t_0) \phi_1^{-\frac{1}{2}}(t) e^{-\frac{1}{2} \int\limits_{t_0}^{t} \frac{\psi_2}{\tilde{\phi}_2} dt} \qquad (t \geqq t_0), \qquad (6.21)$$

it is sufficient that there exist two quadratic forms V and W satisfying the conditions:

1) the function V is nonnegative and satisfies the inequalities

$$\phi_1(t) r^2 \leqq V \leqq \phi_2(t) r^2; \qquad (6.22)$$

2) the function W satisfies the inequalities

$$-\psi_1(t) r^2 \leqq W \leqq -\psi_2(t) r^2; \qquad (6.23)$$

3) the functions $\phi_i(t) > 0$ for $t \geqq 0$; the functions ψ_i/ϕ_i are integrable in any finite interval;

4) the function W is the total derivative with respect to t of the function V as based on system (6.1),

$$\frac{dV}{dt} = W. \tag{6.24}$$

In that Theorem the functions

$$\tilde{\phi}_1 = \sigma_1 \phi_1(t) + \sigma_2 \phi_2(t), \tag{6.25}$$

$$\tilde{\phi}_2 = \sigma_3 \phi_1(t) + \sigma_4 \phi_2(t), \tag{6.26}$$

where

$$\sigma_1 = 1 \text{ for } \psi_1 \geq 0,$$
$$\sigma_1 = 0 \text{ for } \psi_1 < 0,$$
$$\sigma_2 = 1 \text{ for } \psi_1 < 0,$$
$$\sigma_2 = 0 \text{ for } \psi_1 \geq 0;$$

or

$$\sigma_1 = \frac{1 + \operatorname{sgn} \psi_1}{2},$$

$$\sigma_2 = \frac{1 - \operatorname{sgn} \psi_1}{2}.$$

Analogously

$$\sigma_3 = \frac{1 - \operatorname{sgn} \psi_2}{2},$$

$$\sigma_4 = \frac{1 + \operatorname{sgn} \psi_2}{2}.$$

PROOF: We shall assume that there exist two quadratic forms V and W satisfying the conditions of Theorem 17. We shall integrate through relation (6.24) between the limits from t_0 to t, first dividing both members by V; then

$$\int_{t_0}^{t} \frac{dV}{V} = \int_{t_0}^{t} \frac{W}{V} dt,$$

whence

$$V_1 = V(y_{10}, \ldots, y_{n0}, t_0) e^{\int_{t_0}^{t} \frac{W}{V} dt} \tag{6.27}$$

We shall estimate the integral standing in the right-hand member of equality (6.27). For this we shall consider the fraction

$$\frac{W}{V} = \frac{\sum\limits_{j,i=1}^{n} b_{ij} y_i y_j}{\sum\limits_{j,i=1}^{n} a_{ij} y_i y_j}.$$

Applying the inequality (6.23), we shall obtain

$$\frac{-\psi_1 r^2}{V} \leq \frac{W}{V} \leq \frac{-\psi_2 r^2}{V}. \tag{6.28}$$

We shall first estimate from below the left-hand member of inequality (6.28), applying inequalities (6.23). If $\psi_2(t) \geq 0$, then

$$\frac{-\psi_1 r^2}{V} \geq -\frac{\psi_1}{\phi_1}.$$

Whereas if $\psi_1(t) < 0$, then

$$\frac{+\psi_1 r^2}{V} \leq \frac{+\psi_1}{\phi_2}.$$

Combining both inequalities obtained, we shall have

$$\frac{-\psi_1 r^2}{V} \geq \frac{-\psi_1}{\sigma_1 \phi_2 + \sigma_2 \phi_2}. \tag{6.29}$$

Analogously we shall estimate from above the right-hand member of inequality (6.28).

If $\psi_2(t) \geq 0$, then

$$\frac{-\psi_2 r^2}{V} \leq \frac{-\psi_2}{\phi_2}.$$

If $\psi_2(t) < 0$, then

$$\frac{-\psi_2 r^2}{V} \leq \frac{-\psi_2}{\phi_1}.$$

Combining these inequalities into one, we shall obtain

$$\frac{-\psi_2 r^2}{V} \leq \frac{-\psi}{\sigma_3 \phi_1 + \sigma_4 \phi_2}. \tag{6.30}$$

From inequalities (6.29) and (6.30) it follows that

$$\frac{-\psi_1}{\tilde{\phi}_1} \leq \frac{W}{V} \leq \frac{-\psi_2}{\tilde{\phi}_2}. \tag{6.31}$$

Now, applying inequalities (6.31) to the estimation of the integral standing in (6.27), we shall obtain

$$V(y_{10}, \ldots, y_{n0}, t_0)\, e^{-\int_{t_0}^{t} \frac{\psi_1}{\tilde{\phi}_1} dt} \leq V_1 \leq V(y_{10}, \ldots, y_{n0}, t_0)\, e^{-\int_{t_0}^{t} \frac{\psi_2}{\tilde{\phi}_2} dt}$$

Applying to this inequality the estimates (6.22) which are satisfied by the function V, we shall finally obtain that inequality (6.21) holds.

COROLLARY 1. If the function

$$r_0\phi_0^{\frac{1}{2}}(t_0)\phi_1^{-\frac{1}{2}}(t)\ e^{-\frac{1}{2}\int\limits_{t_0}^{t}\frac{\psi_2}{\phi_2}\,dt} = \chi(t, t_0)$$

is bounded for all $t_0 \geq 0$ and $t \geq t_0$, then the homogeneous solution of the system (6.1) will be stable. If, in addition, $\chi(t, t_0) \to 0$ as $t \to \infty$, then the homogeneous solution of the system (6.1) in the presence of quadratic forms V and W satisfying the conditions of Theorem 17 will be asymptotically stable. The proof of this assertion follows from inequality (6.21).

We shall now point out a series of most frequently used methods for finding sufficient criteria for stability and asymptotic stability of the homogeneous solution of the system (6.1).

We shall take an arbitrary quadratic form $V = \sum\limits_{i,j=1}^{n} a_{ij}y_iy_j$, possessing the following properties:

1) $V = 0$ only for $y_1 = \ldots = y_n = 0$;

2) the coefficients $a_{ij}(t)$ are given for $t \geq 0$ and are continuously differentiable (or piecewise-continuously differentiable) there, so that on every finite interval $[O, T]$ the functions $da_{ij}(t)/dt$ have a finite number of discontinuities of the first kind.

We shall find the total derivative of the quadratic form V as based on system (6.1)

$$\frac{dV}{dt} = \sum_{i,j=1}^{n} \frac{d\,a_{ij}}{dt}\,y_iy_j + \sum_{i,j=1}^{n} a_{ij}(t)\,\frac{dy_i}{dt}\,y_j + \sum_{i,j=1}^{n} a_{ij}(t)y_i\,\frac{dy_j}{dt}\,.$$

Substituting dy_i/dt from system (6.1) we shall obtain

$$\frac{dV}{dt} = \sum_{i,j=1}^{n} \frac{da_{ij}}{dt}\,y_iy_j + \sum_{i,j=1}^{n} a_{ij}(t)\,y_j \sum_{k=1}^{n} p_{ik}y_k + \sum_{i,j=1}^{n} a_{ij}y_i \sum_{k=1}^{n} p_{jk}y_k,$$

or, reducing the similar terms,

$$\frac{dV}{dt} = \sum_{i,j=1}^{n} b_{ij}y_iy_j,$$

where

$$b_{ij} = \frac{da_{ij}}{dt} + \sum_{k=1}^{n} p_{ki}a_{kj} + \sum_{k=1}^{n} a_{ik}p_{kj}\,. \tag{6.32}$$

If by Y we denote the vector

$$Y = \left\{ \begin{matrix} y_1 \\ \vdots \\ y_n \end{matrix} \right\},$$

and by Y^* the vector $Y^* = \{y_1, ..., y_n\}$, system (6.1) may be written in the form (6.32):

$$\frac{dY}{dt} = P(t)Y,$$

where $P(t)$ is the matrix of coefficients p_{ij} of system (6.1).

The quadratic form V may be written as $V = Y^*A(t)Y$; then

$$\frac{dV}{dt} = \frac{dY^*}{dt}A(t)Y + Y^*\frac{dA}{dt}Y + Y^*A(t)\frac{dY}{dt}.$$

Substituting dY/dt and dY/dt from system (6.32), we shall obtain

$$\frac{dV}{dt} = [P(t)Y]^*A(t)Y + Y^*\frac{dA}{dt}Y + Y^*A(t)P(t)Y$$

$$= Y^* \left[P^*(t)A(t) + \frac{dA}{dt} + A(t)P(t) \right] Y = W,$$

where $[P(t)Y]^* = Y^*P^*(t)$.

Therefore, matrix B of the quadratic form W has the form

$$B = P^*A + AP + \frac{dA}{dt}.$$

Above, we have obtained the coefficients of W in scalar form.

By $\lambda_1(t), ..., \lambda_n(t)$ we shall denote the characteristic values of the quadratic form V and by $\mu_1(t), ..., \mu_n(t)$, the characteristic values of the quadratic form W, where $\lambda_1(t), \lambda_2(t), ..., \lambda_n(t) \geq 0$ for all $t \geq 0$; $\mu_1(t), \mu_2(t), ..., \mu_n(t) \leq 0$ for all $t \geq 0$.

As has been shown in §2 of chapter I, the quadratic form W satisfies the inequalities

$$\mu_1(t)r^2 \leq V \leq \mu_n(t)r^2. \tag{6.33}$$

Analogously

$$\lambda_1(t)r^2 \leq W \leq \lambda_n(t)r^2. \tag{6.34}$$

And then, according to Theorem 17 every solution of the system (6.1) will satisfy the inequalities (6.21), where one should set

$$\phi_1 = \mu_1; \quad \phi_2 = \mu_n; \quad \psi_1 = -\lambda_1; \quad \psi_2 = -\lambda_n.$$

Thus, the following Theorem holds.

THEOREM 18. If $\lambda_1(t)$, $\lambda_n(t)$ are the lowest and highest characteristic values of matrix $PA + AP + dA/dt$, and $\mu_1(t)$, $\mu_n(t)$ are respectively the lowest and highest characteristic values of matrix $A(t)$, then every solution of system (6.1) satisfies the inequalities

$$r_0 \mu_1^{\frac{1}{2}}(t_0) \mu_n^{-\frac{1}{2}}(t) e^{\frac{1}{2}\int_{t_0}^{t} \frac{\lambda_1}{\tilde{\phi}_1} dt} \leq r(t, y_{10}, \ldots, y_{n0}, t_0) \leq$$

$$\leq r_0 \mu_n^{\frac{1}{2}}(t_0) \mu_1^{-\frac{1}{2}}(t) e^{\frac{1}{2}\int_{t_0}^{t} \frac{\lambda_n}{\tilde{\phi}_2} dt} \qquad (6.35)$$

where

$$\tilde{\phi}_1 = \sigma_1 \mu_1 + \sigma_2 \mu_n,$$

$$\tilde{\phi}_2 = \sigma_3 \mu_1 + \sigma_4 \mu_n;$$

here

$$\sigma_1 = \frac{1 - \operatorname{sgn} \lambda_1}{2},$$

$$\sigma_2 = \frac{1 + \operatorname{sgn} \lambda_1}{2},$$

$$\sigma_3 = \frac{1 + \operatorname{sgn} \lambda_n}{2},$$

$$\sigma_4 = \frac{1 - \operatorname{sgn} \lambda_n}{2}.$$

The proof of Theorem 18 follows from inequalities (6.33) and (6.34), and from Theorem 17.

COROLLARY. If the right-hand member of the inequality (6.35) with fixed r_0 is bounded for all $t_0 \geq 0$ and $t \geq t_0$, then the homogeneous solution of system (6.1) is stable. If, moreover, the function standing in the right-hand member of (6.35) tends to zero as $t \to \infty$, then the homogeneous solution of the system (6.1) is asymptotically stable.

EXAMPLES

Example 1. We shall take $V = \sum_{i=1}^{n} y_i^2$, then

$$W = \frac{dV}{dt} = \sum_{i,j=1}^{n} b_{ij} y_i y_j,$$

where

$$b_{ij} = \frac{p_{ji} + p_{ij}}{2},$$

i.e. the matrix of the quadratic form W is equal to the symmetrized matrix of system (6.1).

We shall find the roots of the equation

$$\left| \frac{P + P^*}{2} - \lambda E \right| = 0$$

and denote them by $\lambda_1, ..., \lambda_n$; then every solution of system (6.1) will satisfy the inequalities

$$r_0 e^{\frac{1}{2}\int_{t_0}^{t} \lambda_1(\tau)d\tau} \leqq r(t, y_{10}, ..., y_{n0}, t_0) \leqq r_0 e^{\frac{1}{2}\int_{t_0}^{t} \lambda_n(\tau)d\tau}, \qquad (6.36)$$

as follows from Theorem 18, since here $\mu_1 = ... = \mu_n = 1$; $\tilde{\phi}_1 = \tilde{\phi}_2 = 1$.

From inequality (6.36) it follows that for stability of the homogeneous solution of system (6.1), it is sufficient that the integral $\int^t \lambda_n(\tau)d\tau$ converge. If that integral tends to $-\infty$ as $t \to \infty$, then the homogeneous solution will be asymptotically stable.

If the integral of the smallest characteristic value of the matrix $P + P^*$ is not bounded from above, then the homogeneous solution in unstable.

Example 2.   We shall set $V = \sum\limits_{i,j=1}^{n} a_{ij}y_iy_j$, where a_{ij} are real constants such that for them Sylvester conditions are satisfied (and the quadratic form V is positive-definite).

We shall set up the total derivative of V as based on system (6.1); then

$$\frac{dV}{dt} = W = \sum\limits_{i,j=1}^{n} b_{ij}y_iy_j,$$

where

$$b_{ij} = \sum\limits_{k=1}^{n} p_{ki}a_{kj} + \sum\limits_{k=1}^{n} a_{ik}p_{kj},$$

as follows from equalities (6.32).

We shall find the roots $\lambda_1, ..., \lambda_n$ of the equation

$$|P^*A + AP - \lambda E| = 0;$$

besides, let μ_1, μ_n be respectively the smallest and largest values of the quadratic form V; then every solution of the system (6.1) satisfies the inequality

$$r_0 \left(\frac{\mu_1}{\mu_n}\right)^{\frac{1}{2}} e^{\frac{1}{2}\int_{t_0}^{t} \frac{\lambda_1(\tau)}{\tilde{\phi}_1(\tau)}d\tau} \leqq r_0(t, y_{10}, ..., y_{n0}, t_0) \leqq r_0 \left(\frac{\mu_n}{\mu_1}\right)^{\frac{1}{2}} e^{\frac{1}{2}\int_{t_0}^{t} \frac{\lambda_n(\tau)}{\tilde{\phi}_2(\tau)}d\tau},$$

where $\tilde{\phi}_i(\tau)$ are step-functions taking only the positive values μ_1 or μ_n.

In order that the homogeneous solution of system (6.1) be stable, it is sufficient that $\int_{t_0}^{t} [\lambda_n(\tau)/\tilde{\phi}_2(\tau)]d\tau$ be bounded from above. Moreover, if it tends to $-\infty$, then the solution of system (6.1) will be asymptotically stable.

In order that the homogeneous solution of system (6.1) be unstable, it is sufficient that $\int_{t_0}^{t} [\lambda_1(\tau)/\tilde{\phi}_1(\tau)]d\tau$ be unbounded from above.

We shall point out that this example contains a method of investigating systems of a rather wide class, as the quadratic form V may be chosen in different ways and, in particular, allowing some variable parameters to remain in it. For instance, one may take the form $V = \sum_{i=1}^{n} a_i y_i^2$, where the a_i are arbitrary positive constants by varying which one may strive for the quadratic form W to satisfy those or other conditions.

Example 3.   Let $V = \sum_{i=1}^{n} a_i(t)y_i^2$, where the $a_i(t)$ are positive, continuously differentiable functions, given for $t \geq 0$.

We shall construct the total derivative function of V as based on system (6.1)

$$\frac{dV}{dt} = W = \sum_{i,j=1}^{n} b_{ij}y_i y_j,$$

where

$$b_{ij} = \delta_{ij}\frac{da_i}{dt} + \frac{p_{ij}a_j(t) + p_{ji}a_i(t)}{2}.$$

Here

$$\delta_{ij} = \begin{cases} 0, & i \neq j \\ 1, & i = j \end{cases}.$$

Let $\lambda_1, \ldots, \lambda_n$ be the characteristic values of the quadratic form W, and let the inequalities $a_1(t) \leq a_2(t) \leq \ldots \leq a_n(t)$ be satisfied. Then, every solution of system (6.1) satisfies the inequality

$$r_0 a_1^{\frac{1}{2}}(t_0) a_n^{-\frac{1}{2}}(t) e^{\frac{1}{2}\int_{t_0}^{t} \frac{\lambda_1(\tau)}{\tilde{\phi}_1(\tau)}d\tau} \leq r(t, y_{10}, \ldots, y_{n0}, t_0) \leq r_0 a_1^{-\frac{1}{2}}(t) a_n^{\frac{1}{2}}(t_0) e^{\frac{1}{2}\int_{t_0}^{t} \frac{\lambda_n(\tau)}{\tilde{\phi}_2(\tau)}d\tau},$$

where

$$\tilde{\phi}_1 = \sigma_1 a_1(t) + \sigma_2 a_n(t),$$
$$\tilde{\phi}_2 = \sigma_3 a_1(t) + \sigma_4 a_n(t),$$

and the σ_i are defined in Theorem 18.

As the function V for finding the sufficient criteria for stability one may choose quadratic forms whose coefficients are known functions of time, depending on some numerical parameters. By varying the parameters one may arrive at one or another set of properties for the quadratic form W.

§ 7. Influence of error in calculating the coefficients of the equation on the behaviour of solutions and stability properties

We shall note that, as a rule, the coefficients in system (6.1) in the investigation of real systems are known approximately for the following two reasons:

1) the equations of motion themselves are of an approximate nature;

2) the free motion which is being investigated for stability is sought from system (1.1) inexactly, and therefore system (1.4) and, consequently, also its linear approximation (6.1) have coefficients whose values differ from those which do actually hold.

It is very important to know what is the influence of these factors upon the solution of the problems of stability and upon those estimates which are satisfied by the solutions of the actual equations since, in general, the criteria for stability and asymptotic stability for the system (6.1) may be satisfied, while in fact instability takes place.

THEOREM 19.   Whatever system (6.1), there exists a nonnegative piecewise-continuous function $\phi(t)$, given for $t \geq 0$, such that every solution of system (6.1) satisfies the inequalities

$$r_0^2 e^{-\int_{t_0}^{t} \phi(\tau)d\tau} \leq r^2(t, y_{10}, \ldots, y_{n0}, t_0) \leq r_0^2 e^{+\int_{t_0}^{t} \phi(\tau)d\tau} \tag{7.1}$$

$$\text{for } t \geq t_0.$$

PROOF: Following [2], we shall calculate the total derivative of the function $V = \sum_{i=1}^{n} y_i^2$ as based on system (6.1). Then

$$\frac{dV}{dt} = \sum_{i,j=1}^{n} \frac{(p_{ij} + p_{ji})}{2} y_i y_j. \tag{7.2}$$

Dividing both members of equality (7.2) by the function V and integrating between the limits t_0 and t, we shall obtain

$$\sum_{i=1}^{n} y_i^2 = r_0^2 e^{\int_{t_0}^{t} \sum_{i,j=1}^{n} \frac{p_{ij} + p_{ji}}{2} y_i y_j \, d\tau} \sim \sum_{i=1}^{n} y_i^2 \qquad (7.3)$$

We shall set

$$\phi(t) = \max \left| \lambda_i(t) \right|$$

$$(i = 1, \ldots, n),$$

where λ_i is the characteristic value of the quadratic form

$$W = \sum_{i,j=1}^{n} \frac{p_{ij} + p_{ji}}{2} y_i y_j.$$

Then, as has been shown in §2, there holds the estimate

$$-\phi(t)r^2 \leqq W \leqq \phi(t)r^2. \qquad (7.4)$$

From (7.3), on the basis of (7.4) we shall obtain

$$r_0^2 e^{-\int_{t_0}^{t} \phi(\tau) d\tau} \leqq r^2(t, y_{10}, \ldots, y_{n0}, t_0) \leqq r_0^2 e^{\int_{t_0}^{t} \phi(\tau) d\tau}.$$

Remark. It is usually very difficult to find the functions $\lambda_1(t), \ldots, \lambda_n(t)$' which for every fixed t are the characteristic values of the matrix $\frac{1}{2}(P^* + P)$, and therefore we shall give a method below for the simplest determination of the function $\phi(t)$ (which, however, gives a more gross estimate).

We shall estimate the absolute value of the function W. Then

$$|W| \leqq \sum_{i,j=1}^{n} \left| b_{ij} y_i y_j \right|.$$

We shall note that $\left| y_i \right| \cdot \left| y_j \right| \leqq \frac{1}{2} r^2$.

Thus, we shall obtain

$$|W| \leqq r^2 \sum_{i,j=1}^{n} \left| \frac{b_{ij}}{2} \right|.$$

Consequently, as function ϕ we may take the function

$$\sum_{i,j=1}^{n} \left| \frac{p_{ij} + p_{ji}}{4} \right|.$$

If by $\rho(t)$ we denote

$$\max_{i,j=1,\ldots,n} |p_{ij}(t)|,$$

then as $\phi(t)$ one may take the function

$$\phi(t) = \tfrac{1}{2} n^2 \rho(t).$$

COROLLARY 1.   If the coefficients of system (6.1) are bounded for $t \geq 0$, then instead of $\rho(t)$ one may take a positive constant, and then we shall obtain that every solution of system (6.1) satisfies the inequalities

$$r_0 e^{-n(t-t_0)} \leq r(t, y_{10}, \ldots, y_{n0}, t_0) \leq r_0 e^{n(t-t_0)} \quad \text{for } t \geq t_0.$$

This inequality has been used by us in Corollary 2 of Theorem 16 with a reference to the book by A. M. Lyapunov.

COROLLARY 2.   If the function $\rho(t)$ is such that $\int_{t_0}^{t} \rho(\tau)d\tau$ converges for $t \to +\infty$, then the homogeneous solution is stable, as every solution of system (6.1) satisfies the inequalities

$$r_0 e^{-\int_{t_0}^{t} \frac{1}{2} n^2 \rho(\tau)\, d\tau} \leq r(t, y_{10}, \ldots, y_{n0}, t_0) \leq r_0 e^{\int_{t_0}^{t} \frac{1}{2} n^2 \rho(\tau)\, d\tau}$$

for $t \geq t_0$, because of (7.1).

We shall now cite a theorem which clarifies the influence of imprecision in the calculation of the coefficients of the system (6.1) upon the estimate of the solutions of the system of equations

$$\frac{dy_s}{dt} = \sum_{i=1}^{n} [p_{si}(t) + \varepsilon_{si}(t)] y_i \quad (s = 1, \ldots, n), \tag{7.5}$$

where $p_{si}(t)$ are the coefficients of system (6.1) and $\varepsilon_{si}(t)$ represent the differences between the actual values of the coefficients and their approximate values $p_{si}(t)$.

Thus, system (7.5) is real.

The problem consists in attempting to estimate the solution of system (7.5) by proceeding from system (6.1), and thus to clarify the influence of errors in calculating the coefficients of system (6.1) upon the estimates of the solutions for system (7.5).

THEOREM 20. If on the basis of system (6.1) there exist two quadratic forms V and W possessing the following properties:

1) the form V is nonnegative and satisfies the inequalities

$$\phi_1(t)r^2 \leq V \leq \phi_2(t)r^2 ; \qquad (7.6)$$

2) the form W satisfies the inequalities

$$-\psi_1(t)r^2 \leq W \leq -\psi_2(t)r^2 ; \qquad (7.7)$$

3) the form W is the total derivative of V as based on the system (6.1), i.e.

$$\frac{dV}{dt} = W; \qquad (7.8)$$

4) the coefficients of the form V satisfy the inequalities $|a_{ij}(t)| \leq a(t)$, and the functions $\varepsilon_{ij}(t)$ satisfy the inequalities $|\varepsilon_{ij}(t)| \leq \varepsilon(t)$, where $a(t)$ and $\varepsilon(t)$ are continuous functions —

then every solution of system (7.5) satisfies the inequalities

$$r_0 \phi_1^{\frac{1}{2}}(t_0)\phi_2^{-\frac{1}{2}}(t)e^{-\frac{1}{2}\int_{t_0}^{t}(\tilde{\psi}_1/\tilde{\phi}_1)\,d\tau} \leq r(t, y_{10}, \ldots, y_{n0}, t_0) \leq$$

$$\leq r_0 \phi_2^{\frac{1}{2}}(t_0)\phi_1^{-\frac{1}{2}}(t)\,e^{-\frac{1}{2}\int_{t_0}^{t}(\tilde{\psi}_2/\tilde{\phi}_2)\,d\tau} \qquad \text{for } t \geq t_0, \qquad (7.9)$$

where all the functions under the integral sign are defined below in such a way that the integrals exist for all $t \geq t_0$.

PROOF: Say there exist two quadratic forms V and W satisfying all the conditions of Theorem 20. We shall show that inequalities (7.9) then hold.

Differentiating the quadratic form V as based on system (7.5), we shall obtain

$$\frac{dV}{dt} = \sum_{i,j=1}^{n} \frac{d\,a_{ij}(t)}{dt}y_iy_j + \sum_{j=1}^{n}\frac{\partial V}{\partial y}\frac{dy_j}{dt} . \qquad (7.10)$$

Substituting dy_j/dt from system (7.5), we shall obtain

$$\frac{dV}{dt} = \sum_{i,j=1}^{n}\frac{d\,a_{ij}(t)}{dt}y_iy_j + \sum_{j=1}^{n}\frac{\partial V}{\partial y_j}\left[\sum_{i=1}^{n}(p_{ji}+\varepsilon_{ji})y_i\right] = W + W_1,$$

where W_1 is the quadratic form

$$W_1 = \sum_{j=1}^{n} \frac{\partial V}{\partial y_j} \left[\sum_{i=1}^{n} \varepsilon_{ji}(t) \, y_i \right]. \tag{7.11}$$

We shall now estimate the quadratic form (7.11). For this we shall first compute the functions $\partial V / \partial y_j$.

$$\frac{\partial V}{\partial y_j} = 2 \sum_{i=1}^{n} a_{ij} y_i,$$

as $a_{ij} = a_{ji}$, whence we have

$$W_1 = \sum_{j=1}^{n} \left(2 \sum_{i=1}^{n} a_{ji} y_i \right) \left(\sum_{i=1}^{n} \varepsilon_{ji} y_i \right).$$

Estimating both members of the last equality according to Bunyakovskiy, we shall obtain

$$|W_1| \leq \sum_{j=1}^{n} 2 \sum_{i=1}^{n} |a_{ij}| \, |y_i| \sum_{i=1}^{n} |\varepsilon_{ji}| \, |y_i| \leq 2a(t) \varepsilon(t) n^2 \left[\sum_{i=1}^{n} |y_i|^2 \right] \tag{7.12}$$

or, since $\sum_{i=1}^{n} |y_i|^2 = r^2$,

$$|W_1| \leq 2a(t) \varepsilon(t) n^2 r^2. \tag{7.13}$$

From (7.13) it follows that the total derivative form as based on system (7.5) $dV/dt = W + W_1$ satisfies the inequalities

$$- \left[\psi_1 + 2a(t) \varepsilon(t) n^2 \right] r^2 \leq W + W_1 \leq - \left[\psi_2 - 2a(t) \varepsilon(t) n^2 \right] r^2,$$

and then, according to Theorem 17, every solution of system (7.5) satisfies the inequalities:

$$r_0 \phi_1^{\frac{1}{2}}(t_0) \, \phi_2^{-\frac{1}{2}}(t) \, e^{- \frac{1}{2} \int_{t_0}^{t} (\tilde{\psi}_1/\tilde{\phi}_1) \, d\tau} \leq r(t, y_{10}, \ldots, y_{n0}, t_0) \leq$$

$$\leq r_0 \phi_2^{\frac{1}{2}}(t_0) \, \phi_1^{-\frac{1}{2}}(t) \, e^{- \frac{1}{2} \int_{t_0}^{t} (\tilde{\psi}_2/\tilde{\phi}_2) \, d\tau},$$

where

$$\tilde{\psi}_1 = \psi_1 + 2a(t) \varepsilon(t) n^2,$$

$$\tilde{\psi}_2 = \psi_2 - 2a(t) \varepsilon(t) n^2,$$

$$\tilde{\phi}_1 = \sigma_1 \phi_1 + \sigma_2 \phi_2,$$

$$\tilde{\phi}_2 = \sigma_3 \phi_1 + \sigma_4 \phi_2,$$

in which σ_i $(i = 1, ..., 4)$ are defined in terms of $\tilde{\psi}_1$, $\tilde{\psi}_2$ according to the formulae

$$\sigma_1 = \frac{1 + \operatorname{sgn} \tilde{\psi}_1}{2},$$

$$\sigma_2 = \frac{1 - \operatorname{sgn} \tilde{\psi}_1}{2},$$

$$\sigma_3 = \frac{1 - \operatorname{sgn} \tilde{\psi}_2}{2},$$

$$\sigma_4 = \frac{1 + \operatorname{sgn} \tilde{\psi}_2}{2}.$$

COROLLARY 1. By $\tilde{\phi}_i(\tilde{\psi}_i)$ we shall denote those functions which have been introduced above in inequalities (7.9), and by $\tilde{\phi}_i(\psi_i)$—those functions which are dealt with in Theorem 17. If there exist two quadratic forms W and V satisfying all the conditions of Theorem 20, and the function

$$\phi_2^{\frac{1}{2}}(t)\,\phi_1^{-\frac{1}{2}}(t)\; e^{\displaystyle -\frac{1}{2}\int_{t_0}^{t} [\psi_2(\tau)/\tilde{\phi}_2(\psi_2)]\,d_\tau} = \chi(t, t_0)$$

for all $t \geqq t_0$ is bounded from above by the function

$$e^{\displaystyle -\int_{t_0}^{t} [a(\tau)\,\varepsilon(\tau)\,n^2/\tilde{\phi}_2(\tilde{\psi}_2)]\,d\tau},$$

then from the stability of the homogeneous solution of system (6.1) follows the stability of the homogeneous solution of system (7.5).

Indeed, in Theorem 20 above it has been shown that every solution of system (7.5) satisfies inequalities (7.9).

We shall note further that the inequality

$$\frac{-\psi_2}{\tilde{\phi}_2(\tilde{\psi}_2)} \leqq \frac{-\psi_2}{\tilde{\phi}_2(\psi_2)} \tag{7.14}$$

holds, since for those t for which $\psi_2(t) > 0$ the right-hand member of that inequality has the form $-\psi_2/\phi_2(t)$, and the left-hand member has either the same form or the form $-\psi_2/\phi_1(t)$, depending on whether $\psi_2(t) \geqq 2a(t)\varepsilon(t)n^2$ or $\psi_2(t) < 2a(t)\varepsilon(t)n^2$.

If $\psi_2(t) < 0$, then in the right-hand member of inequality (7.14) stands the quantity $-\psi_2(t)/\phi_1(t)$. In the left-hand member of that inequality stands the same quantity, since $\tilde{\psi}_2 = \psi_2(t) - 2a(t)\,\varepsilon(t)n^2 < 0$.

From inequality (7.14) it follows that the right-hand member of inequality (7.9) does not exceed the function

$$r_0 \phi_2^{\frac{1}{2}}(t_0) \phi_1^{-\frac{1}{2}}(t) e^{-\frac{1}{2} \int_{t_0}^{t} [\psi_2/\tilde{\phi}_2(t_2)] d\tau} \cdot e^{\int_{t_0}^{t} [a(\tau)\,\varepsilon(\tau)\,n^2/\tilde{\phi}_2(\tilde{\psi}_2)] d\tau}.$$

According to the assumption made above, for $t \geq t_0$ this function does not exceed the quantity $r_0 k$, and consequently the homogeneous solution of system (7.5) is stable.

If in addition

$$\kappa(t, t_0) e^{-\int_{t_0}^{t} [a(\tau)\varepsilon(\tau)\,n^2/\tilde{\phi}_2(\psi_2)] d\tau}$$

tends to zero as $t \to +\infty$, then the homogeneous solution of system (7.5) will be asymptotically stable, as the right-hand member of inequality (7.9) may be bounded from above by the function

$$r_0 \kappa(t, t_0) e^{-\int_{t_0}^{t} [a(\tau)\varepsilon(\tau)\,n^2/\tilde{\phi}_2(\tilde{\psi}_2)] d\tau}.$$

COROLLARY 2. We shall assume that the coefficients of system (6.1) are bounded in absolute value for $t \geq 0$. If there exist two quadratic forms V and W satisfying the conditions:

$$a_1 r^2 \leq V \leq a_2 r^2, \tag{7.15}$$

$$-b_1 r^2 \leq W \leq -b_2 r^2, \tag{7.16}$$

and $dV/dt = W$ as based on system (6.1), and if the errors $\varepsilon_{ij}(t)$ in calculating the coefficients of system (6.1) satisfy the condition

$$\bar{\varepsilon} \leq \frac{b_2}{2n^2 \bar{a}}, \tag{7.17}$$

where $|\varepsilon_{ij}(t)| \leq \bar{\varepsilon}$ and $|p_{ij}(t)| \leq \bar{a}$ — then the homogeneous solution of system (7.5) will be asymptotically stable.

In fact, the right-hand member of estimate (7.9) in that case has the form

$$r_0 \frac{a_2}{a_1^{\frac{1}{2}}} e^{-\frac{(t-t_0)}{a_2}(b_2 - 2\bar{a}\bar{\varepsilon}n^2)},$$

whence by virtue of (7.17) it follows that

$$r(t, y_{10}, \ldots, y_{n0}, t) \to 0 \quad \text{as} \quad t \to +\infty.$$

Now, if the function

$$e^{-\frac{b_2}{2a_2}(t-t_0)} \quad e^{-\int_{t_0}^{t}[a(\tau)\,\varepsilon(\tau)\,n^2/\tilde{\phi}_2(\tilde{\psi}_2)]\,d\tau}$$

is bounded from above, then the homogeneous solution of system (7.5) will be stable. Here $\tilde{\phi}_2(\tilde{\psi}_2)$ are step-functions taking the two values a_1 or a_2.

COROLLARY 3. If in the linear system (7.5) the coefficients differ "little" from some constants, and the system with these constant coefficients has an asymptotically stable homogeneous solution, then the system with variable coefficients will also have an asymptotically stable homogeneous solution. Here one must have in view those upper bounds for the coefficients for which the above assertion holds.

Let the homogeneous solution of the system

$$\frac{dy_s}{dt} = \sum_{i=1}^{n} p_{si}y_i \quad (s = 1, ..., n) \tag{7.18}$$

have an asymptotically stable homogeneous solution. Then there exist two quadratic forms V and W possessing the following properties:

$$a_1 r^2 \leq V \leq a_2 r^2, \tag{7.19}$$

$$-b_1 r^2 \leq W \leq -b_2 r^2 \quad . \tag{7.20}$$

If the functions $\varepsilon_{ji}(t)$ in the system

$$\frac{dy_s}{dt} = \sum_{i=1}^{n} [p_{si} + \varepsilon_{si}(t)]\,y_i \quad (s = 1, ..., n) \tag{7.21}$$

satisfy the estimate indicated in Corollary 2, then the homogeneous solution of system (7.21) will also be asymptotically stable.

Remark. One may propose a more precise estimate for the quadratic form W, obtainable in the following way (following Bunyakovskiy):

$$|W_1| \leq 2\sqrt{\sum_{s=1}^{n}\left[\sum_{i=1}^{n}(\varepsilon_{si}y_i)\right]^2} \cdot \sqrt{\sum_{s=1}^{n}\left[\sum_{i=1}^{n}a_{si}y_i\right]^2} \quad .$$

Under the first square root sign stands the quadratic form whose matrix has the form $\varepsilon^*\varepsilon$, where $\varepsilon = \{\varepsilon_{si}(t)\}$.

Under the second square root sign stands the quadratic form whose matrix coincides with the square of the matrix of the quadratic form V.

Consequently, $|W_1| \leq 2\phi_2(t)\lambda(t)$, where $\lambda^2(t)$ is the largest characteristic value of the matrix $\varepsilon^*\varepsilon$ for every t.

Example. As an example we shall consider the system of equations

$$\frac{dy_s}{dt} = \sum_{i=1}^{n} p_{si} y_i ,$$ (7.22)

where p_{si} are functions of t given for $t \geqq 0$ and, perhaps, even functions of $y_1, \ldots, y_n$ given for $r < R$. We shall assume that there exist constant numbers c_{si} such that $p_{si} \to c_{si}$ as $t \to \infty$ uniformly with respect to $y_1, \ldots, y_n$ from the region $r \leqq R_0 < R$, where R_0 and R are positive constants.

If all the roots of the equation $|C - \lambda E| = 0$ have negative real parts (the matrix $C = \{c_{si}\}$), then system (7.22) may be replaced with a high degree of accuracy in the sense of the behaviour of the solutions starting in the region $r \leqq R_0 < R$ for large values of t, by a system with constant coefficients

$$\frac{dy_s}{dt} = \sum_{i=1}^{n} c_{si} y_i .$$ (7.23)

The proof of this assertion may be obtained by applying the results given above.

In conclusion we shall note the close connection of some of the results of §§ 6 and 7 with work [51].

§ 8. The stability of the homogeneous solution of a linear system with respect to given coordinates

The problem of stability with respect to given coordinates has already been formulated in §4. Now we shall give two methods of solving it in the case of linear systems.

We shall note that even for linear systems with constant coefficients one meets cases in which, with respect to different coordinates, the homogeneous solution is stable and even asymptotically so, while with respect to other coordinates it is unstable. Such an example is analysed in detail by V. K. Chesnokov.

$$\left.\begin{array}{l} \dfrac{dx_1}{dt} = x_1 + x_3, \\[2ex] \dfrac{dx_2}{dt} = -4x_1 - x_2 - x_3, \\[2ex] \dfrac{dx_3}{dt} = -2x_1 - x_2 - x_3. \end{array}\right\}$$ (A)

The principal determinant of the system

$$\Delta(\rho) = \begin{vmatrix} \rho - 1 & 0 & -1 \\ 4 & \rho + 1 & 1 \\ 2 & 1 & \rho + 1 \end{vmatrix} = \rho^3 + \rho^2 - 2$$

has the roots $\rho_1 = 1$ and $\rho_{2,3} = -1 \pm j$.

The solution of the system may be found by the formula

$$x_s = - \sum_{k=1}^{n} x_k^0 \sum_{\lambda=1}^{n} C_\lambda^{(k)} \frac{\Delta_{1s}(\rho_\lambda)}{\Delta'(\rho_\lambda)} e_\lambda^{\rho t},$$

where x_k^0 is the initial value of the variables. Here $\Delta_{1s}(\rho_\lambda)$ are the values of the algebraic cofactors of the elements of the first row of the determinant when the corresponding roots

$$C_\lambda^{(k)} = \frac{\Delta_{ks}(\rho_\lambda)}{\Delta_{1s}(\rho_\lambda)},$$

$$\Delta(\rho_\lambda) = \frac{d\Delta(\rho)}{d\rho}\bigg|_{\rho=\rho_\lambda} = 3\rho^2 + 2\rho\bigg|_{\rho=\rho_\lambda}.$$

are substituted in them. The solution of (A) has the following form

$$x_1 = \tfrac{1}{5}\{[3e^t + 2(\cos t + 2\sin t)e^{-t}]x_1^0 + [-e^t + (\cos t + 2\sin t)e^{-t}]x_2^0 +$$

$$+ [2e^t + (\sin t - 2\cos t)e^{-t}]x_3\},$$

$$x_2 = \tfrac{1}{5}\{[-6e^t + 2(3\cos t - 4\sin t)e^{-t}]x_1^0 + [2e^t + (3\cos t - 4\sin t)e^{-t}]x_2^0 +$$

$$+ [-4e^t + (3\sin t + 4\cos t)e^{-t}]x_3^0\},$$

$$x_3 = (-2x_1^0\sin t - x_2^0\sin t + x_3^0\cos t)e^{-t}.$$

As can be seen, for the coordinate x_3 the motion is stable and for x_1 and x_2 it is unstable. It is essential that the total "perturbation" constituting the right-hand member of the equation for dx_3/dt does not contain increasing terms

$$2x + y = (2x_0\cos t + y_0\cos t + z_0\sin t)e^{-t}.$$

$$2x_1 + x_2 = (2x_1^0\cos t + x_2^0\cos t + x_3^0\sin t)e^{-t}.$$

If the ratio of the coefficients a_{31}/a_{32} differs from the given one by a small quantity, for example, by 1%, then in the coordinate x_3 there will appear an increasing term

$$z \approx \tfrac{1}{5}(0.06x_1^0 + 0.02x_2^0 + 0.04x_3^0)e^t .$$

However, it may be possible in practice to establish the values of the coefficients a_{31} and a_{32} with a degree of accuracy such that in the time interval of interest to us that term be considerably below the admissible deviations, and instability will not arise.

We shall consider the functions $l_i(t)$ given for $t \geq 0$ and decreasing to zero as $t \to +\infty$ $(i = k + 1, ..., n)$.

Further, we shall use the notation

$$r_k^2 = \sum_{i=1}^{k} y_i^2 \quad \text{and} \quad r_t^2 = r_k^2 + \sum_{i=k+1}^{n} l_i y_i^2 .$$

If we now find an estimate for the functions r_t along the integral curves of the linear system (6.1), then taking into account that $l_i \to 0$ as $t \to \infty$, we shall at the same time obtain an estimate for the function r_k, and consequently we can obtain the stability criteria with respect to the coordinates $y_1, ..., y_k$.

This method of establishing stability with respect to the coordinates $y_1, ..., y_n$ is known as the method of damping factors.

We shall note that the functions $l_i(t)$ may always be chosen so that $\sum_{i=k+1}^{n} l_i(t) y_i^2 \to 0$ as $t \to +\infty$, since the growth of the function does not exceed some function $\exp \int_{t_0}^{t} \phi(r)dr$, determined from the system (6.1) itself (see Theorem 19).

THEOREM 21. If there exist two quadratic forms V and W satisfying the following conditions:

1)   the quadratic form V satisfies the inequalities

$$\phi_1(t) r_t^2 \leq V \leq \phi_2(t) r_1^2 ;$$

2)   the quadratic form W satisfies the inequalities

$$-\psi_1(t) r_1^2 \leq W \leq -\psi_2(t) r_1^2 ;$$

3) the function W is the total derivative of the function V as based on system (6.1), i.e. $dV/dt = W$

(Here ϕ_1, ϕ_2 are positive functions given for $t \geqq 0$, and the functions $\psi_1/\tilde{\psi}_1$ and $\psi_2/\tilde{\psi}_2$ are integrable in every interval $[t_0, T]$, where $T \geqq t_0$.) — then every solution of system (6.1) satisfies the estimate

$$r_{t_0}\phi_1^{\frac{1}{2}}(t_0)\,\phi_2^{-\frac{1}{2}}(t)\,e^{-\frac{1}{2}\int\limits_{t_0}^{t}\frac{\psi_1}{\tilde{\phi}_1}\,d\tau} \leqq r(t, y_{10}, \dots, y_{n0}, t_0) \leqq$$

$$\leqq r_{t_0}\phi_2^{\frac{1}{2}}(t_0)\,\phi_1^{-\frac{1}{2}}(t)\,e^{-\frac{1}{2}\int\limits_{t_0}^{t}\frac{\psi_2}{\tilde{\phi}_2}\,d\tau}, \tag{8.1}$$

where

$$r_{t_0}^2 = \sum_{i=1}^{n} y_{i0}^2 + \sum_{i=k+1}^{n} l_i(t_0)\,y_{i0}^2,$$

and $\tilde{\phi}_1, \tilde{\phi}_2$ have the same meaning as in Theorem 17.

The proof of this Theorem is analogous to that of Theorem 17.

COROLLARY 1. From Theorem 21 it follows that if as $l_i(t)$ one chooses the functions

$$e^{-\alpha_i t - \int\limits_{t_0}^{t}\phi(\tau)\,d\tau} \qquad (\alpha_i > 0; i = k+1, \dots n),$$

then from estimate (8.1) we shall obtain

$$r_k^2 + \sum_{i=k+1}^{n} l_i y_i^2 \leqq r_{t_0}^2 \phi_2(t_0)\,\phi_1^{-1}(t)\,e^{-\int\limits_{t_0}^{t}\frac{\psi_2}{\tilde{\phi}_2}\,d\tau}, \tag{8.2}$$

whence we have an estimate for the first k coordinates

$$r_k^2 \leqq r_{t_0}^2 \phi_2(t_0)\,\phi_1^{-1}(t)\,e^{-\int\limits_{t_0}^{t}\frac{\psi_2}{\tilde{\phi}_2}\,d\tau} - \sum_{i=k+1}^{n} l_i(t)\,y_i^2. \tag{8.3}$$

COROLLARY 2. If the function $\phi_2(t_0)\phi_1^{-1}(t)\exp\left[-\int\limits_{t_0}^{t}(\psi_2/\tilde{\phi}_2)d\tau\right]$ is bounded for $t \geqq t_0$, then the homogeneous solution of system (6.1) will be stable with respect to the coordinates $y_1, \dots, y_k$.

Indeed, in the presence of quadratic forms V and W satisfying Theorem 21, estimate (8.3) holds. Discarding the sum in the right-hand member of inequality (8.3) we may only strengthen it, and then the estimate obtained shows that the quantity r_k^2 may be made arbitrarily small for any $t \geqq t_0$ if only the quantity $r_{t_0}^2$ is sufficiently small, i.e. the initial deviations $y_{10}, \ldots, y_{n0}$ are small.

Another method of investigating stability with respect to given coordinates $y_1, \ldots, y_k$ consists in reducing the problem to the investigation of stability of the homogeneous solution with respect to all the coordinates in some new coordinate system.

In system (6.1) we shall carry out a change of variables according to the formulae

$$y_i = x_i \quad (i = 1, \ldots, k);$$

$$y_i = x_i e^{\int_{t_0}^{t} [\alpha_i + \phi(\tau)] \, d\tau} \qquad (i = k+1, \ldots, n), \tag{8.4}$$

where the $\alpha_i > 0$, and $\phi(t)$ are those functions which were dealt with in Theorem 19.

Here $x_1, \ldots, x_n$ are the new functions sought for, which will satisfy the following system of differential equations:

$$\left.\begin{array}{l} \dfrac{dx_s}{dt} = \displaystyle\sum_{i \infty 1}^{k} p_{si}(t) x_i + \sum_{i=k+1}^{n} p_{si}(t) x_i e^{\int_{t_0}^{t} [\alpha_i + \phi(\tau)] \, d\tau} \\[4pt] \text{for } s \leqq k; \\[20pt] \dfrac{dx_s}{dt} = \displaystyle\sum_{i=1}^{k} p_{si}(t) x_i e^{-\int_{t_0}^{t} [\alpha_i + \phi(\tau)] \, d\tau} + \sum_{i=k+1}^{n} p_{si}(t) x_i - (\alpha_s + \phi) x_s \end{array}\right\} \tag{8.5}$$

for $s = k+1, \ldots, n$.

This system is obtained from (6.1) with the aid of substitution (8.4).

We shall note that the homogeneous solution of the system of the form (8.5) is asymptotically stable with respect to the coordinates $x_{k+1}, \ldots, x_n$, which follows from the change of variables (8.4).

THEOREM 2′. In order that the homogeneous solution of system (6.1) be stable with respect to the coordinates $y_1, ..., y_k$, it is necessary and sufficient that the homogeneous solution of system (8.5) also be stable with respect to all the coordinates.

PROOF: *Sufficiency.* Let the homogeneous solution of the system (8.5) be stable. Then from the substitution (8.4) it follows that the solution of system (6.1) will be stable with respect to the first k coordinates, since $x_i = y_i$; $i = 1, ..., k$.

Necessity. As has been noted above, the homogeneous solution of system (8.5) is stable with respect to the coordinates $x_{k+1}, ..., x_n$. According to the assumption, from (8.4) also follows that the homogeneous solution will be stable also with respect to the coordinates $x_1, ..., x_k$. Consequently, the homogeneous solution of system (8.5) is stable.

Remark. An analogous theorem holds also for the case of asymptotic stability.

§9. Investigation of the stability of linear systems by construction of exact solutions

It is well known that the finding of the exact solutions of a linear system with variable coefficients is very difficult. However, if such a construction is made in a form especially adapted for the investigation of the problem of stability of these solutions, then this gives considerable advantage compared with those methods which have been dealt with in the preceding sections.

In the present sections we shall expound a method for constructing a general solution of a linear system of a special type.

In system (6.1) we shall perform the substitution $t = \phi(z)$, where ϕ is a function given for $z \in (0, 1)$ and is differentiable there.

We shall consider that $\phi(1) = 0$ and $\phi(z) \to +\infty$ as $z \to 0$. After this substitution, system (6.1) will take the form

$$\frac{dy_s}{dz} = \phi'(z) \sum_{i=1}^{n} p_{si}(\phi(z)) y_i. \qquad (9.1)$$

We shall assume that the functions $\phi'(z) p_{st}(\phi(z))$ are representable in the form of series

$$\phi'(z) p_{si}(\phi(z)) = \sum_{k=0}^{\infty} p_{si}^{(k)} \frac{z^k}{z^N}, \qquad (9.2)$$

where N is a positive integer; $N \geq 1$. The coefficients $p_{si}^{(k)}$ in series (9.2) we consider to be real constants.

With the assumptions indicated, system (9.1) takes the form

$$z^N \frac{dy_s}{dz} = \sum_{i=1}^{n} y_i \left(\sum_{k=0}^{\infty} p_{si}^{(k)} z^k \right). \tag{9.3}$$

Furthur on, we shall consider system (9.3) in the case when $N = 1$, unless otherwise stipulated.

THEOREM 22.   If all the roots of the equation

$$|P_0 - \lambda E| = 0, \tag{9.4}$$

where $P_0 = \| p_{si}^0 \|$, have positive real parts, then the homogeneous solution of system (9.1) is asymptotically stable and system (9.3) has a general solution represented in the form of series

$$y_s = \sum_{i=1}^{n} z^{\lambda_i} \eta_{si}(z) C_i, \tag{9.5}$$

where $\lambda_1, \ldots, \lambda_n$ are the roots of equation (9.4), and $C_1, \ldots, C_n$ are arbitrary constants.

The quantities η_{si} represent functions of the variable z, representable in the form of series

$$\eta_{si}(z) = \sum_{m=0}^{+\infty} K_{si}^{(m)} (\ln z) z^m, \tag{9.6}$$

converging for $|z| \leq C_0$, where C_0 is a sufficiently small positive constant, and the $K_{si}^{(m)}$ are polynomials in $\ln z$.

PROOF: In system (9.3) we shall perform a change of the independent variable according to the formula $dzd\tau = -z$. Then system (9.3) will take the form:

$$\left. \begin{aligned} \frac{dz}{d\tau} &= -z, \\[2em] \frac{dy_s}{d\tau} &= -\sum_{i=1}^{n} \sum_{k=0}^{\infty} p_{(si)}^{(k)} z^k y_i \quad (s = 1, \ldots, n). \end{aligned} \right\} \tag{9.7}$$

If the system of functions

$$y_s = y_s(z, y_{10}, \ldots, y_{n0}) \tag{9.8}$$

is a solution of system (9.3) (for $z = 1$; $y_s = y_{s0}$), then the functions $z = z_0 e^{-\tau}$

$$y_s = y_s(z_0 e^{-\tau}, y_{10}, \ldots, y_{n0}) \tag{9.9}$$

where $z_0 \in (0, 1]$ are the solutions of system (9.7) with the condition $y_s = y_{s0}$, when $\tau_0 = \ln z_0$.

In fact, differentiating the functions (9.9) with respect to the variable τ, we shall obtain

$$\frac{dy_s}{d\tau} = \frac{dy_s}{dz} \cdot \frac{dz}{d\tau} = -z \frac{dy_s}{dz},$$

whence

$$\frac{dy_s}{d\tau} = - \sum_{i=1}^{n} \sum_{k=0}^{+\infty} p_{si}^{(k)} z^k y_i,$$

as the functions y_s, being functions of the variable z, satisfy system (9.3).

If one has found the general solution of system (9.7)

$$y_s = y_s(\tau, y_{10}, \ldots, y_{n0}, \tau_0) \quad (s = 1, \ldots, n)$$

satisfying the condition $y_s = y_{s0}$ for $\tau = \tau_0$, then by the substitution $\tau = -(\ln z - \tau_0)$ we shall obtain the system of functions

$$y_s = y_s(\ln z - \tau_0) \quad (s = 1, \ldots, n) \tag{9.10}$$

satisfying system (9.3) and the condition $y_s = y_{s0}$ for $z = 1$.

This assertion is established by differentiating the functions (9.10) with respect to the variable τ as based on system (9.7). Thus, we have established a link between the solutions of systems (9.3) and (9.7).

As follows from the theorems on the first method of Lyapunov, system (9.7) has a family of solutions representable in the form of series

$$y_s = \sum_{m+m_1+\ldots+m_n=1}^{+\infty} K_{s m_1, \ldots, m_n}^{(m)}(\tau) C_1^{m_1} \ldots C_n^{m_n} \cdot C^m e^{-t \left(\sum_{i=1}^{n} m_i \lambda_i + m \right)} \quad (s = 1, \ldots, n,) \tag{9.11}$$

converging for $t \geqq 0$ if $|C_s| < \gamma$, where γ is a sufficiently small positive number

The functions $K_{s m_1, \ldots, m_n}^{(k)}(\tau)$ are polynomials in τ.

The right-hand members of system (9.7) are linear with respect to the quantities $y_1, \ldots, y_n$, and therefore series (9.11) will also depend linearly on the arbitrary constants $C_1, \ldots, C_n$. Consequently, they may be represented in the form

$$y_s = \sum_{i=1}^{n} C_i e^{-\lambda_i \tau} \eta_{si} \quad (s = 1, \ldots, n), \tag{9.12}$$

where the quantities η_{si} represent functions expandable in converging series.

$$\eta_{si} = \sum_{m=0}^{+\infty} K_{si}^m(\tau) C^m e^{-m\tau} \quad (s = 1, \ldots, n). \tag{9.13}$$

In those series we shall perform the substitution of the variable z according to the formula $z = Ce^{-\tau}$. Then

$$y_s = \sum_{i=1}^{n} \bar{C}_i z^{\lambda_i} \bar{\eta}_{si} \quad (s = 1, \ldots, n). \tag{9.14}$$

It is easy to see that the functions $\bar{\eta}_{si}$ are represented in the form of series

$$\bar{\eta}_{si} = \sum_{m=0}^{+\infty} \bar{K}_{si}^{(m)} (\ln z) z^m,$$

converging for $|z| < \gamma$. The function $\bar{K}_{si}^{(m)}$ are polynomials in $\ln z$.

The arbitrary constants $\bar{C}_i$ in the form (9.14) differ from the preceding ones by the factors $C^{-\lambda_s}$ and therefore may be again denoted by C_i, and the functions $\bar{\eta}_{si}$ by η_{si}. Then (9.14) coincides with series (9.5).

Thus, it has been shown that system (9.3) has a family of solutions representable in the form of series (9.5).

The characteristic numbers $\lambda_1, \ldots, \lambda_n$ have positive real parts, therefore $y_s \to 0$ as $z \to 0$, and this indicates that the homogeneous solution of the original system is asymptotically stable.

THEOREM 23.   If $\lambda_1, \ldots, \lambda_n$ are the roots of the equation $|P_0 - \lambda E| = 0$, then the general solution of system (9.3) is also representable in the form (9.5).

PROOF: Theorem 23 refers to the case when among the $\lambda_1, \ldots, \lambda_n$ there are numbers with real parts differing in sign, or with zero real parts. Therefore one may not apply directly Lyapunov's theorem on the existence of a general solution in the form of series. In order to avoid that inconvenient state of affairs, in system (9.3) we shall perform the substitution

$$\eta_s z^m = y_s \quad (s = 1, \ldots, n), \tag{9.15}$$

where m is some negative number, and η_s are new functions to be sought.

For the determination of the functions η_s we shall obtain the system of equations

$$z \frac{d\eta_s}{dz} = -m\eta_s + \sum_{i=1}^{n} \sum_{k=0}^{+\infty} p_{si}^{(k)} z^k y \quad (s = 1, \ldots, n). \tag{9.16}$$

System (9.16) is obtained from system (9.3) by replacing in it the functions y_s by the η_s according to formulae (9.15).

We shall note that system (9.16) has the same form as system (9.3), and transformation (9.15) leads only to changing the diagonal elements of the matrix P_0. The roots of the equation $|P_0 - mE - \mu E| = 0$ differ from the numbers $\lambda_1, \ldots, \lambda_n$ by the constant $-m$, i.e. $\mu_i = \lambda_i - m$.

If $-m > \mathrm{Re}\lambda_i$, then the numbers $\mu_1, \ldots, \mu_n$ have positive real parts. Consequently, the homogeneous solution of system (9.16) is asymptotically stable and, as follows from Theorem 22, the general solution of that system is representable in the form of series

$$\eta_s = \sum_{i=1}^{n} C_i z^{\mu_i} \eta_{si} = \sum_{i=1}^{n} C_i z^{\lambda_i - m} \eta_{si}. \tag{9.17}$$

Performing transformation (9.15) in system (9.17), we shall obtain that system (9.3) has a family of solutions represented in the form (9.5), etc.

We shall now dwell on the actual construction of series (9.5). In system (9.3) we shall set $z = Ce^{-\tau}$, then we shall obtain the system

$$\frac{dy_s}{d\tau} = -\sum_{k=0}^{+\infty} \sum_{i=1}^{n} p_{si}^{(k)} y_i C^k e^{-k\tau}. \tag{9.18}$$

The solution of system (9.18) will be expressed in the form of series

$$y_s = \sum_{k=0}^{\infty} y_s^k C^k. \tag{9.19}$$

We shall substitute series (9.19) in system (9.18) and equate the functions standing next to the same powers of C. For their determination we shall obtain a sequence of systems of differential equations of the form

$$\left. \begin{aligned} \frac{dy_s^{(0)}}{d\tau} &= \sum_{i=1}^{n} p_{si}^{(0)} y_i^{(0)} \quad (s = 1, \ldots, n), \\ \frac{dy_s^{(k)}}{d\tau} &= \sum_{i=1}^{n} p_{si}^{(0)} y_i^{(k)} + \sum_{i=1}^{n} \sum_{l=0}^{k-1} p_{si}^{(l)} y_i^l e^{-l\tau}. \end{aligned} \right\} \tag{9.20}$$

We shall find the general solution of the first group of equations entering in (9.20)

$$y_s^{(0)} = \sum_{i=1}^{n} C_i \eta_{si}^{(0)}. \tag{9.21}$$

To find the functions $y_s^{(k)}$ one may apply the method of variation of the arbitrary Lagrange multipliers. We shall set

$$y_s^{(k)} = \sum_{i=1}^{n} \eta_{si}^{(0)} C_i(\tau) \quad (s = 1, \ldots, n). \tag{*}$$

The functions $C_i(\tau)$ with the substitution of (9.21) in system (9.20) will be determined from the equations

$$\sum_{i=1}^{n} \eta_{si}^{(0)} \frac{dC_i}{d\tau} = \sum_{i=1}^{n} \sum_{l=0}^{k-1} p_{si}^{(l)} y_i^{(l)} e^{-l\tau}. \tag{9.22}$$

Solving system (9.22) for the functions $dC_i/d\tau$, we shall obtain for their determination the system of equations

$$\frac{dC_i}{d\tau} = P_i(\tau, y_s^{(0)}, ..., y_s^{(k-1)}) \quad (i = 1, ..., n),\tag{9.23}$$

where the P_i represent linear forms of the functions $y_s^{(l)}$, $l \leqq k - 1$.
From system (9.23) we shall find

$$C_i = \int\limits_{+\infty}^{\tau} P_i(\tau, y_s^{(l)}, ..., y_s^{(k-1)}) \, d\tau.\tag{9.24}$$

From (9.24) it follows that the functions $l_i(\tau)$ are linear forms with respect to the constants $C_1, ..., C_n$ entering in the functions $y_s^{(0)}$ ($s=1, ..., n$). After finding the functions $l_i(\tau)$, with the aid of formulae (*) we shall determine any approximation, and consequently also the solution of the system (9.18)

$$y_s = \sum_{k=0}^{\infty} y_s^{(k)} C^k \quad (s = 1, ..., n).$$

In Theorem 22 the structure of the solutions defining (9.5) is exposed in detail, so that their determination may be reduced to successively finding the solutions of linear systems of algebraic equations.

Indeed, substituting series (9.5) in system (9.18) and equating terms of the same power in the expressions of the form

$$C^m e^{-m\tau} e^{-\lambda_s \tau},$$

we shall obtain a system of algebraic equations for the determination of the polynomials $K_{si}^{(m)}$. Here the polynomials corresponding to $m = 0$ are determined from the system of differential equations which is the first group in system (9.20).

We shall now turn to the case when the right-hand member of the system of equations has a pole $z = 0$ of the order $N > 1$.

We shall assume that all the roots of the equation $|P - \lambda E| = 0$ have positive real parts. Then the equation in partial derivatives

$$\sum_{s=1}^{n} \frac{\partial V}{\partial y_s} \sum_{i=1}^{n} p_{si}^{(0)} y_i = \sum_{i=1}^{n} y_i^2$$

has a solution in the form of a positive-definite quadratic form [2].

We shall find the total derivative of this form as based on system (9.3); then

$$z^N \frac{dV}{dz} = z^N \sum_{i=1}^{n} y_i^2 + \sum_{s=1}^{n} \frac{\partial V}{\partial y_s} \sum_{i=1}^{n} \sum_{k=1}^{\infty} p_{si}^{(k)} z^k y_i = W.\tag{9.25}$$

As follows from (9.25), there exists a positive number z_0 such that the following estimates will hold:

$$b_1 z^N \sum_{i=1}^{n} y_i^2 \leq W \leq b_2 z^N \sum_{i=1}^{n} y_i^2 \text{ for } z \leq z_0, \quad b_1, b_2 > 0. \tag{9.26}$$

From inequality (9.26) it follows that function V decreases as $z \to 0$ and, consequently, $\sum_{i=1}^{n} y_i^2 \to 0$ as $z \to 0$, i.e. the homogeneous solution of system (9.3) is asymptotically stable.

Besides, one can propose an estimate characterizing the decrease of any solution as $z \to 0$.

For this we shall set $d\tau = - dz/z^N$. Then system (9.3) will be transformed into a system of the form

$$\frac{dy_s}{d\tau} = - \sum_{i=1}^{n} \sum_{k=0}^{\infty} p_{si}^{(k)} z^k(\tau) y_i, \tag{9.27}$$

where

$$z(\tau) = \frac{z_0}{\sqrt[N-1]{1 + z_0^{N-1}\tau}}.$$

It is not hard to see that the total derivative of the function V as based on system (9.27) $dV/d\tau = W_1$ satisfies the following conditions

$$- b_2 \sum_{i=1}^{n} y_i^2 \leq W_1 \leq - b_1 \sum_{i=1}^{n} y_i^2. \tag{9.28}$$

The function W is a positive-definite quadratic form, and therefore satisfies the inequalities

$$a_1 \sum_{i=1}^{n} y_i^2 \leq W \leq a_2 \sum_{i=1}^{n} y_i^2. \tag{9.29}$$

From inequalities (9.28) and (9.29) we shall find that with the condition indicated, every solution of system (9.23) satisfies the inequalities

$$p_1 r_0 e^{-p_i \tau} \leq r \leq q_1 r_0 e^{-q_i \tau},$$

where p_i, q_i are positive constants $(i = 1, 2)$,

$$r_0 = \sqrt{\sum_{i=1}^{n} y_{i0}^2},$$

and r is the distance from the integral curve to the coordinate origin.

Thus, the assertion of Theorem 23 on the stability of the homogeneous solution holds for any $N \geqq 1$.

Remark. We shall note that the problem of presenting the solutions of system (9.3) for $N = 1$ has been dealt with by many authors: [16], [17], [18], [19], and [20]. Here, however, we give the solution of the problem of representing the integral curves of system (9.3) on the basis of the first method of Lyapunov [2].

§ 10.   Investigation of the behaviour of transient processes in a linear system in a finite time interval by the method of approximate integration

Say one is given the system of linear equations

$$\frac{dy_s}{dt} = \sum_{i=1}^{n} p_{si}(t, C_{01}, \ldots, C_{0k}) y_i \quad (s = 1, \ldots, n), \tag{10.1}$$

representing a linear approximation in system of equations (1.4). We shall consider that the functions $p_{si}(t, \omega_1, \ldots, \omega_k)$ are given for $t \in [t_0, t_0 + T]$ and are piecewise-continuous there, and the variables $\omega_1, \ldots, \omega_k$ are the parameters of the automatic control system, taking various values from the region Ω of admissible values.

In an extensive class of cases encountered in the theory of automatic control, it may be considered that the functions $p_{si}(t, \omega_1, \ldots, \omega_k)$ are polynomials in $\omega_1, \ldots, \omega_k$. We shall recall that the original system (1.1) is known, in general, only approximately. The steady state (1.2) is therefore known also approximately. Therefore all the functions of time encountered in system (1.4) represent the actual picture of the flow of the transient processes in the real system only approximately. This assertion is all the more correct in relation to system (10.1). Consequently, within the framework of the limits of accuracy with which the functions $p_{si}(t, \omega_1, \ldots, \omega_k)$ are known, they may be replaced by other functions $q_{si}(t, \omega_1, \ldots, \omega_k)$. Here every conclusion on the transient processes in system (10.1) will be just as correct as a conclusion on the transient processes in the system

$$\frac{dy_s}{dt} = \sum_{i=1}^{n} q_{si}(t, \omega_1, \ldots, \omega_k) \quad (s = 1, \ldots, n). \tag{10.2}$$

This simple consideration may be put as the basis of the following method of an approximate construction of the transient processes in system (10.1):

a) we shall split up the interval $[t_0, t_0 + T]$ by means of the points $h_0 < h_1 < \ldots < h_m$; $h_0 = t_0$; $h_m = t_0 + T$;

b) we shall compute the values of the functions $p_{si}(t, \omega_1, \ldots, \omega_k)$ at the points $h_0, \ldots, h_{m-1}$.

We shall define the functions $q_{si}(t, \omega_1, \ldots, \omega_k)$ in system (10.2) in such a way that the equality

$$q_{si}(t, \omega_1, \ldots, \omega_k) = p_{si}(h_{l-1}, \omega_1, \ldots, \omega_k) \qquad (10.3)$$

hold for $t \in [h_{l-1}, h_l]$ $(l = 1, \ldots, m)$.

It is clear, that the functions $q_{si}(t, \omega_1, \ldots, \omega_k)$ are piecewise-continuous step-functions given in $[t_0, t_0 + T]$;

c) we shall find the fundamental system of solutions for linear system (10.2), in which the functions q_{si} are defined by relations (10.3).

By Y_l we shall denote the matrix

$$Y_l = e^{tP(h_{l-1}, \omega_1, \ldots, \omega_k)} C_l \text{ for } t \in [h_{l-1}, h_l] \quad (l = 1, \ldots, m), \qquad (10.4)$$

where P is the matrix of the coefficients of systems (10.1); C_l are some constants of the matrix.

It is clear that matrix (10.4) will be a solution of system (10.2) in the time interval indicated.

We shall now choose the constants of the matrix C_l in such a way that the conditions of conjugation

$$e^{h_l P(h_{l-1}, \omega_1, \ldots, \omega_k)} C_l = e^{h_l P(h_l, \omega_1, \ldots, \omega_k)} C_{l+1} \quad (l = 1, \ldots, m-1) \qquad (10.5)$$

be satisfied.

We shall consider C_0 to be a unit matrix. From (10.5) we shall obtain the recurrence relation

$$C_{l+1} = e^{-h_l P(h_l, \omega_1, \ldots, \omega_k)} e^{h_l P(h_{l-1}, \omega_1, \ldots, \omega_k)} C_l,$$

which will allow us to determine successively all the constants of matrix C_l

By R_l we shall denote the matrix

$$R_l = e^{(h_l - h_{l-1}) P(h_{l-1}, \omega_1, \ldots, \omega_k)}.$$

Utilizing these matrices, we shall find that

$$C_{l+1} = e^{-h_l P(h_l, \omega_1, \ldots, \omega_k)} R_l R_{l-1} R_{l-2} \ldots R_1.$$

Thus, the function-matrix

$$Y_{l+1} = e^{(t-h_l) P(h_l, \omega_1, \ldots, \omega_k)} R_l R_{l-1} \ldots R_1. \qquad (10.6)$$

Now we shall define a matrix Y in such a way that the following equalities hold:

$$Y(t) = Y_l(t) \text{ for } t \in [h_{l-1}, h_l] \quad (l = 1, \ldots, m). \tag{10.7}$$

The elements of the matrix, defined by relations (10.6), are continuous functions of the variable t in the interval $[t_0, t_0 + T]$.

From the way in which the matrix $Y(t)$ was constructed, it follows that the matrix represents a fundamental system of solutions for the system of equations (10.2), where $Y(t_0) = E$. Consequently, any transient process in system (10.2) may be written in the form

$$Y = Y(t) Y_0, \tag{10.8}$$

where $Y_0 = \left\{ \begin{array}{c} y_{10} \\ \vdots \\ y_{n0} \end{array} \right\}$.

Y_0 is a vector representing the totality of the initial data of the transient process Y.

Remark 1. In the case when the points $h_0, h_1, \ldots, h_{m-1}$ are chosen so that for all admissible values of the parameters $\omega_1, \ldots, \omega_k$ the inequalities

$$|p_{si}(t, \omega_1, \ldots, \omega_k) - q_{si}(t, \omega_1, \ldots, \omega_k)| \leq l \tag{10.9}$$

will be satisfied, where l is some positive constant characterizing the error in the calculation of the coefficients $p_{si}(t, \omega_1, \ldots, \omega_k)$ in system (10.1) only, then the transient processes in system (10.1) are just as reliably described by equation (10.8) in the interval $[t_0, t_0 + h_{m-1}]$, as by the exact solutions of system (10.1) itself.

If one increases the number of points of division, then it may be shown that the vectorial function Y, defined by (10.8), tends to the exact solutions of (10.1) as $(h_l - h_{l-1}) \to 0$.

The increase in the number of points of division leads to a considerable increase in the volume of computation, whereas in reality the precision of the representation of the transient processes in terms of (10.8) need not necessarily increase. Therefore, the points $h_0, h_1, \ldots, h_m$ should be chosen only so as to satisfy relation (10.9).

This remark would not be complete if to it we did not add that inequality (10.9) may be realized in general only when the region of admissible values of the parameters $\omega_1, \ldots, \omega_k$ is bounded; moreover, the number of points $h_0, h_1, \ldots, h_{m-1}$ may be chosen smaller, the smaller the diameter of the region Ω.

If the region Ω is not bounded, or has considerable dimensions, from the point of view of the influence on the uniform fulfillment of inequality (10.9), it is recommended that the region Ω be divided first into a series of regions in each of which inequality (10.9) is satisfied by choosing the smallest possible number of points $h_0, h_1, ..., h_m$.

Remark 2. In performing the calculation of the fundamental system of solutions $Y(t)$, it is necessary to know the matrices R_l, which may be easily constructed if one knows the fundamental system of solutions for the system of equations

$$\frac{dy_s}{dt} = \sum_{i=1}^{n} p_{si}(h_{l-1}, \omega_1, ..., \omega_k) y_i \quad (s = 1, ..., n). \tag{10.10}$$

The calculation of the fundamental system of solutions for (10.10) may be carried out by using Laplace transforms.

We shall take the system of equations

$$\frac{dy_s}{dt} = \sum_{i=1}^{n} p_{si}(\tau, \omega_1, ..., \omega_k) y_i \quad (s = 1, ..., n), \tag{10.11}$$

which is obtained from system (10.1) by replacing the independent variable t by the parameter τ, independent of t.

System (10.11) is a system with coefficients independent of time, therefore one may find the fundamental system of solutions

$$Y_1 \left[(t - t_0), \tau, \omega_1, ..., \omega_k \right] = e^{(t-t_0) p(\tau, \omega_1, ... \omega_k)} .$$

It is easy to see that $R_l = Y_1(h_l - h_{l-1}, h_{l-1}, \omega_1, ..., \omega_k)$. Hence, it follows that if the fundamental system of solutions for system (10.11) is found, then the transient processes in system (10.1) may be constructed with the aid of formula (10.8) with the desired degree of accuracy by making use only of the operations of multiplication and addition necessary for the computation of the function Y_l.

The consideration lying at the basis of the construction for transient process (10.1) just expounded may be used as the basis of another method, consisting of the following.

In system (10.1) one introduces auxiliary parameters $\varepsilon_1, ..., \varepsilon_r$ such that the coefficients of the newly obtained system

$$\frac{dy_s}{dt} = \sum_{i=1}^{n} p_{si}(t, \varepsilon_1, ..., \varepsilon_r, \omega_1, ..., \omega_k) y_i \quad (s = 1, ..., n) \tag{10.12}$$

possess the following property

$$p_{si}(t, \varepsilon_1, ..., \varepsilon_r, \omega_1, ..., \omega_k) \equiv p_{si}(t, \omega_1, ..., \omega_k)$$

for $\varepsilon_1 = \varepsilon_2 = ... = \varepsilon_r = 1$.

In an extensive class of cases these parameters may be introduced in such a way that the coefficients in system (10.12) be piecewise-continuous functions of the independent variable t in the interval $[t_0, t_0 + T]$ and be polynomials in the quantities $(\varepsilon_1, ..., \varepsilon_r, \omega_1, ..., \omega_k)$.

Thus, the functions $p_{si}(t, \varepsilon_1, ..., \varepsilon_r, \omega_1, ..., \omega_k)$ may be represented in the form

$$p_{si}(t, \varepsilon_1, ..., \varepsilon_r, \omega_1, ..., \omega_k) = \sum_{l=0}^{p} p_{si}^{(l)}(t, \varepsilon_1, ..., \varepsilon_r, \omega_1, ..., \omega_k),$$

where $p_{si}^{(l)}$ are homogeneous forms of some power in the quantities $\varepsilon_1, ..., \varepsilon_r$ with coefficients dependent on $t, \omega_1, ..., \omega_k$.

In system (10.12) we shall introduce the parameters in such a way that for $\varepsilon_1 = ... = \varepsilon_r = 0$ system (10.12) become a system of easily integrable equations

$$\frac{dy_s}{dt} = \sum_{i=1}^{n} p_{si}^{(0)}(t, \omega_1, ..., \omega_k) y_i \quad (s = 1, ..., n). \tag{10.13}$$

We shall seek the solution of system (10.12) in the form of series in powers of the parameters $\varepsilon_1, ..., \varepsilon_r$,

$$Y(t, \varepsilon_1, ..., \varepsilon_r, \omega_1, ..., \omega_k) = \sum_{l=0}^{\infty} Y^{(l)}, \tag{10.14}$$

where the $Y^{(l)}$ are homogeneous forms of the degree l in $\varepsilon_1, ..., \varepsilon_r$ whose coefficients are matrices to be determined.

We shall write system (10.12) in matrix form

$$\frac{dy}{dt} = \sum_{l=0}^{p} P^{(l)} Y, \tag{10.15}$$

where $P^{(l)}$ are homogeneous forms in $\varepsilon_1, ..., \varepsilon_r$ whose coefficients are known matrices of the variables $t, \varepsilon_1, ..., \varepsilon_r, \omega_1, ..., \omega_k$. Substituting series (10.14) in system (10.15) and equating the terms of the same power in $\varepsilon_1, ..., \varepsilon_r$, we shall obtain a system of equations of the form

$$\frac{dY^{(0)}}{dt} = P^{(0)} Y^{(0)},$$

$$\frac{dY^{(l)}}{dt} = P^{(0)} Y^{(l)} + \sum_{i=0}^{l-1} P^{(l-i)} Y^{(i)} \quad (l = 1, 2, 3, ...), \tag{10.16}$$

where $P^{(l)} \equiv 0$ for $l > p$.

From system (10.16) one successively determines the sought matrices according to the following recurrence formulae.

Say that the matrix $Y^{(0)}$ which is the fundamental solution for the first group of equations of system (10.16) is found.

We shall seek $Y^{(l)}$ in the form

$$Y^{(l)} = Y^{(0)}C, \tag{10.17}$$

where C is a matrix defined by the condition $C = 0$ for $t = t_0$.

Substituting (10.17) in system (10.16), we shall obtain

$$\frac{dY^{(0)}}{dt} C + Y^{(0)}\frac{dC}{dt} = P^{(0)} Y^{(0)} C + \sum_{i=0}^{l-1} P^{(l-i)}Y^{(i)},$$

whence

$$\frac{dC}{dt} = [Y^0]^{-1} \sum_{i=0}^{l-1} P^{(l-i)}Y^{(i)}.$$

Consequently

$$C(t) = \int_{t_0}^{t} [Y^0]^{-1} \sum_{i=0}^{l-1} P^{(l-i)}Y^{(i)}dt.$$

Likewise from (10.17) we shall find

$$Y^{(l)} = Y^{(0)}(t) \int_{t_0}^{t} [Y^0]^{-1} \sum_{i=0}^{l-1} P^{(l-i)}Y^{(i)}dt. \tag{10.18}$$

Relation (10.18) represents a recurrence formula, allowing one to determine all the coefficients of system (10.14).

If in series (10.14) one sets $\varepsilon_1 = \ldots = \varepsilon_r = 1$, then we shall obtain a fundamental system of solutions for system (10.1) and, consequently, every transient process may be written in the form

$$Y(t) = Y(t, \varepsilon_1, \ldots, \varepsilon_r, \omega_1, \ldots, \omega_r) Y^{(0)}$$

for $\varepsilon_1 = \ldots = \varepsilon_r = 1$.

If in series (10.14) one dispenses with all terms for which $l > q$, then for $\varepsilon_1 = \ldots = \varepsilon_r = 1$ we shall obtain a matrix which will approximately represent the fundamental system of solutions for system (10.1), as series (10.14) converge for all values of $\varepsilon_1, \ldots, \varepsilon_r$. We shall now prove it.

Series (10.14) converge uniformly on every finite interval $t \in [t_0, t_0 + T_1]$, as these series have a majorant in the terms of the positive converging series

$\bar{Y} = e^{t\bar{P}}$ where $\bar{P}$ is a constant matrix obtained from the matrix $P(t, \omega_1, \ldots, \omega_k, \varepsilon_1, \ldots, \varepsilon_r)$ by replacing the functions of time entering in P by the largest value of their moduli in the interval $[t_0, t_0 + T_1]$. Therefore, series (10.14) may be approximated by the partial sum $\sum\limits_{l=0}^{q} Y^{(l)}$ with any degree of accuracy in the finite interval $[t_0, t_0 + T_1]$ provided only that q is sufficiently large.

A more precise pronouncement of this kind, connected with the estimate of the remainder of the series in relation to the number q, cannot be managed, as the estimates then obtained are of an exponential type and are unsatisfactory. However, this state of affairs may be ignored if one takes the following consideration into account.

The system of equations under consideration, as has already been noted, is not exact, i.e. with the choice of its coefficients one admits now and then a considerable leeway, of the order of 10–20%. Therefore, as solution of such a system one may take any continuously differentiable functions satisfying the system of equations with sufficient accuracy.

This consideration may be laid at the basis of the construction of the approximate solution.

We shall take the function $Y_q = \sum\limits_{l=0}^{q} Y^{(l)}$ and substitute it in system (10.13). Then we shall obtain

$$Z_q = \sum_{l=0}^{P} P^{(l)} Y_q - \frac{d}{dt} Y_q = \sum_{l+\mu=q+1}^{P+q} P^{(l)} Y^{(\mu)} .$$

Thus, it is proposed to consider the matrix Y_q as representing the solution sufficiently well if Z_q is in a certain sense small for $\varepsilon_1 = \ldots = \varepsilon_r = 1$; $\omega_1, \ldots, \omega_k \in \Omega$.

We shall further point out two of the simplest variants of the method just described for constructing solutions of the system

The first variant consists in the introduction of a unique parameter ε in the system of equations. Then the process of computing the approximations is considerably simplified and, besides, one may distinguish just those terms in the matrix of coefficients which demonstrate in general the greatest influence upon the behaviour of the solutions of the system.

Indeed, one may set the parameter ε and its powers in front of different terms of the matrix P by taking into account the number of these terms.

Thus, for example, the system of equations

$$\frac{dx}{dt} = (1 + 0.1 \sin t) x + (10 + 0.1 t \sin t) y,$$

$$\frac{dy}{dt} = (3 + t) x - (0.1 \sin t) y,$$

may be replaced by the system

$$\frac{dx}{dt} = (\varepsilon + 0.1 \, \varepsilon^3 \sin t) x + (10 + 1.0 \varepsilon^3 t \sin t) y,$$

$$\frac{dy}{dt} = (3 + \varepsilon t) x - (0.1 \varepsilon^3 \sin t) y.$$

If one is interested in the solutions of this system for t from zero to unity, then we shall obtain them with a high degree of accuracy by retaining in the solution only the terms up to ε^3.

The other variant of the method indicated above consists in the following.

We shall introduce the parameters $\varepsilon_1, \ldots, \varepsilon_r$ in such a way that a part or all of them stand as factors in front of the quantities $\omega_1, \ldots, \omega_k$. Then series (10.14) will consist of homogeneous forms in $\varepsilon_1, \ldots, \varepsilon_r$. Then the coefficients of these forms will be the known forms in $\omega_1, \ldots, \omega_k$ with the coefficients dependent on time. These latter coefficients are not dependent on the system parameters and are defined only by its constant part being given, and therefore may be calculated once and for all. Such a representation of series (10.14) allows one to study them in dependence on the behaviour of the parameters $\omega_1, \ldots, \omega_k$.

This is particularly valuable when the system of equations embraces a large class of different problems.

Here one should point out works [2] and [26], in which the method applied in this section has been first developed, and also works [21] and [22].

§ 11. New method of constructing the regions of stability in the space of admissible parameters of the automatic control system

In the theory of automatic control one very often meets with problems of the following type.

Given is the constant part of the automatic control system and one has some leeway in the choice of parameters defining the functioning of the control organs. It is required to choose these parameters in such a way that the fixed behaviour (steady-state motion) be stable.

In the present section we give a new method of finding the regions of stability in the space of admissible values of the parameters, not connected with the construction of the characteristic polynomial.

We shall pass to the exposition of this method.

Say that as the steady-state motion one has chosen a system of quantities $x_1 = x_2 = \ldots = x_n = 0$, where $x_1, x_2, \ldots, x_n$ are the coordinates describing the functioning of the system of interest to us. Then the investigation of that steady motion may be reduced to the study of the behaviour of the solutions of the system of equations

$$\frac{dx_i}{dt} = f_i(t, x_1, \ldots, x_n, \lambda_1, \ldots, \lambda_m) \quad (i = 1, \ldots, n), \tag{11.1}$$

where f_i are real functions of the variables $t, x_1, \ldots, x_n, \lambda_1, \ldots, \lambda_m$, given for $t \geqq 0; -\infty < x_i < +\infty$ $(i = 1, \ldots, n); \lambda_1, \lambda_2, \ldots, \lambda_m \in \Omega$, where Ω is the region of the admissible values of the parameters of the system.

From the preceding it follows that $f_i(t_i, 0, \ldots, 0, \lambda_1, \ldots, \lambda_m) \equiv 0$.

Let the system of linear equations

$$\frac{dx_i}{dt} = \sum_{j=1}^{n} p_{ij} x_j \quad (i = 1, \ldots, n) \tag{11.2}$$

represent a linear approximation for system (11.1). Then, as is known (see § 14), from the asymptotic stability of the homogeneous solution of system (11.2) will follow the stability of the steady motion in system (11.1) with sufficiently broad assumptions relative to the nonlinear terms.

We shall consider that the coefficients of system (11.2) do not depend on t, but are known functions of the parameters of the system $\lambda_1, \ldots, \lambda_m$.

It is known that the homogeneous solution of system (11.2) is asymptotically stable if and only if the real parts of the roots of the equation

$$|P - \lambda E| = 0 \tag{11.3}$$

are negative, where P is the matrix of coefficients of system (11.2) and E is a unit matrix.

In other words, the homogeneous solution of system (11.2) is asymptotically stable if and only if all the roots (11.3) lie in the of left halfplane of the complex variable λ.

We shall map that half plane on the unit circle of the plane of the complex variable ρ by means of the function

$$\lambda = \frac{\rho - 1}{\rho + 1}. \tag{11.4}$$

Under this transformation the roots of equation (11.3) will become the roots of the equation

$$\left| P - E \frac{\rho - 1}{\rho + 1} \right| = 0. \tag{11.5}$$

Multiplying (11.5) by $(\rho + 1)^n$, we shall obtain

$$\left| P + E - \rho(E - P) \right| = 0. \tag{11.6}$$

In (11.6) replacing ρ by $-\rho$ and multiplying both members by $\left| (P - E)^{-1} \right|$, we shall obtain

$$\left| B - \rho E \right| = 0, \tag{11.7}$$

where

$$B = (P - E)^{-1}(P + E).$$

The homogeneous solution of system (11.2) will be asymptotically stable if and only if all the roots of equation (11.7) lie within the unit circle.

We shall denote these roots by $\rho_1, \ldots, \rho_n$.

It is known [3] that the matrix B^k will have the roots $\rho_1^k, \ldots, \rho_n^k$. Hence it follows that the homogeneous solution of system (11.2) will be asymptotically stable if and only if the elements of the matrix B^k tend to zero as $k \to +\infty$. This condition will be satisfied if for any k it turns out that the modulus of every element of the matrix B^k does not exceed the number α/n, where α is any positive number less than unity and n is the number of equations.

Thus, the following proposition holds.

The homogeneous solution of system (11.2) will be asymptotically stable if and only if there exists an integer $k > 0$ such that the element b_{ij}^k of the matrix B^k satisfies the inequality

$$\left| b_{ij}^{(k)} \right| \leq \frac{\alpha}{n}. \tag{11.8}$$

The necessary and sufficient stability criterion given above may be applied to the approximate construction of the region of stability in the space of admissible values of the parameters $\lambda_1, \ldots, \lambda_m$.

As has been explained above, criterion (11.8) is based on constructing the the matrix

$$B = (P - E)^{-1}(P + E) = (P - E)^{-1}[(P - E) + 2E],$$

whence follows that

$$B = E + 2(P - E)^{-1}; \tag{11.9}$$

consequently, matrix B will be constructed if one finds the matrix

$$C = (P - E)^{-1}. \tag{11.10}$$

Matrix (11.10) may be found from system (11.2) if one solves the latter with respect to $x_1, ..., x_n$ and then we replace the values p_{ii} by $p_{ii} - 1$. Or else, instead of system (11.2), we consider the system

$$\frac{dx_i}{dt} = \sum_{j=1}^{n} (P_{ij} - \delta_{ij}) x_j, \tag{11.11}$$

where

$$\delta_{ij} = \begin{cases} 1, & i = j \\ 0, & i \neq j \end{cases}.$$

From system (11.11) we shall find the quantities $x_1, ..., x_n$, having expressed them in terms of $dx_1/dt, ..., dx_n/dt$. The matrix of coefficients of these expressions will then coincide with (11.10).

We shall denote the coefficients of matrix (11.10) by b_{ij}. Then the homogeneous solution of system (11.2) will be asymptotically stable if the relation

$$|\delta_{ij} + 2b_{ij}| \leq \frac{\alpha}{n} < \frac{1}{n} \quad (i,j = 1, ..., n) \tag{11.12}$$

is satisfied.

Inequalities (11.12) define a region Ω_0 in the set Ω, such that in it system (11.2) is asymptotically stable.

We shall find the matrix C^2. Its elements will be the quantities $\sum_{j=1}^{n} b_{ij}b_{ik}$ $(i,k = 1, ..., n)$. Then the inequalities

$$\left| \delta_{ij} + 4b_{ij} + 4 \sum_{k=1}^{n} b_{ik}b_{kj} \right| \leq \frac{\alpha}{n} < \frac{1}{n} \tag{11.13}$$

define a region Ω_1 in set Ω in which system (11.2) is asymptotically stable.

We shall note that the application of this method in the sense of inequalities (11.12) and (11.13) gives the condition for stability in which all the roots of equation (11.7) lie sufficiently close to the centre of the circle $|\rho| \leq 1$, i.e. all the roots of equation (11.3) lie in the neighbourhood of the point $\lambda = -1$ and do not approach the imaginary axis.

However, it is possible to make an improvement in this method. We shall make one remark.

It is known that the region of asymptotic stability in the parameter space is contained in the set of those of them which satisfy the relation

$$\sum_{i=1}^{n} p_{ii}(\lambda_1, ..., \lambda_m) < 0. \tag{11.14}$$

Since with computing machines finding of powers of numerically given matrices has been well mastered, it is proposed to split the set of parameters satisfying condition (11.14) into a grid of points at which one computes the elements of the matrix B, and with the aid of computing machines one finds powers of these matrices (for example up to the 128-th degree, as can be obtained in the seventh step, since $2^7 = 128$).

If it turns out that the elements of the matrix B^k are less than $1/n$, then the point chosen belongs to the region of asymptotic stability.

In constructing the programme of the computing machine it is proposed to proceed in such a way that one always first verifies the inequality

$$\sum_{i=1}^{n} b_{i_i}^{(k)} \leqq n,$$

as in the presence of the root whose modulus exceeds unity, that sum, as a rule, will grow sharply with increasing k and as soon as $\sum_{i=1}^{n} b_{ii}^{(k)} > n$. Then the point of parameter space under consideration does not belong to the region of asymptotic stability.

For completeness of exposition, we give below (for comparison with the above method) the stability criteria for automatic control systems which have obtained the most extensive application.

Hurwitz Criteria

This criterion requires the construction of a characteristic polynomial, i.e. the expansion of the determinant

$$\left| P - \lambda E \right| = a_0 \lambda^n + a_1 \lambda^{n-1} + a_2 \lambda^{n-2} + \dots + a_{n-1} \lambda + a_n . \qquad (11.15)$$

We shall note that automatic control systems contain, as a rule, parameters which have to be chosen in such a way that asymptotic stability hold. This state of affairs complicates even more the expansion of the determinant in computing the coefficients of polynomial (11.15).

The Hurwitz stability criteria are such that for the presence of asymptotic stability in an automatic control system it is necessary and sufficient that the inequalities

$$\Delta_0 > 0; \ \Delta_1 > 0; \ \Delta_2 > 0; \dots; \Delta_n > 0$$

be satisfied, where

$$\Delta_0 = a_1; \quad \Delta_1 = \begin{vmatrix} a_1 & a_0 \\ a_3 & a_2 \end{vmatrix}; \quad \Delta_2 = \begin{vmatrix} a_1 & a_0 & 0 \\ a_3 & a_2 & a_1 \\ a_5 & a_6 & a_3 \end{vmatrix}; \dots$$

$$\dots \Delta_n = \begin{vmatrix} a_1 & a_0 & 0 & 0 & 0 & 0 & 0 & 0 & \dots \\ a_3 & a_2 & a_1 & a_0 & 0 & 0 & 0 & 0 & \dots \\ a_5 & a_4 & a_3 & a_2 & a_1 & a_0 & 0 & 0 & \dots \\ a_7 & a_6 & a_5 & a_4 & a_3 & a_2 & a_1 & a_0 & \dots \\ \cdot & \cdot & \cdot & \cdot & \cdot & \cdot & \cdot & \cdot & \cdot \end{vmatrix} . \qquad (11.16)$$

Mikhaylov Criteria

This set of criteria also require the construction of the characteristic polynomial (11.15), but is not connected with the evaluation of determinants (11.16).

In polynomial (11.15) we shall replace the variable λ by $i\omega$. In the expression obtained we shall separate the real and imaginary parts.

Then we shall obtain

$$|P - i\omega E| = U(\omega) + iV(\omega),$$

where

$$U(\omega) = a_n - a_{n-2}\omega^2 + a_{n-4}\omega^4 \dots; \qquad (11.17)$$

$$V(\omega) = a_{n-1}\omega - a_{n-3}\omega^3 + a_{n-5}\omega^5 - \dots . \qquad (11.18)$$

We shall construct the hodograph of the vector $R = U(\omega) + iV(\omega)$ as ω varies from 0 to ∞.

In order that the automatic control system be asymptotically stable, it is necessary and sufficient that the vector R, whose vertex describes the hodograph, rotate by an angle $\frac{1}{2}n\pi$ counterclockwise, starting from the positive direction of the real axis, as ω varies from 0 to ∞ for $a_0 > 0$.

In constructing Mikhaylov's curve one has to evaluate polynomials $U(\omega)$ and $V(\omega)$ at a large number of points. Even in evaluating the polynomials by a modified Horner scheme, for large n the volume of computations remains considerable.

Nyquist–Mikhaylov Frequency Criterion

This criterion is related to the concepts of transfer functions of open and closed systems.

In order to clarify these concepts we shall consider an automatic control system, the equation of whose objective may be written in the form

$$D_0(p)x(t) = M_0(p)f(t) + C_0(p)Z(t);\qquad(11.19)$$

the controller equation:

$$B(p)Z(t) = N(p)\varepsilon(t);\qquad(11.20)$$

the error equation:

$$\varepsilon(t) = g(t) - x(t).\qquad(11.21)$$

Here by $D_0(p)$, $M_0(p)$, $C_0(p)$, $B(p)$, $N(p)$ one denotes linear differential operators with constant real coefficients. By p one denotes the symbol of differentiation with respect to time, $f(t)$ is the perturbing action, $g(t)$ is the controlling action.

We shall perform the Laplace transformation over equations (11.19), (11.20), (11.21).

Then we shall obtain

$$X(S) = \frac{KW(s)}{1+KW(s)}G(s) + \frac{V(s)F(s)}{1+KW(s)} + \frac{V_H(s)}{1+KW(s)}\qquad(11.22)$$

$$E(S) = \frac{1}{1+KW(s)}G(s) - \frac{V(s)F(s)}{1+KW(s)} - \frac{V_H(s)}{1+KW(s)},\qquad(11.23)$$

where

$$KW(s) = \frac{C_0(s)N(s)}{D_0(s)B(s)};$$

$$V(s) = \frac{M_0(s)}{D_0(s)};$$

$$V_H(s) = \frac{M_H(s)}{D_0(s)B(s)}.$$

The function

$$\frac{KW(s)}{1+KW(s)} = \Phi(s)\qquad(11.24)$$

is called the transfer function of the automatic control system with respect to the control action $g(t)$.

The function $KW(s)$ is called the transfer function of the open automatic control system with respect to the control action $g(t)$.

In the plane of the complex variable s we shall construct the hodograph of the vector $R = KW(i\omega)$ as ω varies from 0 to ∞.

In the presence of asymptotic stability in the open system, for asymptotic stability of the closed system it is necessary and sufficient that the hodograph of the vector $R(i\omega)$ does not enclose the point $(-1, 0i)$.

If the open system is unstable and its characteristic polynomial has m roots with positive real parts, then for asymptotic stability of the closed system it is necessary and sufficient that the hodograph of the vector $R(i\omega)$ enclose the point $(-1, 0i)$ in the positive direction $\frac{1}{2}m$ times.

To simplify the application of the criterion, in practice one frequently uses the hodograph of the vector $W^{-1}(i\omega) = 1/W(i\omega)$, and also logarithmic scales.

Besides the stability criteria mentioned above, one extensively uses the method of D-expansions, which allows one to construct the region of stability with respect to any parameter.

This method is also based on the construction of the characteristic polynomial and is cumbersome to apply to the construction of the region of stability with respect to several parameters.

CHAPTER III

ESTIMATION OF THE BEHAVIOUR OF TRANSIENT
PROCESSES IN NONLINEAR SYSTEMS

§ 12. Method of estimates — Technical stability

In the first section we gave the concept of technical stability of the homo-geneous solution of system (1.4). This concept consists in the following.

Say one is given an interval of time variation $[T_0, T_0 + T]$ and two sets G_{t_0} and G_t in the n-dimensional space $y_1, ..., y_n$. If there exists a set F in the space of admissible values of the parameters such that the integral curves of system (1.4), starting at $t = 0$ from the set G_{t_0}, remain in the set G_t for $t \in [T_0, T_0 + T]$, then the homogeneous solution of system (1.4) is called *technically stable*.

As has already been noted in §1, the set G_{t_0} is defined, as a rule, by the technical conditions of the functioning of the real system. The set G_t is for-mulated from the definite requirement demanded of the design system. In a broad class of cases it may be considered that the sets G_{t_0} and G_t are spheres with radii r_{t_0} and r_t.

In that case the problem of technical stability is posed in such a way that one has to find estimates of the behaviour of the solutions of system (1.4) with respect to all the coordinates. Here the coordinates are regarded as equivalent in the sense of the requirements imposed on them.

In §4 examples were given in which it was very important to carry out a detailed investigation of the behaviour of the solutions with respect to some given coordinates (stability with respect to given coordinates).

In a broad class of cases of such kind as the sets G_{t_0} and G_t, n-dimensional ellipsoids may be given. It should be noted in this connection, that the method of damping coefficients developed in §8 consists in choosing ellipsoids in which the axes corresponding to those variables with respect to which the stability is being investigated, do not increase relative to the axes of the remaining variables, and the axes corresponding to the latter increase without limit as $t \to +\infty$.

The considerations given above allow one to reduce the solution of the problem of technical stability to the finding of estimates for some function $R(y_1, ..., y_n, t)$ such that from $R_1(t, y_{10}, ..., y_{n0}, t_0) \leq f(t, y_{10}, ..., y_{n0}, t_0)$ it follows that the integral curves $y_s = y_s(t, y_{10}, ..., y_{n0}, t_0)$ $(s = 1, ..., n)$ of system (1.4) starting in the set G_{t_0} fall within the set G_t for $t \in [T_0, T_0 + T]$.

Above we have denoted by $R_1(t, y_{10}, \ldots, y_{n0}, t_0)$ the value of the function $R(y_1, \ldots, y_n, t)$ on that integral curve.

It is clear that the function $R(y_1, \ldots, y_n, t)$ is in some sense defined by the geometrical properties of the sets G_{t_0} and G_t.

We shall assume that there exist two functions $V(y_1, \ldots, y_n, t)$ and $W(y_1, \ldots, y_n, t)$ satisfying the following conditions:

1) the functions V and W are given for $t \in [T_0, T_0 + T]$ and $\sum_{i=1}^{n} y_i^2 < \alpha^2$, where α and T are positive constants;

2) the function $V(y_1, \ldots, y_n, t)$ satisfies the inequalities

$$\phi_1(t) R^{l_1}(t, y_1, \ldots, y_n) \leqq V \leqq \phi_2(t) R^{l_2}(t, y_1, \ldots, y_n), \qquad (12.1)$$

where $\phi_1(t)$ and $\phi_2(t)$ are piecewise-continuous positive functions given in the interval $[T_0, T_0 + T_1]$.

The function $R(t, y_1, \ldots, y_n)$ is given for $t \in [T_0, T_0 + T_1]$, $\sum_{i=1}^{n} y_i^2 < \alpha^2$; and $R(t, y_1, \ldots, y_n) = 0$ for $y_1 = y_2 = \ldots = y_n = 0$; l_1 and l_2 are positive numbers such that $l_1 \geqq l_2$;

3) the functions $W(y_1, \ldots, y_n, t)$ satisfy the inequalities

$$- \psi_1(t) R^{k_1}(t, y_1, \ldots, y_n) \leqq W \leqq - \psi_2(t) R^{k_2}(t, y_1, \ldots, y_n), \qquad (12.2)$$

where $\psi_1(t)$ and $\psi_2(t)$ are piecewise-continuous functions in the interval $[T_0, T_0 + T_1]$; k_1 and k_2 are positive numbers such that $k_1 \leqq k_2$;

4) the function W is the total derivative of the function V as based on system (1.4)

$$\frac{dV}{dt} = W. \qquad (12.3)$$

THEOREM 24.   If there exist two functions V and W satisfying the preceding four conditions, if the functions $\psi_i(t)$ are positive, and if $k_i/l_1 = \lambda_i > 1$ $(i = 1,2)$, then every integral curve of system (1.4) satisfies the inequalities

$$\sqrt[l_2]{\phi_2^{-1}(t) V_0} \sqrt[1-\lambda_1]{1 + (\lambda_1 - 1) V_0^{\lambda_1 - 1} \int_{t_0}^{t} \psi_2(\tau) \phi_2^{-\lambda_1}(\tau) d\tau} \leqq$$

$$\leqq R_1(t, y_{10}, \ldots, y_{n0}, t_0) \leqq$$

$$\leqq \sqrt[l_1]{\phi_1^{-1}(t) V_0} \sqrt[1-\lambda_2]{1 + (\lambda_2 - 1) V_0^{\lambda_2 - 1} \int_{t_0}^{t} \psi_2(\tau) \phi_2^{-\lambda_2}(\tau) d\tau} \qquad (12.4)$$

$$\text{for } t \in [T_0, T_0 + T_1],$$

where $V_0 = V(y_{10}, \ldots, y_{n0}, t_0)$.

PROOF: We shall take an integral curve of system (1.4) and substitute it in equality (12.3). Then it is transformed into the identity $dV/dt \equiv W$. Multiplying both members of that identity by the function $V^{-\lambda}$, where $\lambda > 1$, and integrating between the limits t_0 and t, we shall obtain

$$\int_{t_0}^{t} V^{-\lambda} dV = \int_{t_0}^{t} WV^{-\lambda} dt,$$

whence follows

$$\frac{V^{1-\lambda} - V_0^{1-\lambda}}{1 - \lambda} = \int_{t_0}^{t} WV^{-\lambda} dt. \tag{12.5}$$

Carrying out identical transformations in equality (12.5) we shall obtain

$$V = \frac{V_0}{\sqrt[\lambda-1]{1 + (1 - \lambda) V_0^{\lambda-1} \int_{t_0}^{t} WV^{-\lambda} dt}} \tag{12.6}$$

We shall now deal with the estimation of the expression under the integral sign in formula (12.6).

In (12.6) we shall set $\lambda = \lambda_2$.

The function W satisfies the inequalities

$$- \psi_1(t) R^{k_1}(t, y_1, \ldots, y_n) \leqq W \leqq - \psi_2(t) R^{k_2}(t, y_1, \ldots, y_n).$$

The functions $V^{-\lambda_2}$ satisfy the inequalities

$$\phi_2^{-\lambda_2}(t) R^{-\lambda_2 l_2}(t, y_1, \ldots, y_n) \leqq V^{-\lambda_2} \leqq \phi_1^{-\lambda_2}(t) R^{-\lambda_2 l_1}(t, y_1, \ldots, y_n).$$

From these inequalities it follows that

$$- WV^{-\lambda_2} \geqq \psi_2(t) \psi_2^{-\lambda_2}(t), \tag{12.7}$$

as $\lambda_2 = k_2/l_2$.

From inequalities (12.7) and relation (12.6) we shall obtain, for $\lambda = \lambda_2$, that

$$V \leqq \frac{V_0}{\sqrt[\lambda_2-1]{1 + (\lambda_2 - 1) V_0^{\lambda_2-1} \int_{t_0}^{t} \psi_2(t) \phi_2^{-\lambda_2}(t) \, dt}} \tag{12.8}$$

In (12.6) setting $\lambda = \lambda_1$ and utilising inequalities (12.1) and (12.2) we shall obtain

$$- WV^{-\lambda_1} \leq \phi_1(t)\psi_1^{-\lambda_1}(t). \tag{12.9}$$

From inequality (12.9) and relation (12.6) for $\lambda = \lambda_1$ we shall obtain

$$V \geq \frac{V_0}{\sqrt[\lambda_1-1]{1 + (\lambda_1 - 1) V_0^{\lambda_1-1} \int\limits_{t_r}^{t} \psi_1(t)\phi_1^{-\lambda_1}(t)dt}} \tag{12.10}$$

From inequality (12.7) it follows that the function $R(t, y_1, ..., y_n)$ satisfies the inequalities

$$\sqrt[l_2]{\phi_2^{-1}(t)V} \leq R(t, y_1, ..., y_n) \leq \sqrt[l_1]{\phi_1^{-1}(t)V}. \tag{12.11}$$

Substituting in the right-hand member of inequality (12.11), instead of the function V, the right-hand member of inequality (12.8), and substituting in the left-hand member of inequality (12.11), instead of the function V, the left-hand member of inequality (12.10), we shall obtain in equality (12.4).

Remark. Estimate (12.4) holds only along those integral curves which lie in the region for which the functions V and W are given.

This remark is not of the nature of a limitation upon the region of applicability of estimate (12.4), but only assumes that the functions V and W extend with respect to the variables $y_1, ..., y_n$ over the entire phase space.

THEOREM 25.   If there exist two functions V and W satisfying conditions 1–4 given above, and $\lambda_i > 1$ $(i = 1, 2)$, then for $l_1 = l_2 = l$ every integral curve satisfies inequalities of the form

$$\sqrt[l]{\phi_2^{-1}(t)V_0} \sqrt[1-\lambda_1]{1 + (\lambda_1 - 1)V_0^{\lambda_1-1}\int\limits_{t_0}^{t} f_1(\tau)d\tau} \leq R_1(t, y_{10}, ..., y_{n0}, t_0) \leq$$

$$\leq \sqrt[l]{\phi_1^{-1}(t)V_0} \sqrt[1-\lambda_2]{1 + (\lambda_2 - 1)V_0^{\lambda_2-1}\int\limits_{t_0}^{t} f_2(\tau)d\tau}, \tag{12.4'}$$

where

$$
f_1 = \begin{cases} \psi_1(t)\,\phi_1^{-\lambda_1}(t) & \text{when } \psi_1(t) \geq 0, \\ \psi_1(t)\,\phi_2^{-\lambda_1}(t) & \text{when } \psi_1(t) \leq 0; \end{cases}
$$

$$
f_2 = \begin{cases} \psi_2(t)\,\phi_2^{-\lambda_2}(t) & \text{when } \psi_2(t) \geq 0, \\ \psi_2(t)\,\phi_1^{-\lambda_2}(t) & \text{when } \psi_2(t) \leq 0. \end{cases}
$$

PROOF: We shall take an integral curve of system (1.4) and substitute it in equality (12.3). Then, by means of the same transformation as has been performed in the proof of the preceding Theorem, we shall obtain for $\lambda > 1$ a relation of the form (12.6).

We shall carry out an estimate of the quantity $-WV^{-\lambda}$ standing under the integral sign in (12.6).

In the proof of the preceding Theorem it has been shown that for $\psi_2(t) > 0$, inequality (12.7) holds for $\lambda_2 = \lambda$.

If $\psi_2 < 0$, then the quantity $-WV^{-\lambda}$ satisfies the inequality

$$
-WV^{-\lambda_2} \geq \psi_2 \phi_1^{-\lambda_2}(t); \tag{12.12}
$$

thus, from inequality (12.12) and (12.7) it follows that there holds inequality

$$
-WV^{-\lambda_2} \geq f_2(t), \tag{12.13}
$$

where

$$
f_2(t) = \begin{cases} \psi_2 \phi_2^{-\lambda_2} & \text{for } \psi_2 \geq 0, \\ \psi_2 \phi_1^{-\lambda_2} & \text{for } \psi_2 \leq 0. \end{cases}
$$

From inequality (12.13) and relation (12.6) it follows that

$$
V \leq \frac{V_0}{\sqrt[\lambda_2-1]{1 + (\lambda_2-1)\,V_0^{\lambda_2-1} \int\limits_{t_0}^{t} f_2(\tau)\,d\tau}}. \tag{12.14}
$$

Carrying out analogous estimates from above for the quantity $-WV^{-\lambda}$ for $\lambda = \lambda_1$, we shall obtain

$$
V \geq \frac{V_0}{\sqrt[\lambda_1-1]{1 + (\lambda_1-1)\,V_0^{\lambda_1-1} \int\limits_{t_0}^{t} f_1(\tau)\,d\tau}}, \tag{12.15}
$$

where

$$f_1 = \begin{cases} \psi_1 \phi_1^{-\lambda_1} \text{ for } \psi_1 \geqq 0, \\ \psi_1 \phi_2^{-\lambda_1} \text{ for } \psi_1 \leqq 0. \end{cases}$$

In the preceding Theorem it has been noted that the function R satisfies the inequalities (12.11). Utilising that inequality and the inequalities (12.14) and (12.15), we shall obtain the required estimates.

Remark. The estimates given here hold for those curves which lie in the region where the functions V and W are given. Besides, these estimates hold only for those values of $t \geqq t_0$ for which the expressions under the square root sign occurring in the formulae are nonnegative.

Theorem 25 is stronger than the preceding one, as the functions ψ_i may take values of differing signs. This remark would be incomplete if we did not also note that Theorem 24 refers to a wider class of functions V. However, the form of those functions depends in every case on the way they are chosen. On our choice depends also the function R, and therefore the condition $l_1 = l_2$ is not too constraining.

THEOREM 26. If there exist two functions V and W, satisfying the conditions 1–4, and $\lambda_1 = \lambda_2 = 1$, $\psi_i \geqq 0$, then every solution of system (1.4) will satisfy the inequalities

$$\sqrt[l_2]{\phi_2^{-1}(t) V_0 e^{-\int_{t_0}^{t} \psi_1 \tilde{\phi}_1^{-1} d\tau}} \leqq R_1(t, y_{10}, \ldots, y_{n0}, t_0) \leqq \sqrt[l_1]{\phi_1^{-1}(t) V_0 e^{-\int_{t_0}^{t} \psi_2 \tilde{\phi}_2^{-1} d\tau}}$$

$$(12.16)$$

PROOF: Say there exist two functions V and W satisfying the conditions of Theorem 26. We shall take an integral curve of system (1.4) and substitute it in relation (12.3). We shall multiply the identity obtained by the function V^{-1} and integrate it between the limits t_0 and t. Then we shall obtain

$$\int_{t_0}^{t} V^{-1} dV = \int_{t_0}^{t} W V^{-1} dt,$$

whence

$$V = V_0 e^{\int_{t_0}^{t} W V^{-1} dt}. \qquad (12.17)$$

We shall note that the integral standing in the right-hand member of equality (12.17) may be estimated by the same method as had been used in §6 for the proof of Theorem 15. Then we shall have

$$-\psi_1\phi_1^{-1} \leq WV^{-1} \leq -\psi_2\phi_2^{-1} \ . \tag{12.18}$$

From this inequality and inequality (12.11) we have inequality (12.16).

Remark. If ψ_1 and ψ_2 change sign, then inequalities (12.18) hold only for those t for which $\psi_1(t) > 0$, $\psi_2(t) > 0$. If $\psi_1 < 0$ and $\psi_2 < 0$, then the function WV^{-1} will satisfy the inequality:

for $\psi_2 < 0$

$$WV^{-1} \leq -\psi_2\phi_1^{-1} \ ;$$

for $\psi_1 < 0$

$$WV^{-1} \geq -\psi_1\phi_2^{-1} \ .$$

From these inequalities and inequality (12.11) we shall obtain

$$\sqrt[l_2]{\phi_2^{-1}(t)\, V_0\, e^{-\int_{t_0}^{t} \psi_1\tilde{\phi}_1^{-1}\, d\tau}} \leq R_1(t, y_{10}, \ldots, y_{n0}, t_0) \leq \sqrt[l_1]{\phi_1^{-1}(t)\, V_0\, e^{-\int_{t_0}^{t} \psi_2\tilde{\phi}_2^{-1}\, d\tau}}, \tag{12.19}$$

where

$$\tilde{\phi}_1 = \sigma_1\phi_1(t) + \sigma_2\phi_2(t),$$

$$\tilde{\phi}_2 = \sigma_3\phi_1(t) + \sigma_4\phi_2(t) \ ;$$

where

$$\sigma_1 = \frac{1 + \operatorname{sgn}\psi_1}{2},$$

$$\sigma_2 = \frac{1 - \operatorname{sgn}\psi_1}{2},$$

$$\sigma_3 = \frac{1 - \operatorname{sgn}\psi_2}{2},$$

$$\sigma_4 = \frac{1 + \operatorname{sgn}\psi_2}{2}.$$

THEOREM 27.   If there exist two functions V and W satisfying conditions 1–4, and $\lambda_1 = 1$, $\lambda_2 > 1$, and $l_1 = l_2 = l$, then every solution of the system of equations (1.4) will satisfy the inequalities

$$\sqrt[l]{\phi_2^{-1}(t)\, V_0\, e^{-\int_{t_0}^{t} \psi_1 \tilde{\phi}_1^{-1}\, d\tau}} \leq R_1(t, y_{10}, \ldots, y_{n0}, t_0) \leq$$

$$\leq \sqrt[l]{\phi_1^{-1}(t)\, V_0}^{\,1-\lambda_2} \sqrt{1 + (\lambda_2 - 1)\, V_0^{\lambda_2 - 1} \int_{t_0}^{t} f_2(\tau)\, d\tau}, \qquad (12.20)$$

where

$$f_2(t) = \begin{cases} \psi_2 \phi_2^{-\lambda_2} & \text{for } \psi_2 \geq 0, \\ \psi_2 \phi_1^{-\lambda_2} & \text{for } \psi_2 \leq 0. \end{cases}$$

PROOF: The left-hand part of inequality (12.20) may be obtained from the remark to Theorem 26.

The right-hand part of that inequality may be obtained by the method applied in the proof of Theorem 25.

Remark.   An analogous theorem also holds for $\lambda_1 > 1$, $\lambda_2 = 1$, $l_1 = l_2 = l$. In this case every solution of system (1.4) will satisfy the inequalities

$$\sqrt[l]{\phi_2^{-1}(t)\, V_0}^{\,1-\lambda_1} \sqrt{1 + (\lambda_1 - 1)\, V_0^{\lambda_1 - 1} \int_{t_0}^{t} f_1(\tau)\, d\tau} \leq$$

$$\leq R_1(t, y_{10}, \ldots, y_{n0}, t_0) \leq \sqrt[l]{\phi_1^{-1}(t)\, V_0\, e^{-\int_{t_0}^{t} \psi_2 \tilde{\phi}_2^{-1}\, d\tau}}, \qquad (12.21)$$

where

$$f_1(t) = \begin{cases} \psi_1(t)\, \phi_1^{-\lambda_1}(t) & \text{for } \psi_1(t) \geq 0, \\ \psi_1(t)\, \phi_2^{-\lambda_2}(t) & \text{for } \psi_1(t) \leq 0. \end{cases}$$

We shall note that the inequalities dealt with in all the Theorems formulated in this section hold only for values of $t \geq t_0$ where the integral curves of system (1.4) lie within the region in which there exist functions V and W satisfying conditions (12.1), (12.2), (12.3). Besides, it should also be noted that these inequalities are meaningful only as long as the expressions under the square root signs which occur in them are nonnegative.

All the Theorems formulated in this section constitute the main content of the method which may be proposed for the solution of the problem of technical stability of the homogeneous solution of system (1.4).

THEOREM 28. Let there be given: a number $T > 0$ and two sets G_{t_0} and G_t. If there exist two functions V and W satisfying conditions 1–4 and such that one of the inequalities (12.4), (12.4'), (12.16), (12.20), (12.21) possesses the property that if $(y_{10},...,y_{n0}) \in G_{t_0}$ then $(y_1,...,y_n) \in G_t$ for $t \in [T_0, T_0 + T]$, then the homogeneous solution of (1.4) is technically stable.

This Theorem will give, in general, only the sufficient conditions for technical stability. Here an unsuccessful choice of the functions R and V may lead to rigid sufficient conditions. For a final clarification of these conditions it is necessary to take several instances of functions R and V and thereupon extend the investigation of the obtained sufficient conditions as far as possible by the application of an electronic model of system (1.4).

Below examples are given of applications of the method given here.

§ 13.   Stability in a finite interval

In the works of G. V. Kamenkov [23] and A. A. Lebedev [24] a theory of stability was developed for the homogeneous solution in the finite time interval. This theory has a very close connection with the concept of technical stability. In the present section we shall expose the main results connected with stability in a finite interval.

In the preceding sections it has been noted that the values of some function V on the integral curves of the system of differential equations (1.4) allow one to judge as to the behaviour of these curves. The same idea lies at the basis of the theory of stability in a finite interval.

DEFINITION 14. The homogeneous solution of system (1.4) is called *stable* for a given t_0 in relation to a positive definite function $V(y_1, ..., y_n, t)$ in the interval τ, if from $V(y_{10}, ..., y_{n0}, t_0) = a$, it follows that $V_1(t, y_{10},...,y_{n0}, t_0) \leq a$ for $t_0 < t \leq t_0 + \tau$ for every choice of a sufficiently small positive quantity a. Here, just as above, $V_1(t, y_{10}, ..., y_{n0}, t_0)$ denotes the value of the function $V(y_1, ..., y_n, t)$ on an integral curve of system (1.4), passing at $t = t_0$ through the point $(y_{10}, ..., y_{n0})$.

DEFINITION 15. The homogeneous solution of the system (1.4) is called *stable* in a finite interval for a given t_0, if there exists a positive number $\tau > 0$ and a positive-definite function $V(y_1, ..., y_n, t)$ such that in relation to it the homogeneous solution of system (1.4) is stable in the finite interval τ.

We shall consider the system of differential equations

$$\frac{dy_s}{dt} = \sum_{i=1}^{n} p_{si}(t) y_i + f_s(t, y_1, ..., y_n) \qquad (s = 1, ..., n), \qquad (13.1)$$

where the $p_{si}(t)$ are real functions, given for $t \geq 0$ and continuous there.

The functions $f_s(t, y_1, ..., y_n)$, given for $t \geq 0$ and $\sum_{i=1}^{n} y_i^2 \leq \alpha^2$, where α is a positive constant, are continuous and satisfy the inequality

$$|f_s| \leq \phi_s(t) \left[\sum_{i=1}^{n} y_i^2 \right]^c, \qquad (13.2)$$

where $c > \frac{1}{2}$; $\phi_s(t)$ are continuous positive functions given for $t \geq 0$.

System (13.1) may be considered as one of the possible variants of system (1.4).

THEOREM 29. In order that the homogeneous solution of system (13.1) for a given t_0 be stable in a finite interval, with respect to some fixed positive-definite quadratic form V, for every choice of the functions f_s satisfying the inequalities (13.2), it is necessary and sufficient that the roots of the equation

$$|P(t_0) - \lambda E| = 0 \qquad (13.3)$$

have negative real parts, where $P(t_0)$ is a matrix whose elements are the numbers $p_{si}(t_0)$.

Before we go on to the proof of the Theorem, we shall note that the homogeneous solution of the linear system

$$\frac{dy_s}{dt} = \sum_{i=1}^{n} p_{si}(t_0) y_i \qquad (s = 1, ..., n) \qquad (13.4)$$

with constant coefficients is asymptotically stable if and only if all the roots of the equation (13.3) have negative real parts.

It is known that in the case of asymptotic stability every solution satisfies the inequality

$$\sum_{i=1}^{n} y_i^2 \leq c_1 \sum_{i=1}^{n} y_{i0}^2 e^{-c_2 t},$$

where c_1, c_2 are positive constants. Then, as has been shown in § 6, there exist two quadratic forms V and W satisfying the following inequalities

$$a_1 \sum_{i=1}^{n} y_i^2 \leq V \leq a_2 \sum_{i=1}^{n} y_i^2 \,,$$

$$-b_1 \sum_{i=1}^{n} y_i^2 \leq W \leq - b_2 \sum_{i=1}^{n} y_i^2 \,,$$

where a_i, b_i $(i = 1, 2)$ are positive constants.

We shall note that these forms may be chosen in such a way that their coefficients be constant numbers.

Indeed, let the homogeneous solution of system (13.4) be asymptotically stable. We shall take an arbitrary negative-definite quadratic form W. Following the method expounded in the proof of Theorem 15, we shall set

$$V = - \int_{0}^{+\infty} W dt \,. \tag{13.5}$$

It is easy to see that the function V is a quadratic form in the variables $y_{10}, \ldots, y_{n0}$, positive-definite, and independent of t. Here $dV/dt = W$, where dV/dt is the total derivative of the form V as based on system (13.4). Hence it follows that this relation has the aspect

$$\sum_{i=1}^{n} \frac{\partial V}{\partial y_i} \sum_{k=1}^{n} p_{ik}(t_0) y_k = W. \tag{13.6}$$

The form V, defined by (13.5), is the unique solution of equation (13.6) in the class of the quadratic form. Thus, the following assertion is obtained.

If the homogeneous solution of the system is asymptotically stable, i.e. if the roots of equation (13.3) have negative real parts, then for every choice of a negative-definite quadratic form W, independent of t, there exists a positive-definite quadratic form V satisfying equation (13.6).

This assertion was first formulated by A. M. Lyapunov and proved by him by means of the theory of differential determinants. We shall note that the algebraic form of this theorem of Lyapunov is very useful.

We shall take the matrix B, real and symmetrical with negative characteristic values. Then the system of equations

$$P^*(t) A + A P(t_0) = B \tag{13.7}$$

has a unique solution A, representing a real symmetric matrix with positive characteristic values if and only if all the roots of equation (13.3) have negative real parts.

From Theorem 15 one may derive a generalization of this Theorem, consisting in the following.

We shall consider the linear differential equation in matrix form

$$P^*(t)A(t) + AP + \frac{dA}{dt} = B(t),\qquad(13.8)$$

where $B(t)$ and $P(t)$ are given matrices, and $A(t)$ is the matrix sought. The solution of that equation $A(t)$, representing a real symmetric matrix, exists provided $B(t)$ has a quadratic form which satisfies condition (6.4) if and only if all the solutions of equation (6.1) satisfy condition (6.2).

We shall now go on to the sufficiency proof of Theorem 29.

Let the roots of equation (13.6) have negative real parts. We shall take the function $W = -\sum_{i-1}^{n} y_i^2$ and shall construct a function V equal to

$$V = \sum_{i,j=1}^{n} a_{ij}y_iy_j,$$

where the a_{ij} are the elements of the matrix A determined from the linear system (13.7).

From the above, it follows that the quadratic form V will be positive-definite and, besides, the total derivative of the form V as based on system

$$\frac{dy_s}{dt} = \sum_{i=1}^{n} p_{si}(t_0)y_i \qquad (s=1,...,n)\qquad(13.9)$$

coincides with the function W.

We shall find the total derivative of the function V as based on system (13.1). Then we shall obtain

$$\frac{dV}{dt} = \sum_{s=1}^{n} \frac{\partial V}{\partial y_s}\left[\sum_{i=1}^{n} p_{si}(t)y_i + f_s(t,y_1,...,y_n)\right]$$

$$= -\sum_{i=1}^{n} y_i^2 + \sum_{s=1}^{n} \frac{\partial V}{\partial y_s}\sum_{i=1}^{n}[p_{si}(t) - p_{si}(t_0)]y_i + \sum_{s=1}^{n} \frac{\partial V}{\partial y_s}f.\qquad(13.10)$$

In view of continuity of the functions $p_{si}(t)$ and of the fulfillment of conditions (13.2), there exist two positive numbers A and τ such that the total derivative of the function V as based on (13.1) will be nonpositive for $t\in[t_0, t_0+\tau]$ and for $\sum_{i=1}^{n} y_i^2 \leq A^2$.

We shall find the number $\mu = \inf V$ for $\sum_{i=1}^{n} y_i^2 = A^2$.

It is clear that for all $a < \mu$, there will follow from the inequality $V(t, y_{10}, ..., y_{n0}, t_0) \leqq a$ that $V_1(t, y_{10}, ..., y_{n0}) \leqq a$ for $t \in [t_0, t_0 + \tau]$, where V_1 denotes a quadratic form evaluated on the integral curves of system (13.1).

Necessity. We shall assume that there exists a quadratic positive-definite form $V(t, y_1, .., y_n, t_0)$ such that with respect to it, for any choice of the functions f_s satisfying conditions (13.2), the homogeneous solution of system (13.1) is stable in the finite interval.

From the definition of stability in a finite interval it follows that the total derivative of the function V as based on system (13.1), for $t = t_0$, is nonpositive. It is easy to convince oneself, that this derivative coincides with the total derivative of the function V as based on the system

$$\frac{dy_s}{dt} = \sum_{i=1}^{n} p_{si}(t_0) y_i + f_s(t_0, y_1, ..., y_n) \qquad (s = 1, ..., n) . \qquad (13.11)$$

Consequently, the homogeneous solution of (13.11) is stable for every choice of function f_s $(s = 1, ..., n)$, satisfying conditions (13.2).

From Lyapunov's theorem it is known that such a state of affairs holds if and only if all the roots of equation (13.3) have negative real parts.

Remark 1. Definition 14 may be replaced by a more general one, namely: as function V one may take a function possessing the following properties:

1) the function V is given in the region $\sum_{i=1}^{n} y_i^2 < \alpha^2$, $\alpha > 0$ and $t \in [t_0, t_0 + \tau_1]$;

2) $V(t, 0, ..., 0) \equiv 0$;

3) $V > 0$ for $\sum_{i=1}^{n} y_i^2 \neq 0$.

This lightening of the requirements imposed on the function V allows one to use a broader class of functions for finding the stability in a finite interval. In this connection, the quadratic form with respect to which stability is being established in Theorem 29, may be chosen so that only the properties 1–3 of those mentioned above need be fulfilled.

Remark 2. A. A. Lebedev has proposed a definition for stability in a finite interval, which includes the requirement that the diameter of the region $V(t, y_1, ..., y_n) \leqq A$ does not exceed the diameter of the region $V(t, y_{10}, ..., y_{n0}) \leqq A$. In the definitions given above, this requirement is omitted and consequently the concept of stability in a finite interval of time is wider than the one proposed by Lebedev. Nevertheless, this comparison of the two definitions would be incomplete if we did not recall the fact that the definition given by Lebedev permits, in the presence of stability in a finite interval, an estimate of the distance from the integral curve to the coordinate origin, but it is true that these estimates are more gross than those which are given in §12. Thus, in the presence of stability in a finite interval it is proposed to carry out a further investigation (in the sense of finding estimates) by the methods indicated in §12.

In the proof of Theorem 29 in the part on sufficiency, the analysis of the quantities A, μ, τ has been omitted. In reality these quantities play a considerable role.

We shall give one of the methods of finding these quantities.

By τ_1 we shall denote the time interval on which the form

$$W_1 = \sum_{i,\,s=1}^{n} \frac{\partial V}{\partial y_s} p_{si}(t)\, y_i$$

remains negative for $\sum_{i=1}^{n} y_i^2 \neq 0$. It is clear that τ_1 is the smallest of the values for which one of the inequalities

$$(-1)^k \Delta k(t) > 0 \qquad (k = 1, \ldots, n),$$

is violated, where $\Delta k(t)$ are the successive principal minors of the matrix of the quadratic form W_1.

By $\lambda_1(t), \ldots, \lambda_n(t)$ we shall denote the characteristic values of the matrix of the quadratic form W_1. Then the form W_1 will satisfy the inequality

$$\lambda_1(t) \sum_{i=1}^{n} y_i^2 \leqq W_1 \leqq \lambda_n(t) \sum_{i=1}^{n} y_i^2,$$

where $\lambda_1(t)$ is the smallest and $\lambda_n(t)$ is the largest characteristic value of the characteristic values of the form W_1. Here $\lambda_n(t) < 0$ for $t \in [t_0, t_0 + \tau_1]$.

The functions f_s satisfy conditions (13.2). Therefore there exists a number A so small that if $\sum_{i=1}^{n} y_i^2 \leqq A^2$ then

$$\left| \sum_{s=1}^{n} \frac{\partial V}{\partial y_s} f_s \right| \leqq c(t) A^{\alpha} \sum_{i=1}^{n} y_i^2,$$

where $c(t)$ is a function determined by means of an estimate for the coefficients of the form V and the functions $\phi_s(t)$.

The total derivative dV/dt, as based on system (13.1), will satisfy the inequality

$$\frac{dV}{dt} \leqq [\lambda_n + c(t)A^\alpha] \sum_{i=1}^{n} y_i^2, \tag{13.12}$$

whence follows that for any number $\tau < \tau_1$ there exists a number A such that the total derivative of function V, as based on system (13.1), will be negative.

We shall find the characteristic values of the quadratic form V, $\mu_1 \leqq \mu_2 \leqq \ldots \leqq \mu_n$. It is clear that

$$\inf V = \mu_1 A^2 \quad \text{for} \quad \sum_{i=1}^{n} y_i^2 = A^2,$$

consequently the stability in the interval $[t_0, t_0 + \tau]$ will hold for all $a \leqq \mu_1 A^2$.

Thus, to find τ and the region of variation of the quantity a, it is necessary to know the estimate for the quadratic form W_1 from above, and for V from below.

To conclude the investigation it remains to find the form of the function $c(t)$. Let p be the largest in absolute value of the coefficients of the form V. Applying the Bunyakovskiy inequality, we shall obtain

$$\left| \sum_{s=1}^{n} \frac{\partial V}{\partial y_s} f_s \right| \leqq \sqrt{\sum_{s=1}^{n} f_s^2} \sqrt{\sum_{s=1}^{n} \left(\frac{\partial V}{\partial y_s}\right)^2} \leqq 2pn \sqrt{\sum_{s=1}^{n} \phi_s^2(t)} \left[\sum_{i=1}^{n} y_i^2\right]^{\frac{1}{2}+c},$$

whence it is clear that as $c(t)$ one may take a function

$$c(t) = 2pn \sqrt{\sum_{s=1}^{n} \phi_s^2(t)} \ ,$$

$$\alpha = c + \tfrac{1}{2}.$$

We shall give an example of a calculation of the interval in which stability in the sense of Definition 14 holds.

We shall consider the equation

$$\frac{dy}{dt} = -\frac{y}{1+t} + by^2 . \tag{13.13}$$

We shall set $V = \frac{1}{2}y^2$. Then

$$\frac{dV}{dt} = -\frac{y^2}{1+t} + by^3.$$

Below we shall carry out the analysis of the interval, showing that the method proposed by Kamenkov sometimes leads to erroneous conclusions.

Here we shall set $W_1 = -y^2/(1+t)$. W_1 is a negative-definite form for all $t \geq 0$, in the sense that $W_1 < 0$ for $y \neq 0$. According to Kamenkov, in that case the stability of the homogeneous solution $y = 0$ of equation (13.13) holds in the semi-infinite interval $(0, +\infty)$, considering that $t_0 = 0$. However, this is not the case.

We shall take an arbitrary number $\tau > 0$

$$\frac{dV}{dt} < -\frac{y^2}{1+\tau} + b|y|^3 \text{ for } t \in (0, \tau).$$

We shall set $y^2 < a^2(\tau)$ where the quantity a is such that

$$\frac{-y^2}{1+\tau} + b|y|^3 < 0 \text{ for } y^2 \leq a^2(\tau);$$

it is clear that

$$a(\tau) < \frac{1}{b(1+\tau)}.$$

The quantity $A(\tau) = \frac{1}{2} a^2(\tau)$.

Thus, for equation (13.13) the homogeneous solution $y = 0$ will be stable in the finite interval τ if only $V(y_0) < A(\tau)$, where $y_0 = y(0)$.

Clearly, as $\tau \to +\infty$, $A(\tau) \to 0$.

Equation (13.13) may be integrated. Its solution, which becomes y_0 at $t = 0$, will have the form

$$y = \frac{y_0}{(t+1)[1 - by_0 \ln(t+1)]}.$$

For $t = \exp(1/by_0) - 1$, and for any positive value of y_0 arbitrarily small the solution $y(t, y_0)$ escapes to infinity, which confirms the qualitative analysis carried out on the basis of the theory developed above.

§ 14.   Stability of nonlinear systems in the first approximation

A. M. Lyapunov [2] has shown that from asymptotic stability of the homogeneous solution of the system of equations

$$\frac{dy_s}{dt} = \sum_{i=1}^{n} p_{si} y_i \quad (s = 1, \dots, n) \tag{14.1}$$

there follows the asymptotic stability of the homogeneous solution of the system of equations

$$\frac{dy_s}{dt} = \sum_{i=1}^{n} p_{si} y_i + f_s(t, y_1, \dots, y_n) \quad (s = 1, \dots, n), \tag{14.2}$$

where $f_s(t, y_1, \ldots, y_n)$ are holomorphic functions with respect to $y_1, \ldots, y_n$ in equal powers for all $t \geq 0$, and continuous and bounded functions with respect to t, given for $t \geq 0$.

Here it is assumed that the expansions of the functions $f_s(t, y_1, \ldots, y_n)$ do not contain linear terms in $y_1, \ldots, y_n$.

This state of affairs, as was shown for example in work [25], holds also in the case when the functions f_s satisfy the inequalities

$$\left| f_s(t, y_1, \ldots, y_n) \right| < cr^{1+\alpha} \, ,$$

for $t \geq 0$

$$r \leq R, \quad r = \sqrt{\sum_{i=1}^{n} y_i^2} \; ;$$

where α and c are positive constants.

In the case when the coefficients in system (14.1) are variable and bounded functions of time for $t \geq 0$ and it is known that every solution of that system satisfies the estimate

$$r \leq c_1 r_0 e^{-c_2 (t - t_0)},$$

the situation indicated above also holds [6].

One speaks of theorems of this sort as of theorems on stability in the first approximation.

In its general formulation, the problem of stability in the first approximation may be set in the following way.

Given are two systems of differential equations

$$\frac{dy_s}{dt} = g_s(t, y_1, \ldots, y_n), \tag{14.3}$$

$$\frac{dy_s}{dt} = g_s(t, y_1, \ldots, y_n) + f_s(t, y_1, \ldots, y_n), \tag{14.4}$$

each of which has a homogeneous solution.

The question arises: when, from the stability of the homogeneous solution of system (14.3), does there follow the stability of the homogeneous solution of system (14.4)? One of the general approaches to the solution of this problem was proposed in work [33].

THEOREM 30.   If there exist two functions $V(t, y_1, \ldots, y_n)$ and $W(t, y_1, \ldots, y_n)$ satisfying the following conditions:

1)   the function V is positive-definite and admits of an infinitely small upper bound;

2) the function W is negative and is the total derivative of the function V as based on system (14.3);

3) the function V has continuous partial derivatives with respect to the variables $t, y_1, \ldots, y_n$ —

then the homogeneous solution of system (14.4) is stable for any choice of functions f_s satisfying the inequality

$$\sqrt{\sum_{s=1}^{n} f_s^2} \leq -W \div \sqrt{\sum_{s=1}^{n} \left(\frac{\partial V}{\partial y_s}\right)^2}$$

In fact, the total derivative of the function V as based on system (14.4) will be nonpositive, whence follows the correctness of the Theorem. If the functions V and W satisfy some properties which are in the nature of estimates, then the problem of stability in the first approximation may be solved more completely.

We shall consider that the right-hand members of systems (14.3) and (14.4) are given in the interval $[t_0, t_0 + T]$.

We shall find estimates for the solution of system (14.4) with the aid of estimates satisfied by the solutions in system (14.3). We shall assume, for example, that there exist two functions V and W satisfying the following conditions:

1) the function V is nonnegative and satisfies the inequalities

$$\phi_1(t) r^l \leq V \leq \phi_2(t) r^l \quad \text{for } t \geq t_0 ; \tag{14.5}$$

2) the function W is nonpositive and satisfies the inequalities

$$-\psi_1(t) r^k \leq W \leq -\psi_2(t) r^k \quad \text{for } t \geq t_0, \ k \geq l > 0. \tag{14.6}$$

Here $\phi_i(t), \psi_i(t) \ (i = 1, 2)$ are continuous functions $\phi_i > 0$.

Then, as is known from §12, every solution of system (14.3) will satisfy inequalities (12.4) in which one should set

$$k_1 = k_2 = k; \quad l_1 = l_2 = l; \quad R_0 = r_0; \quad R = r.$$

We shall now assume that the function B is continuously differentiable with respect to the variable $t, y_1, \ldots, y_n$ and, besides, that its partial derivatives satisfy the inequality

$$\left|\frac{\partial V}{\partial y_t}\right| \leq \gamma \phi_2(t) r^{l-1},$$

where γ is some positive constant.

Then every solution of system (14.4) may also be subjected to analogous inequalities, if the functions f_s will satisfy the inequalities

$$|f_s| < g(t)\,r^{(-l+k+1+\alpha)}, \quad \alpha > 0 \text{ for } r \le R;$$

where R, α are positive constants; $g(t)$ is a positive continuous function given for $t \in [t_0, t_0 + T]$.

We shall compute the total derivative of the function V as based on system (14.4).

$$\frac{dV}{dt} = W + \sum_{s=1}^{n} \frac{\partial V}{\partial y_s} f_s = W_1.$$

The function W_1 satisfies the inequalities

$$-\psi_1' r^k \le W_1 \le -\psi_2' r^k \text{ for } r \le R; \quad 1 > R > 0; \quad t \ge t_0,$$

where

$$\left.\begin{aligned}
\psi_1' &= \psi_1 + n\gamma\phi_2(t)\,g(t), \\
\psi_2' &= \psi_1 - n\gamma\phi_2(t)\,g(t).
\end{aligned}\right\} \tag{14.7}$$

From Theorem 29 it follows that in the presence of the functions V and W_1 satisfying inequalities (14.5) and (14.7), every solution of system (14.4) will satisfy inequalities of the form (12.4′) in which one has set $k_1 = k_2 = k$.

The solution of the problem of stability in the first approximation is of considerable importance, as it permits one to consider instead of the complicated systems (14.4), simpler systems of the form (14.3) for which the problem of stability is solved, as a rule, much more easily. Of all the theorems on stability in the first approximation, one should distinguish particularly the theorem of Lyapunov surpassing all the others in its conclusiveness. We shall recall that this theorem refers to the case when the linear approximation in the system of equations has constant coefficients and the roots of the characteristic equation have negative real parts.

In chapter VI we shall give theorems on stability in the first approximation close in their nature to that theorem of Lyapunov's .In these theorems, directly from the properties of the functions $g_s(t, y_1, \ldots, y_n)$ and $f_s(t, y_1, \ldots, y_n)$ we shall deduce conditions for the stability of homogeneous solutions of a system of type (14.4).

§ 15. System with lag

We shall consider an automatic control system in which the time of formation of the control signal does not coincide with the time of its execution by executive organs. One says of such automatic control systems that in them there occurs a lag. The mathematical equations describing transient processes in such systems relate the velocities of the generalized coordinates calculated at a given instant t with those calculated at instants not exceeding t. In a broad class of cases these equations may be written in the form

$$\frac{dy_s}{dt} = f_s[t, y_1, ..., y_n, y_1(t - h_{s11}), ..., y_n(t - h_{snk})] \qquad (s = 1, ..., n), \qquad (15.1)$$

where by $y_1, ..., y_n$ we denote the sought functions calculated at the instant t; h_{sij} are positive constants or positive functions of time possessing the property

$$|h_{sij}| < h < +\infty \quad .$$

The intial problem for system (15.1) consists in the following [34].

Given is a system of continuous functions $\phi_1(t), ..., \phi_n(t)$ in the interval $[t_0 - h, t_0]$. It is required to find a system of continuous functions $y_1(t), ..., y_n(t)$ possessing the following properties:

1) $y_i = \phi_i(t)$ for $t \in [t_0 - h, t_0]$;

2) the functions y_i satisfy system (15.1) for $t \in [t_0, t_0 + h]$. Here those functions $y_i(t - h_{sij})$ in the system (15.1) in which the argument does not exceed t_0 are replaced by the functions $\phi_i(t - h_{sij})$.

If the right-hand members of the system (15.1) are real and continuous with respect to all their arguments, and also satisfy the Lipschitz condition for all variables except t, then the initial problem for system (15.1) may be solved. Here we consider that the right-hand members of the system are given for all $t \geq t_0$ and $-\infty < y_i < +\infty$ $(i = 1, ..., n)$.

We shall assume that system (15.1) has a homogeneous steady-state motion, i.e. $f_s(t, 0, ..., 0) \equiv 0$. (This does not limit generality, since any steady state may be reduced to a homogeneous one by means of the transformation indicated in § 1.)

The concept of stability of the homogeneous solution for system (15.1) is carried over from § 1 almost literally, namely: the homogeneous solution of system (15.1) is called stable if for every $\varepsilon > 0$ there exists a number $\delta(\varepsilon, t_0) > 0$ such that if $\left| \sum_{i=1}^{n} \phi_i^2(t) \right| < \delta^2$ then $t \in [t_0 - h, t_0]$ implies $\sum_{i=1}^{n} y_i^2(t) < \varepsilon^2$ for $t \geq t_0$.

In work [9] a theorem was developed on the stability of invariant sets of general systems, first introduced in work [36]. As noted by V. R. Petukhov, from that theory follows that all the theorems formulated in § 3 are carried over also to systems with lag, provided only that one replaces the Lyapunov function in these theorems by a functional defined on continuous curves. Thus, one may judge as to the stability of the homogeneous solution of system (15.1) by means of these theorems.

We shall assume that the right-hand members of system (15.1) may be represented in the form

$$\frac{dy_s}{dt} = \sum_{i=1}^{n} \sum_{k=1}^{m} p_{si}^{(k)} y_i (t - h_{sik}) + r_s \quad (s = 1, ..., n), \tag{15.2}$$

where the $p_{si}^{(k)}$ are real constants; $h_{sik} \geqq 0$, and the functions r_s represent a set of nonlinear terms contained in (15.1) and may be estimated in terms of the sum of the moduli of their arguments, excluding t, multiplied by a sufficiently small positive constant.

Let the homogeneous solution of the linear system

$$\frac{dy_s}{dt} = \sum_{i=1}^{n} \sum_{k=1}^{m} p_{si}^{(k)} y_i(t - h_{sik}) \quad (s = 1, ..., n) \tag{15.3}$$

be asymptotically stable. Then every solution of system (15.3) satisfies the inequality

$$\sum_{i=1}^{n} y_i^2 < c_1 M(\phi) e^{-c_2(t-t_0)} ,$$

where

$$M(\phi) = \sup_{t \in [t_0-h,\ t_0]} \left\{ \sum_{i=1}^{n} \phi_i^2(t) \right\} ,$$

and the homogeneous solution of system (15.2) is asymptotically stable.

This theorem was formulated by R. Bellman [37] and is an extension of the Lyapunov theorem mentioned above. In works [38], [39] generalizations are contained of Bellman's theorem; besides, in work [38] and also in works [40], [41], theorems are given which allow one to reduce the investigation of stability of the homogeneous solution of system (15.1) to the investigation of analogous systems of ordinary differential equations obtained from (15.1) by discarding the lag.

The above-mentioned method of investigating the problem of stability of the homogeneous solution of system (15.1) by means of functionals is a simpe. carry-over of the results of work [9] and therefore is not given here. Nevertheless it should be noted that its exposition became possible after the publication of works [42], [43].

We shall note that in the theory of automatic control one also encounters systems with lag described by systems of equations simultaneously containing ordinary and partial derivatives [52]. These are the so-called systems with distributed parameters.

Appendix II develops only the general theory of linear systems with constant coefficients and constant lags. Therefore to acquaint oneself with the theory of equations with distributed parameters, we may recommend the above-mentioned monograph by E. P. Popov.

CHAPTER IV

CONSTRUCTION OF SOLUTIONS FOR NONLINEAR SYSTEMS OF DIFFERENTIAL EQUATIONS IN THE NEIGHBOURHOOD OF A REGULAR SINGULARITY

§ 16. Auxiliary theorems from the theory of equations with partial derivatives

WE SHALL consider the system of equations

$$\frac{dz_j}{dt} + \sum_{s=1}^{n} \frac{dz_j}{\partial x_s} \left[\sum_{i=1}^{n} p_{si}(t) x_i + X_s(t, x_1, \ldots, x_n, z_1, \ldots, z_k) \right] =$$

$$= \sum_{i=1}^{k} q_{ji}(t) z_i + \sum_{i=1}^{n} r_{ji}(t) x_i + Z_j(t, x_1, \ldots, x_n, z_1, \ldots, z_k),$$

$$(j = 1, \ldots, k). \tag{16.1}$$

The functions X_s and Z_j are expanded in series of integral positive powers of the quantities $x_1, \ldots, x_n, z_1, \ldots, z_k$, converging for all $t \in (0, +\infty)$ and for sufficiently small $|x_s|$, $|z_j|$.

The coefficients in the expansions of the functions X_s and Z_j, and also the coefficients $p_{si}(t)$, $p_{ji}(t)$, $r_{ji}(t)$ are given for $t \in [0, +\infty]$, real, continuous, and bounded.

We shall assume, further, that the expansion of the functions X_s, Z_j does not contain terms linear in the quantities $x_1, \ldots, x_n, z_1, \ldots, z_k$.

We shall consider the system of ordinary differential equations, corresponding to system (16.1):

$$\frac{dx_s}{dt} = \sum_{i=1}^{n} p_{si}(t) x_i + X_s \quad (s = 1, \ldots, n); \tag{16.2}$$

$$\frac{dz_j}{dt} = \sum_{i=1}^{k} q_{ji}(t) z_i + \sum_{i=1}^{n} r_{ji}(t) x_i + Z_j \quad (j = 1, \ldots, k).$$

By $\mu_1, \ldots, \mu_{n+k}$ we shall denote the characteristic values of the linear system forming the first approximation for the system (16.2).

We shall consider that $\mu_1, \ldots, \mu_n$ are the characteristic values of the system

$$\frac{dx_s}{dt} = \sum_{i=1}^{n} p_{si}(t) x_i \quad (s = 1, \ldots, n), \tag{16.3}$$

and $\mu_{n+1}, \ldots, \mu_{n+k}$ are the characteristic values of the system

$$\frac{dz_j}{dt} = \sum_{i=1}^{k} q_{ji}(t) z_i \quad (j = 1, \ldots, k). \tag{16.4}$$

THEOREM 31. If:

1) $\mu_i > 0$; $i \leq n$;
2) $\mu_i = \mu_{n+i}$; $i \leq l$;
3) systems (16.3) and (16.4) are correct —

then the system of equation (16.1) has a family of solutions dependent on l arbitrary constants representable in the form of series

$$z_j = \sum_{m=1}^{\infty} z_j^{(m)}(t, c_1, \ldots, c_l, x_1, \ldots, x_n) \quad (j = 1, \ldots, k), \qquad (16.5)$$

converging for $|c_s| < c_0$, $|x_s| < x_0(t)$, where c_0 is a constant > 0 and $x_0(t)$ is a positive function approaching zero sufficiently fast as $t \to +\infty$.

The functions $z_j^{(m)}$ are homogeneous forms of degree m in the quantities $x_1, \ldots, x_n$, whose coefficients are continuous functions of t given for $t \geq 0$, with nonnegative characteristic values, and at the same time are polynomials in $c_1, \ldots, c_l$.

PROOF: Following A. M. Lyapunov [2], we shall construct for system (16.2) a family of solutions corresponding to the characteristic values μ_i, $i \leq n + l$:

$$x_s = \sum_{m_1 + \ldots + m_{n+l} \geq 1} L_s^{(m_{10}, \ldots, m_{n+l})}(t) e^{-t \left(\sum_{i=1}^{n+l} \mu_i m_i \right)} \alpha_1^{m_1}, \ldots, \alpha_{n+l}^{m_{n+l}} \quad (s = 1, \ldots, n), \qquad (16.6)$$

$$z_j = \sum_{m_1 + \ldots + m_{n+l} \geq 1} M_j^{(m_1, \ldots, m_{n+l})}(t) e^{-t \left(\sum_{i=1}^{n+l} \mu_i m_i \right)} \alpha_1^{m_1}, \ldots, \alpha_{n+l}^{m_{n+l}} \quad (s = 1, \ldots, k). \qquad (16.7)$$

Series (16.6) and (16.7) converge for $t \geq 0$ if $|\alpha_i| \leq \alpha$ $(i = 1, \ldots, n + l)$ $\alpha > 0$ is a sufficiently small number. Here the characteristic values of the functions $L_s^{(m_1, \ldots, m_{n+l})}(t)$ and $M_j^{(m_1, \ldots, m_{n+l})}(t)$ are nonnegative.

We shall set $\alpha_{n+i} = c_i \alpha_i$, $i \leq l$ and

$$\beta_s = e^{-\mu_{st}} \alpha_s, \quad (s \leq n). \qquad (16.8)$$

It is easy to see that the Jacobian of functions (16.6) with respect to quantities (16.8) for $\beta_s = 0$ $(s = 1, \ldots, n)$ coincides with the determinant of the fundamental system of solutions for system (16.3), if one multiplies the latter by the quantity $e^{t(\mu_1 + \ldots + \mu_n)}$,

$$\frac{D(x_1, \ldots, x_n)}{D(\beta_1, \ldots, \beta_n)} \bigg|_{\beta_1 = \ldots = \beta_n = 0} = c e^{\int_0^t \sum_{i=1}^{n} [p_{ss}(t) + \mu_s] dt}, \qquad (16.9)$$

where $c \neq 0$.

We shall solve (16.6) for quantities (16.8), which is possible on the basis of (16.9).

We have

$$\beta_s = \phi_s(t, c_1, \dots, c_l, x_1, \dots, x_n) \quad (s = 1, \dots, n). \tag{16.10}$$

Making use of relation (16.10), we shall eliminate quantities (16.8) from the system of equations (16.7). As a result of this, we shall obtain the family of solutions (16.5) for system (16.1).

Remark 1. We shall consider the case when all the coefficients in the expansions of the functions X_s and Z_j and the quantities p_{si}, q_{ji}, r_{ji} are constant. With this assumption, we shall denote system (16.1) as (16.1').

By $\lambda_1, \dots, \lambda_n$ we shall denote the roots of the equation

$$|P - \lambda E| = 0; \quad \{P\}_{ik} = p_{ik} \quad (i, \ k = 1, \dots, n),$$

and by $\kappa_1, \dots, \kappa_k$, the roots of the equation

$$|Q - \kappa E| = 0; \quad \{Q\}_{ji} = q_{ji} \quad (i, \ j = 1, \dots, k).$$

It is clear that $\mu_i = - \text{Re}(\lambda_i)$, $i \leqq n$; $M_{n+i} = \text{Re}(\Psi_i)$; $i \leqq k$.

If the conditions of Theorem 31 are fulfilled for system (16.1'), then the coefficients of the forms $z_j^{(m)}$ $(t, c_1, \dots, c_l, x_1, \dots, x_n)$ may be represented in the form of polynomials in t, $c_1, \dots, c_l$ whose coefficients in their turn are trigonometric multinomials. These trigonometric multinomials will be periodic functions of t if the quantities $\lambda_i - \kappa_i$, $i \leq l$, are commensurate. In the contrary case they will be almost-periodic functions.

If $\lambda_i - \kappa_i = 0$, $i \leq l$, then the coefficients of the forms $z_j^{(m)}$ are polynomials in $c_1, \dots, c_l$ and t.

Remark 2. By means of a nonsingular linear transformation over the sought functions $z_1, \dots, z_k$ and over the independent variables $x_1, \dots, x_n$, system (16.1') may be brought into the form

$$\frac{\partial \bar{z}_j}{\partial t} + \sum_{s=1}^{n} \frac{\partial \bar{z}_j}{\partial \bar{x}_s} (\varepsilon_{s-1} \bar{x}_{s-1} + \lambda_s \bar{x}_s + \bar{X}_s) = \delta_{j-1} \bar{z}_{j-1} + K_j \bar{z}_j + \sum_{i=1}^{n} \bar{r}_{ji} \bar{x}_i + Z_j$$

$$(j = 1, \dots, k), \tag{16.11}$$

where $\varepsilon_o = \delta_0 = 0$; ε_s, δ_j are equal to zero or unity.

If $\mathrm{Re}(\lambda_s) < 0$, $s \leq n$, and $\Psi_i = \lambda_i$, $i \leq l$, then system (16.11) has the family of solutions

$$\bar{z}_j = \sum_{m=1}^{\infty} \bar{z}_j^{(m)}(t,\ c_1, \ldots, c_l,\ \bar{x}_1, \ldots, \bar{x}_n) \qquad (j = 1, \ldots, k). \qquad (16.12)$$

In (16.12) we shall set $t = (1/\lambda_1) \ln \bar{x}_1$ and the newly obtained functions we shall denote by σ_j $(j = 1, \ldots, k)$.

It is clear that the functions

$$\sigma_j = \sum_{m=1}^{\infty} \bar{z}_j^{(m)} (\lambda_1^{-1} \ln \bar{x}_1,\ c_1, \ldots, c_l,\ \bar{x}_1, \ldots, \bar{x}_n), \qquad (j = 1, \ldots, k) \quad (16.13)$$

will satisfy the system of equations

$$\sum_{s=1}^{n} \frac{\partial \sigma_j}{\partial \bar{x}_s}[\varepsilon_{s-1}\bar{x}_{s-1} + \lambda_s\bar{x}_s + \bar{X}_s(\bar{x}_1, \ldots, \bar{x}_n,\ \sigma_1, \ldots, \sigma_k)] = \delta_{j-1}\sigma_{j-1} + \Psi_j\sigma_j +$$

$$+ \sum_{i=1}^{n} \bar{r}_{ji}\bar{x}_i + Z_j(\bar{x}_1, \ldots, \bar{x}_n,\ \sigma_1, \ldots, \sigma_k). \qquad (16.14)$$

THEOREM 32. If:
1) $\mathrm{Re}(\lambda_i) < 0$, $i \leq n$;
2) $\Psi_i = \lambda_i$, $i \leq l$ —

then with $\bar{X}_1 \equiv 0$, the system of equations (16.14) has the family of solutions (16.13), dependent on l arbitrary constants. Here the coefficients of the forms $\bar{z}_j^{(m)}$ are polynomials in $c_1, \ldots, c_l$, $\ln \bar{x}_1$.

Series (16.13) converge for $|c_s| < c_0$,

$$|\bar{x}_s| < x_0 |\ln|\bar{x}_{10}| - \ln|\lambda_1||,$$

where x_0 is the function dealt with in Theorem 1, $|\bar{x}_{10}|$ is sufficiently small.

Further, we shall indicate a case when functions (16.13) do not depend on $\ln \bar{x}_1$.

THEOREM 33. If:
1) $\mathrm{Re}(\lambda_i) < 0$, $i \leq k$;
2) $\lambda_i = \Psi_i$, $i \leq l$;
3) $\varepsilon_i = \delta_i$, $i \leq l - 1$;
4) $\varepsilon_l = 0$, $r_{ij} = 0$; $i, j \leq l$;

5) there exist no relations form the of $\sum_{i=1}^{n} m_i\lambda_i = \kappa_j$, $j \leq k$, for any integral nonnegative m_i, $\sum_{i=1}^{n} m_i \geq 1$, with the exception of the cases $\lambda_i = \Psi_i$, $i \leq l$ — then system (16.1′) [and also (16.11) and (16.14)] have a family of holomorphic solutions dependent on l arbitrary constants, representable in the form of series

$$z_j = \sum_{m=1}^{\infty} \tilde{z}_j^{(m)}(c_1, ..., c_l, x_1, ..., x_n) \quad (j = 1, ..., k), \tag{16.15}$$

where $\tilde{z}_j^{(m)}$ are homogeneous forms of degree m in $x_1, ..., x_n$ whose coefficients are polynomials in $c_1, ..., c_l$.

Series (16.15) converge for $|c_s| \leq c_o$, $|x_s| \leq r$; $r > 0$, $c_o > 0$.

PROOF: We shall carry out the proof for system (16.14). For this purpose we shall substitute into (16.14) the series

$$\sigma_j = \sum_{m=1}^{\infty} \sigma_j^{(m)}(\bar{x}_1, ..., \bar{x}_n) \quad (j = 1, ..., k), \tag{16.16}$$

where $\sigma_j^{(m)}$ are homogeneous forms of power m in $\bar{x}_1, ..., \bar{x}_n$ with the coefficients to be determined.

Equating the forms of the same degree, we shall obtain a system of equations for determining $\sigma_j^{(m)}$

$$\sum_{s=1}^{n} \frac{\partial \sigma_j^{(m)}}{\partial \bar{x}_s}(\varepsilon_{s-1}\bar{x}_{s-1} + \lambda_s\bar{x}_s) = \delta_{j-1}\sigma_{j-1}^{(m)} + \kappa_j\sigma_j^{(m)} + R_j^{(m)}. \tag{16.17}$$

The functions $R_j^{(m)}$ are homogeneous forms of degree m in $\bar{x}_1, ..., \bar{x}_n$ depending on the expansions of the functions $\bar{X}_s$, $\bar{Z}_j$ and on the forms $\sigma_j^{(\mu)}$ $(j = 1, ..., k; \mu = 1, ..., m-1)$.

If the function $R_j^{(m)}$ for $m > 1$ is defined, then from condition 5 of Theorem 33 it follows [1] that system (16.17) has a unique solution in terms of forms $\sigma_j^{(m)}(x_1, ..., x_n)$ $(j = 1, ..., k)$.

We shall show, that system (16.17) for $m = 1$ has a solution in the guise of a system of linear forms $\sigma_j^{(1)}$ depending on l arbitrary constants.

We shall set

$$\sigma_j^{(1)} = y_j^{(1)} + y_j^{(2)} \quad (j = 1, ..., k), \tag{16.18}$$

where $y_j^{(1)}$ is a linear form in $\bar{x}_1, ..., \bar{x}_l$, and $y_j^{(2)}$ is a linear form in $\bar{x}_{l+1}, ..., \bar{x}_n$.

For the determination of these forms we have the equations:

$$\sum_{s=1}^{l} \frac{\partial y_j^{(1)}}{\partial \bar{x}_s}(\varepsilon_{s-1}\bar{x}_{s-1} + \lambda_s \bar{x}_s) = \delta_{j-1}y_{j-1}^{(1)} + \kappa_j y_j^{(1)} \quad (j = 1, ..., l), \quad (16.19)$$

$$\sum_{s=l+1}^{n} \frac{\partial y_j^{(2)}}{\partial \bar{x}_s}(\varepsilon_{s-1}\bar{x}_{s-1} + \lambda_s \bar{x}_s) = \delta_{j-1}y_j^{(2)} + \Psi_j y_j^{(2)} + \sum_{i=l+1}^{n} \bar{r}_{ji}\bar{x}_i \quad (j = l+1, ..., n). \quad (16.20)$$

On the basis of conditions 4 and 5, system (16.20) has a unique solution in the form of a system of linear forms $y_j^{(2)}$.

Let the functions $\bar{x}_i = t^{l_i}e^{\lambda_i t}/l_i$ be the solution of the system

$$\frac{dx_i}{dt} = \varepsilon_{i-1}\bar{x}_{i-1} + \lambda_i \bar{x}_i \quad (i = 1, ..., l). \quad (16.21)$$

Then the matrix of the fundamental system of solutions $X(t)$ for (16.21) will have the form

$$
\begin{vmatrix}
x_1 & 0 & 0 & 0 & \cdots & & & & & & & & & & & \cdots & 0 & 0 & 0 \\
x_2 & x_1 & 0 & 0 & \cdots & & & & & & & & & & & \cdots & 0 & 0 & 0 \\
x_3 & x_2 & x_1 & 0 & \cdots & & & & & & & & & & & \cdots & 0 & 0 & 0 \\
\cdot & & & & \cdot & & & & & & & & & & & & & & \\
\cdot & & & & \cdot & & & & & & & & & & & & & & \\
\cdot & & & & \cdot & & & & & & & & & & & & & & \\
x_{k_1} & x_{k_1-1} & x_{k_1-2} & & \cdots & x_1 & & & & & & & & & & & & & \\
0 & 0 & 0 & & \cdots & 0 & x_{k_1+1} & 0 & 0 & 0 & \cdots & & & & & & & & \\
0 & 0 & 0 & & \cdots & 0 & x_{k_1+2} & x_{k_1+1} & 0 & 0 & \cdots & & & & & & & & \\
0 & 0 & 0 & & \cdots & 0 & x_{k_1+3} & x_{k_1+2} & x_{k_1+1} & 0 & \cdots & & & & & & & & \\
\cdot & & & & & & & & & & & & & & & & & & \\
\cdot & & & & & & & & & & & & & & & & & & \\
\cdot & & & & & & & & & & & & & & & & & & \\
0 & 0 & 0 & & \cdots & 0 & x_{k_2} & x_{k_2-1} & x_{k_2-2} & \cdots & x_{k_2+1} & & & & & & & & \\
0 & 0 & 0 & & \cdots & 0 & 0 & 0 & 0 & \cdots & 0 & x_{k_2+1} & 0 & \cdots & & & & & \\
0 & 0 & 0 & & \cdots & 0 & 0 & 0 & 0 & \cdots & 0 & x_{k_2+2} & x_{k_2+1} & \cdots & & & & & \\
\cdot & & & & & & & & & & & & & & & & & & \\
\end{vmatrix}
$$

It is clear that

$$Y(t) = X(t)C, \quad (16.22)$$

where

$$
C = \begin{bmatrix} c_1 \\ \cdot \\ \cdot \\ \cdot \\ \cdot \\ \cdot \\ c_l \end{bmatrix} ; \quad Y = \begin{bmatrix} y_1^{(1)} \\ y_2^{(1)} \\ \cdot \\ \cdot \\ y_l^{(1)} \end{bmatrix}
$$

gives the general solution of system (16.21) and, at the same time, the functions $y_j^{(1)}$ $(j = 1, ..., l)$ considered as linear forms in the quantities $\bar{x}_i$; $(i = 1, ..., l)$ are a solution of system (16.19).

Thus, the linear forms $\sigma_j^{(1)}$ for $j = 1, ..., l$ are determined.

The forms $\sigma_j^{(1)}$ for $j \geqq l + 1$ are uniquely determined from the system (16.17) for $m = 1$.

Thus, the system of formal series (16.16) is completely determined.

Convergence of series (16.16) follows from Theorem 31.

§ 17. Representation of the solutions of systems of ordinary differential equations in the neighbourhood of a singularity

We shall consider the system

$$
z \frac{dy_s}{dz} = \sum_{i=1}^{n} p_{si}(z)y_i + p_s(z)z + Y_s(z, y_1, ..., y_n) \quad (s = 1, ..., n). \quad (17.1)
$$

The functions Y_s are expanded in series

$$
Y_s = \sum_{m+m_1+...+m_n \geqq 2} p_s^{(m, m_1, ..., m_n)}(z)z^{(m)}y_1^{m_1}, ..., y_n^{m_n} \quad (s = 1, ..., n),
$$

converging for $|z| < z_1$, $|y_j| < y_0$ $(j = 1, ..., n)$, where $z_1 > 0$, $y_0 > 0$ are constants.

$$
p_{si}(z), \; p_s(z), \; p_s^{(m, m_1, ..., m_n)}(z) \quad (17.2)
$$

are given for $z \in [0,1]$, real, continuous, and bounded.

For system (17.1) at the point $y_1 = ... = y_n = 0$, $z = 0$ the conditions for the existence of a solution are not satisfied. Therefore the question arises under what conditions there exists a solution of system (17.1) $y_s = y_s(z)$, $(s = 1, ..., n)$ such that $y_s \to 0$ for $z \to 0$.

Later on we shall derive these conditions and give an analytic representation of such solutions.

By 1, $\mu_1, ..., \mu_n$ we shall denote the characteristic values of the system

$$\frac{dz}{dt} = -z; \tag{17.3}$$

$$\frac{dy_s}{dt} = -\left[\sum_{i=1}^{n} p_{si}(e^{-t}) y_i + p_s(e^{-t}) z \right] \quad (s = 1, ..., n).$$

THEOREM 34. If:

1) $\mu_i > 0$ for $i \leq l$;
2) system (17.3) is correct —

then the system of equations (17.1) has a family of solutions dependent on l arbitrary constants, representable in the form of series

$$\tag{17.4}$$

$$y_s = \sum_{m+m_1+ ... +m_l \geq 1} K_s^{(m,m_1,...,m_l)}(z) z^{(m+m_1\mu_1+...+m_l\mu_l)} c_1^{m_1}, ..., c_l^{m_l} \quad s = 1, ..., n,$$

convergent for $|z| \leq z_0$, $|c_j| \leq c_0$ $(i = 1, ..., l)$; here $z_0 < \beta$ and $c_0 z_0 < \beta$, where β is a sufficiently small constant; c_0, z_0 are positive constants.

The functions $K_s^{(m, m_1, ..., m_l)}(z)$ possess the property $K_s^{(m, m_1, ..., m_l)}(z) \, z^\alpha \to 0$ as $z \to 0$, where α is a positive constant.

PROOF: We shall consider the system of equations

$$-\sum_{j=1}^{l} \frac{\partial y_s}{\partial x_j} \mu_j x_j - z \frac{\partial y_s}{\partial z} + \frac{\partial y_s}{\partial t} = -\sum_{i=1}^{n} p_{si}(e^{-t}) y_i - p_s(e^{-t}) z - Y_s. \tag{17.5}$$

For system (17.5), the conditions of Theorem 31 are satisfied. Therefore there exists a system of functions

$$y_s(t, c_1, ..., c_l, x_1, ..., x_l, z) = \sum_{m=1}^{+\infty} y_s^{(m)}(t, c_1, ..., c_l, x_1, ..., x_l, z),$$

$$(s = 1, ..., n), \tag{17.6}$$

satisfying system (17.5).

It is clear that the forms $y_s^{(m)}$ have the aspect

$$y_s^{(m)} = \sum_{\bar{m}+\bar{m}_1+...+\bar{m}_l = m} K^{(\bar{m}, \bar{m}_1, ..., \bar{m}_l)} z^{\bar{m}} x_1^{\bar{m}_1}, ..., x_l^{\bar{m}_l} c_1^{\bar{m}_1} ... c_l^{\bar{m}_l}; \quad (s = 1, ..., n), \tag{17.7}$$

where $m \geq 1$.

In (17.6) we shall set

$$x_j = z^{\mu_j}, \quad t = -\ln z. \tag{17.8}$$

Then we shall obtain a family of solutions (17.4) satisfying system (17.1), of which one may convince oneself by a direct substitution.

Remark 1. Let functions (17.2) be real constants. In that case we shall denote system (17.1) as (17.1′).

By $\lambda_1, ..., \lambda_n$ we shall denote, just as above, the roots of the equation $|P - \lambda E| = 0$, $\{P\}_{ik} = p_{ik}$.

It is easy to see that for system (17.1′), $\mu_i = \mathrm{Re}(\lambda_i)$.

Thus, for $\mathrm{Re}(\lambda_i) > 0$, $i \le l$, system (17.1′) has a family of solutions (17.4). Here the functions $K_s^{(m, m_1, \cdots, m_l)}(z)$ are polynomials in $\ln z$ whose coefficients are trigonometric polynomials.

Remark 2. In system (17.1′) we shall bring the matrix P into the canonical form. Then we shall obtain

$$z \frac{\partial \bar{y}_s}{\partial z} = \varepsilon_{s-1} \bar{y}_{s-1} + \lambda_s \bar{y}_s + \bar{p}_s z + \bar{Y}_s \quad (s = 1, ..., n), \tag{17.9}$$

where $\varepsilon_0 = 0$.

We shall consider the system of equations with partial derivatives, corresponding to (17.9),

$$-\sum_{j=1}^{l} \frac{\partial \bar{y}_s}{\partial x_j} \left(\varepsilon_{j-1} x_{j-1} + \lambda_j x_j - z \frac{\partial \bar{y}_s}{\partial z} \right) = -(\varepsilon_{s-1} \bar{y}_{s-1} + \lambda_s \bar{y}_s + \bar{Y}_s + P_s z). \tag{17.10}$$

According to Theorem 32, that system has a solution in the form of the converging series

$$\bar{y}_s = \sum_{m+m_1+...+ml=1}^{\infty} \tilde{K}_s^{(m, m_1, \cdots, m_l)}(z) c_1^{m_1}, ..., c_l^{m_l} z^m x_1^{m_1}, ..., x_l^{m_l};$$

$$(s = 1, ..., n), \tag{17.11}$$

where $\tilde{K}_s^{(m, m_1, \cdots, m_l)}(z)$ are polynomials in powers of $\ln z$.

If $m + \sum_{i=1}^{l} m_i \lambda_i \ne \lambda_j$ $(j = 1, ..., l)$ for all integral nonnegative $m, m_1, ..., m_l$ such that $m + m_1 + ... + m_l \ge 2$, then the quantities $\tilde{K}_s^{(m, m_1, \cdots, m_l)}$ are constants.

We shall set

$$x_j = \frac{(\ln z)^{l_j} z^{\lambda_j}}{l_j}, \tag{17.12}$$

where the constants l_j are chosen so that functions (17.12) satisfy the system

$$z\frac{dx_j}{dz} = \varepsilon_{j-1}x_{j-1} + \lambda_j x_j.$$

If functions (17.12) are substituted in series (17.11), then we shall obtain a family of solutions of system (17.9).

The following Theorem holds.

THEOREM 35. If among the characteristic values of the matrix P in system (17.1′) there exists an l with positive real parts, then there exists a family of solutions of system (17.1′) representable in the form of the series

$$y_s = \sum_{m+m_1 \ldots + m_l = 1} N_s^{(m, m_1, \ldots, m_l)} (\ln z) z^{m + \sum\limits_{i=1}^{l} m_i \lambda_i} (\ln z)^{\sum\limits_{i=1}^{l} m_i l_i} c_1^{m_1} \ldots c_l^{m_l},$$

$$(17.13)$$

converging for $|z| \leqq z_0$, $|c_j| \leqq c_0$ $(j = 1, \ldots, n)$, $z_0 < \beta$, $c_0 z_0 < \beta$, where $N_s^{(m, m_1, \ldots, m_l)} (\ln z)$ are polynomials in $\ln z$.

Now if $m + \sum\limits_{i=1}^{l} m_i \lambda_i \neq \lambda_i$ $(j = 1, \ldots, l)$ for $m + \sum\limits_{i=1}^{l} m_i \geqq 1$ with the exception of the cases $\lambda_i = \lambda_j$, then the quantites $N_s^{(m, m_1, \ldots, m_l)}$ are constant.

We shall now consider the case when the original system of differential equations is not represented in the normal form

$$F_s(z, y_1, \ldots, y_k, y_1^{(1)}, y_1^{(2)}, \ldots, y_1^{(n_1)}, \ldots, y_k^{(1)}, \ldots, y_k^{(n_k)}) = 0; \quad (s = 1, \ldots, k). \quad (17.14)$$

We shall consider that the functions F_s are single-valued and analytic in the neighbourhood of the point $z = 0$,

$$y_s^{(j)} = 0 \begin{pmatrix} s = 1, \ldots, k \\ j = 0, \ldots, n_s \end{pmatrix}$$

and can be expanded in a series of the following type

$$F_s = \sum_{i=1}^{k} \sum_{j=1}^{n_i} p_{si}^{(j)} y_i^{(j)} + \sum_{\substack{\sum m_i^j > 1}} \prod_{\substack{i=1, \ldots, k \\ j=0, \ldots, n_i}} P_s^{m_i^j} (y_i^{(j)})^{m_i^j}$$

$$(s = 1, \ldots, k). \quad (17.15)$$

The second sum represents the set of nonlinear terms in the sought functions $y_1, \ldots, y_k$ and of all their derivatives up to the order $n_j (j = 1, \ldots, k)$, consequently the summation in that sum is carried out over all nonnegative integers m_i^j $(j = 0, 1, \ldots, n_i; \ i = 1, 2, \ldots, k)$, such that

$$\sum m_i^j = \sum_{i=1}^{k} \sum_{j=0}^{n_i} m_i^j > 1.$$

The coefficients of series (17.15) are single-valued analytic functions of z in the neighbourhood of $z = 0$ and are represented in the form

$$p_{si}^{(j)}(z) = z \bar{p}_{si}^{(j)},$$

$$P_s^{(m_i^j)}(z) = z^{m_i^j} \bar{P}_s^{(m_i^j)},$$

where $\sum m_i^j$ is extended over all values of i $(i = 1, \ldots, k)$ and j $(j = 1, \ldots, n_{i-1})$. The $\bar{P}$ are also analytic functions in the neighbourhood of $z = 0$.

We shall consider that in the j-th equation of system (17.14) there enters the function $y_j^{(n_j)}$, also $\bar{p}_{jj}^{(n_j)} \neq 0$ for $z = 0$.

We shall consider the linear system of equations

$$\sum_{i=1}^{k} \sum_{j=0}^{n_i} z^j Q_{si}^{(j)} y_i^{(j)} = 0 \qquad (s = 1, \ldots, k), \tag{17.17}$$

where the $Q_{si}^{(j)}$ are the free terms in the expansion of the functions $\bar{p}_{si}^{(j)}$ in powers of z.

We shall seek the solution of that linear system in the form

$$y_i = c_i z^{\lambda} \qquad (i = 1, \ldots, k). \tag{17.18}$$

We shall substitute (17.18) in (17.17). Then we shall obtain

$$\sum_{i=1}^{n} \sum_{j=0}^{n_i} z^{\lambda} f_{ij}(\lambda) Q_{si}^{(j)} c_i = 0 \qquad (s = 1, \ldots, k), \tag{17.19}$$

where

$$f_{ij}(\lambda) = \begin{cases} 1 & \text{for } j = 0 \\ \lambda(\lambda - 1) \ldots (\lambda - j + 1) & \text{for } j = 1, \ldots, n_i. \end{cases}$$

Equations (17.19) are linear and homogeneous. Consequently, in order for a nonhomogeneous solution to exist for these equations, it is necessary and sufficient that the determinant constructed from the matrix $\{c_{si}\}$, whose elements are the expressions $\sum_{j=0}^{n_i} f_{ij}(\lambda) Q_{si}^{(j)} = c_{si}$, be equal to zero.

We shall denote that determinant by $\Delta(\lambda)$. It is clear that $\Delta(\lambda)$ is a polynomial in λ of degree $n = \sum\limits_{i=1}^{k} n_i$.

Let $\lambda_1, \lambda_2, \ldots, \lambda_n$ be the roots of the equation

$$\Delta(\lambda) = 0. \tag{17.20}$$

THEOREM 36. If among the roots of equation (17.20) there is an l with positive real parts, then the system of equations (17.14) has a family of solutions possessing the property that $y_i(z) \to 0$ as $z \to 0$. This family of solutions is represented in the form of a series

$$y_s = \sum_{m+m_1+\ldots+m_l \geq 1} N_s^{(m, m_1, \ldots, m_l)}(\ln z)z^{m+\sum\limits_{i=1}^{l} m_i\lambda_i} c_1^{m_1} \ldots c_l^{m_l}; \quad (s = 1, \ldots, k), \tag{17.21}$$

convergent for $|c_i| < c$ and $|z| < z_0$, where c and z_0 are sufficiently small positive constants.

PROOF: We shall bring the system under consideration, (17.14), into the normal form. For this we shall eliminate from the equation with the number j the higher derivatives of the sought functions $y_s(s \neq \gamma)$. Thereupon we shall obtain a system of equations in which in the j-th equation will enter the higher derivative of the order n_j o f the function y_j. only

Then we shall introduce new sought functions according to the formulae

$$x_{i,1} = y_i; \quad x_{i,2} = z\frac{dx_{i,1}}{dz}; \quad \ldots \; ; \quad x_{i,n_i-1} = z\,\frac{dx_{i,n_i-2}}{dz},$$

whence we find the derivatives of the functions $y_1, \ldots, y_k$ with respect to the variable z according to the formula

$$y_i^{(1)} = \frac{x_{i,2}}{z}; \quad y_i^{(2)} = \frac{1}{z^2}[x_{i,3} - x_{i,2}]; \quad \text{etc.}$$

As a result of this substitution, the original system is reduced to a system of the form (17.1'). Consequently, according to Theorem 35 the transformed syste m has a family of solutions dependent on l arbitrary constants. Taking into acc ount the inverse transformations to the system (17.14), we shall find that it has a family of solutions represented in the form of series (17.21), in which $\bar{N}_s^{(m, m_1, \ldots, m_l)}(\ln z)$ are polynomials in $\ln z$.

We shall now dwell on the history of the problem considered in this chapter. In work [44], the equation

$$x \frac{dy}{dx} = ax + \lambda y + \sum_{i+k=2}^{\infty} a_{ik} x^i y^k$$

was considered, and it was shown that, with the condition $\lambda \neq N$, it has a holomorphic solution satisfying the condition $y = 0$ for $x = 0$. Henri Poincaré [45] has found a family of solutions for this equation, represented in powers of x and x^λ, and also, in the case $\lambda = N$, in powers of $\ln x$, where N is a positive integer. In work [45] an extension of Poincaré's results has been adapted to systems of equations subject to a series of constraining conditions. In work [46] an attempt was made to remove these constraints for a system of two equations. However, Horn did not succeed in resolving this problem.

Bendixon [47] and a series of other authors have occupied themselves with the problem of representing solutions in the neighbourhood of a singular point. Only in work [9] has the complete solution of the problem of Briot and Bouquet been give in its classical formulation. In this chapter the basic results are given with some modifications, as it became clear that there exists a group of problems in the theory of automatic control which is reduced to the study of the behaviour of solutions of systems of differential equations in the neighbourhood of a singularity of a similar type.

CHAPTER V

ESTIMATION OF THE INFLUENCE OF CONSTANTLY ACTING
PERTURBATIONS UPON TRANSIENT PROCESSES IN
A NONSTATIONARY SYSTEM

§ 18.   Influence of constantly acting perturbations

IN THE theory of stability of motion there exists a series of theories on the influence of constantly acting perturbations upon the behaviour of transient processes.

We shall consider the system of equations

$$\frac{dy_s}{dt} = g_s(t, y_1, \ldots, y_n) \qquad (s = 1, \ldots, n), \tag{18.1}$$

whose right-hand members possess the same properties as in system (1.4). [It may be considered that this system is obtained from the same considerations as system (1.4).]

We shall further consider the system of equations

$$\frac{dy_s}{dt} = g_s(t, y_1, \ldots, y_n) + r_s(t, y_1, \ldots, y_n) \qquad (s = 1, \ldots, n). \tag{18.2}$$

The functions $r_s(t, y_1, \ldots, y_n)$ in system (18.2) characterize constantly acting perturbations, to which the real system is subjected.

We shall consider that these functions are such that system (18.2) has a solution corresponding to each choice of initial conditions $y_{10}, \ldots, y_{n0}, t_0$.

Subsequently, without limiting the generality, it may be considered that the right-hand members of the system in (18.1) and (18.2) are given for $t \in [t_0, t_0 + T]$.

The concept of stability under constantly acting perturbations consists in the following.

The steady-state motion $y_1 = y_2 = \ldots = y_n = 0$ in system (18.1) is called stable under constantly acting perturbations if for every $\varepsilon > 0$ there exist two numbers $\gamma > 0$ and $\delta > 0$ such that if $|r_s(t, y_1, \ldots, y_n)| < \gamma$ for all initial conditions $\sum_{i=1}^{n} y_{i0}^2 < \delta^2$, then

$$\sum_{i=1}^{n} y_i^2(t, y_{10}, \ldots, y_{n0}) < \varepsilon^2, \tag{18.3}$$

where $y_i(t, y_{10}, ..., y_{n0})$ $(i = 1, ..., n)$ are functions defining the transient process in system (18.2).

We shall assume that the homogeneous solution of system (18.1) is uniform-asymptotically stable and the functions $g_s(t, y_1, ..., y_n)$ have continuous and bounded partial derivatives with respect to t. Then it may be asserted that the homogeneous solution of system (18.1) is stable under constantly acting perturbations.

Indeed, under the conditions indicated there exists a positive-definite function $V(t, y_1, ..., y_n)$ admitting of an infinitely small upper bound and whose total derivative, as based on system (18.1), represents a negative-definite function $W(y_1, ..., y_n)$. Here the function W may be chosen so that the functions V have bounded derivatives with respect to the variables $y_1, ..., y_n$ in the neighbourhood of the point $y_1 = y_2 = ... = y_n = 0$.

We shall find the total derivative of the function V as based on system (18.2)

$$\frac{dV}{dt} = W + W_1, \tag{18.4}$$

where

$$W_1 = \sum_{i=1}^{n} \frac{\partial V}{\partial y_i}. \tag{18.5}$$

We shall take an arbitrary number $\varepsilon > 0$ (without limiting the generality, it may be considered as sufficiently small). We shall find a number

$$\lambda = \inf_{\sum_{i=1}^{n} y_i^2 = \varepsilon^2} V(t, y_1, ..., y_n), \ t \geq 0. \tag{18.6}$$

We shall choose a number δ such that

$$V < \lambda \quad \text{for} \quad \sum_{i=1}^{n} y_i^2 < \delta^2; \tag{18.7}$$

we shall choose a number γ such that the function $W + W_1$ be negative in the spherical annulus $\delta^2 \leq \sum_{i=1}^{n} y_i^2 \leq \varepsilon^2$. Then any solution of system (18.2) which starts on the surface of the sphere $\sum_{i=1}^{n} y_i^2 = \delta^2$ and remains in the spherical annulus possesses the property that the function V decreases along it, i.e. there holds the inequality

$$V(t_0, y_{10}, \ldots, y_{n0}) > V_1(t, y_{10}, \ldots, y_{n0}). \tag{18.8}$$

If there exists an integral curve starting in the region $\sum_{i=1}^{n} y_i^2 < \delta^2$ and emerging outside the region $\sum_{i=1}^{n} y_i^2 < \varepsilon^2$, then there exists an instant t_1 such that

$$\sum_{i=1}^{n} y_i^2 (t_1, y_{10}, \ldots, y_{n0}, t_0) = \varepsilon^2, \tag{18.9}$$

and then

$$V_1 (t, y_{10}, \ldots, y_{n0}) \geq \lambda, \tag{18.10}$$

which contradicts the condition

$$V_1 (t_1, y_{10}, \ldots, y_{n0}) < V (t_0, y_{10}, \ldots, y_{n0}) < \lambda. \tag{18.11}$$

The contradiction obtained shows that all the integral curves of system (18.2) starting in the sphere of radius δ remain as time increases in a sphere of radius ε.

The argument given above is contained in work [12].

This assertion may be strengthened by dispensing with the constraints on functions $g_s(t, y_1, \ldots, y_n)$, consisting in the presence of bounded partial derivatives of the functions with respect to the variables $y_1, \ldots, y_n$ in the neighbourhood of the point $y_1 = y_2 = \ldots = y_n = 0$. We shall note that these constraints do not correspond to some problems encountered in investigating some nonstationary automatic control systems. However, these theorems have a considerable deficiency in that the actual link between the magnitudes γ, δ, and ε is not known. Later on we shall cite theorems free of this deficiency. The results obtained in these theorems are more profound than the ones described above and therefore require a deeper knowledge of system (18.1) and of the forces $r_s(t, y_1, \ldots, y_n)$ exerting a constant action upon system (18.1).

THEOREM 37. If there exists a quadratic form

$$V = \sum_{i, k=1}^{n} a_{ik}(t) y_i y_k \tag{18.12}$$

satisfying the conditions:

1. V satisfies the inequalities

$$\phi_1(t) r^2 \leq V \leq \phi_2(t) r^2, \tag{18.13}$$

where $\phi_i(t) > 0$ $(i = 1, 2)$ are continuous positive functions given in the interval $t \in [t_0, t_0 + T]$;

2. the total derivative of V, calculated as based on system (18.1), satisfies the inequalities

$$- \psi_1(t) r^2 \leqq W \leqq -\psi_2(t) r^2 \tag{18.14}$$

for $r \leqq R$, where $\psi_i(t)$ $(i = 1, 2)$ are continuous functions given for $t \in [t_0, t_0 + T]$, R is a positive number, and $r = \sqrt{\sum_{i=1}^{n} y_i^2}$;

3. the constantly acting perurbations have the form

$$r_s(t, y_1, \ldots, y_n) = a_s(t) + \sum_{i=1}^{n} q_{si}(t) y_i + P_s(t, y_1, \ldots, y_n) \quad (s = 1, \ldots, n), \tag{18.15}$$

where $a_s(t)$, $q_{si}(t)$ are real functions, given for $t \in [t_0, t_0 + T]$ and having a finite number of discontinuities in every interval $[t_0, T_1]$; $t_0 < T_1 < t_0 + T$. The functions $P_s(t, y_1, \ldots, y_n)$ include nonlinear terms of the constantly acting perturbations and satisfy the inequalities

$$| P_s(t, y_1, \ldots, y_n) | \leqq b_s(t) r^{1+\alpha}; \quad 0 < \alpha = \mathrm{const}; \quad r \leqq R;$$

the $b_s(t)$ are nonnegative functions satisfying the same conditions as the $a_s(t)$ — then every solution of system (18.2) will satisfy the inequalities

$$\phi_2^{-\frac{1}{2}}(t) e^{\int_{t_0}^{t} g_2(\tau) d\tau} \left[\rho_0 - \int_{t_0}^{t} a(\tau) \phi_2(\tau) \phi_1^{-1}(\tau) e^{-\int_{t_0}^{\tau} g_2(\theta) d\theta} d\tau \right] \leqq$$

$$\leqq r \leqq \phi_1^{-1}(t) e^{\int_{t_0}^{t} g_2(\tau) d\tau} \left[\rho_0 + \int_{t_0}^{t} a(\tau) \phi_2(\tau) \phi_1^{-1}(\tau) e^{-\int_{t_0}^{\tau} g_2(\theta) d\theta} d\tau \right]$$

for all $t \geqq t_0$, as long as $r(t) \leqq R$, where

$$g_1 = -\tfrac{1}{2} \cdot \frac{\psi_2}{\phi_2} + \lambda(t) \phi_2(t) \phi_1^{-1}(t) + b(t) \phi_2(t) R^\alpha \phi_1^{-1}(t),$$

$$g_2 = -\tfrac{1}{2} \cdot \frac{\psi_1}{\phi_1} - \lambda(t) \phi_2(t) \phi_1^{-1}(t) - b(t) \phi_2(t) R^\alpha \phi_1^{-1}(t).$$

Here

$$a(t) = \sqrt{\sum_{i=1}^{n} a_i^2(t)}; \quad b(t) = \sqrt{\sum_{i=1}^{n} b_i^2(t)};$$

and λ^2 is the largest characteristic value of the matrix Q^*Q, where Q is a matrix whose elements are the functions $q_{si}(t)$ and Q^* is the transpose of the matrix Q.

PROOF: We shall calculate the total derivative of the quadratic form (12.18), as based on system (18.2). Then we shall obtain

$$\frac{dV}{dt} = W + W_1, \tag{18.16}$$

where W is the total derivative of V, as based on system (18.1), and W may be represented in the form of three components

$$W_1 = \sigma_1 + \sigma_2 + \sigma_3, \tag{18.17}$$

where

$$\sigma_1 = \sum_{i=1}^{n} a_i \frac{\partial V}{\partial y_i}, \quad \sigma_2 = \sum_{i=1}^{n} \frac{\partial V}{\partial y_i} \sum_{s=1}^{n} q_{is} y_s, \quad \text{and} \quad \sigma_3 = \sum_{i=1}^{n} p_i \frac{\partial V}{\partial y_i}.$$

We shall estimate these functions. From the Bunyakovskiy inequality we shall have

$$|\sigma_1| \leqq \sqrt{\sum_{i=1}^{n} a_i^2(t)} \sqrt{\sum_{i=1}^{n} \left(\frac{\partial V}{\partial y_i}\right)^2};$$

$$|\sigma_3| \leqq \sqrt{\sum_{i=1}^{n} p_i^2} \sqrt{\sum_{i=1}^{n} \left(\frac{\partial V}{\partial y_i}\right)^2}.$$

The function V is a quadratic form. Therefore

$$\frac{\partial V}{\partial y_i} = 2 \sum_{k=1}^{n} a_{ik} y_k.$$

One may convince oneself that $\sum_{i=1}^{n} (\partial V / \partial y_i)^2$ therefore represents a fourth degree quadratic form, the matrix of whose coefficients coincides with the square of the matrix of coefficients of form (18.12). It is known that the characteristic values of such a form will be equal to the squares of the corresponding characteristic values of the quadratic form (18.12). Hence there follow the inequalities

$$\left.\begin{array}{l} |\sigma_1| \leqq 2a(t) \phi_2(t) r; \\ |\sigma_3| \leqq 2b(t) \phi_2(t) r^{2+\alpha}. \end{array}\right\} \tag{18.18}$$

We shall now estimate the function σ_2.
Applying the Bunyakovskiy inequality, we shall obtain

$$|\sigma_2| \leqq \sqrt{\sum_{i=1}^{n} \left(\frac{\partial V}{\partial y_i}\right)^2} \sqrt{\sum_{i=1}^{n} \left(\sum_{i=1}^{n} q_{is} y_s\right)^2}.$$

The function $\sum_{i=1}^{n} \left(\sum_{s=1}^{n} q_{is} y_s \right)^2$ is a quadratic form, the matrix of whose coefficients is obtained by multiplying the matrix Q by its transpose Q^*, where
Q is a matrix the elements of which are functions $q_{si}(t)$.

By $\lambda^2(t)$ we shall denote the largest characteristic value of that quadratic
form. Then

$$|\sigma_2| \leq 2\lambda(t)\phi_2(t) r^2. \tag{18.19}$$

We shall set $\rho = \sqrt{V}$. We shall divide both members of (18.16) by 2ρ, then
we shall obtain

$$\frac{dp}{dt} = \tfrac{1}{2} \frac{W}{V}\rho + \frac{\sigma_1}{2\rho} + \frac{\sigma_2}{2\rho} + \frac{\sigma_3}{2\rho} \tag{18.20}$$

From inequalities (18.13) we shall find

$$r \leq \sqrt{V}\phi_1^{-\frac{1}{2}}(t) \leq \rho\phi_1^{-\frac{1}{2}}(t).$$

Hence, and from inqequalities (18.18) and (18.19), we shall find

$$\left. \begin{aligned} \frac{|\sigma_1|}{2\rho} &\leq a(t)\phi_2(t)\phi_1^{-\frac{1}{2}}(t); \\[2mm] \frac{|\sigma_2|}{2\rho} &\leq \lambda(t)\phi_2(t)\phi_1^{-1}(t)\rho; \\[2mm] \frac{|\sigma_3|}{2\rho} &\leq b(t)\phi_2(t)\rho r^\alpha \phi_1^{-1}(t) \text{ for } r \leq R. \end{aligned} \right\} \tag{18.21}$$

Inequalities (18.21) allow us to estimate from above and from below the
derivative of the sought function ρ.

We shall note first that the function W/V may be estimated just as has been
done in § 6 by means of the inequalities

$$-\frac{\psi_1}{\tilde{\phi}_1} \leq \frac{W}{V} \leq -\frac{\psi_2}{\tilde{\phi}_2}.$$

Taking these inequalities into account, we shall find

$$\frac{dp}{dt} \leq \rho\left[-\tfrac{1}{2}\frac{\psi_2}{\tilde{\phi}_2} + \lambda(t)\phi_2(t)\phi_1^{-1}(t) + b(t)\phi_2(t)r^\alpha\phi_1^{-1}(t) \right] + a(t)\phi_2(t)\phi_1^{-\frac{1}{2}}(t). \tag{18.22}$$

On the other hand,

$$\frac{dp}{dt} \geq \rho\left[-\tfrac{1}{2}\frac{\psi_1}{\tilde{\phi}_1} - \lambda(t)\phi_2(t)\phi_1^{-1}(t) - b(t)\phi_2(t)r^\alpha\phi_1^{-1}(t) \right] - a(t)\phi_2(t)\phi_1^{-\frac{1}{2}}(t).$$

We shall integrate these inequalities on the assumption that $r_0 \leqq r_1 \leqq R$. Then, because of continuity for some $t \geqq t_0$, the inequality $r(t) \leqq R$ will be satisfied, and therefore the nonlinear differential inequalities obtained above may be replaced by linear differential inequalities by substituting R^α for r^α.

Taking this consideration into account, from (18.22) we shall obtain

$$\rho \leqq e^{\int_{t_0}^{t} g_1(\tau)d\tau} \left[\rho_0 + \int_{t_0}^{t} a(\tau)\phi_2(\tau)\phi_1^{-\frac{1}{2}}(\tau) e^{-\int_{t_0}^{\tau} g_1(\theta)d\theta} d\tau \right]. \qquad (18.23)$$

On the other hand

$$\rho \geqq e^{\int_{t_0}^{t} g_2(\tau)d\tau} \left[\rho_0 - \int_{t_0}^{t} a(\tau)\phi_2(\tau)\phi_1^{-\frac{1}{2}}(\tau) e^{\int_{t_0}^{\tau} g_2(\theta)d\theta} d\tau \right]. \qquad (18.24)$$

By combining the last two inequalities, we shall obtain what is required.

COROLLARY 1. The existence of the function V as a quadratic form, satisfying all the conditions of the Theorem, may be guaranteed for the system of equations (18.1), with the behaviour of their solutions determined by their linear approximation

$$\frac{dy_s}{dt} = \sum_{i=1}^{n} p_{si}y_i, \qquad (18.25)$$

i.e. when coefficients in the system (18.25) are constant, and the roots of the characteristic equation have negative real parts and the nonlinear functions are bounded with respect to t. In that case the function V may be chosen as a quadratic form with constant coefficients and, consequently, as the functions $\phi_i(t)$ and $\psi_i(t)$ one may choose positive constants.

If the coefficients of the system of equations (18.25) are dependent on time, and any of its solutions

$$y_1(t, y_{10}, \ldots, y_{n0}, t_0), \ldots, y_n(t, y_{10}, \ldots, y_{n0}, t_0)$$

satisfies the conditions (6.9), then

$$p_1 r_0 \phi^{\frac{1}{2}}(t_0)\phi^{-\frac{1}{2}}(t) e^{-p_2 \int_{t_0}^{t} (\psi/\phi)dt} \leqq r(t, y_{10}, \ldots, y_{n0}, t_0) \leqq q_1 r_0 \phi^{\frac{1}{2}}(t_0)\phi^{-\frac{1}{2}}(t) e^{-q_2 \int_{t}^{t} (\psi/\phi)dt}$$

$$\text{for } t \geqq t_0,$$

where $\phi(t)$ and $\psi(t)$ are positive functions, $\phi(t) > 0$ and $\psi(t) \geqq 0$, given for $t \geqq t_0$ and continuous; p_i, q_i $(i = 1, 2)$ are positive constants.

Now if the nonlinear terms in system (18.1) satisfy the inequality

$$\left| g_s - \sum_{i=1}^{n} p_{si} y_i \right| \le c\psi(t) r^{1+\alpha}, \quad c > 0, \; \alpha > 0,$$

then all the conditions of the Theorem are satisfied, and therefore all the solutions of system (18.2) satisfy the inequalities indicated in the statement of the Theorem, in which one should set

$$\left. \begin{array}{l} p_i \phi = \phi_i \\ q_i \psi = \psi_i \end{array} \right\} \; i = 1, 2; \; p_i, \; q_i \text{ are positive constants.}$$

In fact, according to Theorem 16 there exist two quadratic forms V and W satisfying the estimates indicated in Theorem 16.

We shall set up the total derivative of the quadratic form V as based on system (18.1), and shall make an estimate of it using the inequalities of the preceding section, which will demonstrate the correctness of the assertion made.

COROLLARY 2. Cases are encountered when the function V, because of some considerations, may not be chosen in the aspect of a quadratic form. We shall assume, however, that there exists a function V satisfying the following conditions:

1) $\phi_1(t) r^k \le V \le \phi_2(t) r^k$;

2) $\left| \partial V / \partial y_i \right| \le c(t) r^{k-1}$;

3) the total derivative of the function V, calculated on the basis of system (18.1), satisfies the inequality

$$- \psi_1 r^k \le W \le - \psi_2 r^k .$$

Then every solution of system (18.2) satisfies the modified inequalities indicated in the Theorem. This modification is obtained in an obvious way, if in the proof one takes for ρ the function $\rho = \sqrt[k]{V}$.

Remark 1. One may look upon the functions $a_s(t)$, $q_{si}(t)$, $g_s(t, y_1, \ldots, y_n)$ $(s, i = 1, \ldots, n)$ as upon random functions. Then to fixed initial conditions $y_{10}, \ldots, y_{n0}, t_0$ there corresponds a stochastic process each of whose realizations satisfies system (18.2) and the initial conditions. In this case one may consider the inequalities indicated in the Theorem as estimates of the deviation of any realization of this process from the steady-state motion.

Remark 2. The function $\lambda(t)$ dealt with in the proof of the Theorem, generally peaking, cannot be found. Nevertheless, as $\lambda(t)$ one may take a function

$\lambda(t) = q(t)n$, where $q(t)$ is the greatest value of the function $|q_{si}(t)|$ $(s, i = 1, \ldots, n)$.

This makes the inequalities more gross, but less complicated to compute.

§ 19. Constantly acting perturbations of a random nature

We shall consider a system of random functions $X_1(t), X_2(t), \ldots, X_k(t)$, forming a random process $X(t)$. Following work [53], we shall say that this process is completely given if one knows the complete system of correction functions

$$m_{n_1, n_2, \ldots, n_k} = M\left[x_1(t_{11}) x_1(t_{12}) \ldots x_1(t_{1\,n_1}) \ldots x_k(t_{k\,n_k})\right]$$

for any real t_{ij}

$$\begin{cases} i = 1, \ldots, k ; \\ j = 1, \ldots, n_i , \end{cases}$$

where k and n_i are any nonnegative integers.

We shall consider the system of differential equations

$$\frac{dy_s}{dt} = f_s(t, y_1, \ldots, y_n) \quad (s = 1, \ldots, n). \tag{19.1}$$

We shall consider that the right-hand members of the system represent a stochastic process, whose realizations with probability one belong to the set of functions $F = \{g_s(t, y_1, \ldots, y_n)\}$ $(s = 1, \ldots, n)$ continuous with respect to the variables $y_1, \ldots, y_n, t$.

We shall consider that $g_s(t, y_1, \ldots, y_n)$ $(s = 1, \ldots, n)$ are real functions, given for $-\infty < y_i < +\infty$, $t_0 \leq t < t_0 + T$. Then to every set of real numbers $y_{10}, \ldots, y_{n0}$ there corresponds the stochastic process

$$y_s = y_s(t, y_{10}, \ldots, y_{n0}, t_0) \quad (s = 1, \ldots, n), \tag{19.2}$$

the realizations of which are continuously differentiable functions of the variable t, satisfying system (15.1) and the conditions $y_s = y_{s0}$ for $t = t_0$ $(s = 1, \ldots, n)$ with probability one.

We shall call stochastic process (19.2) the *stochastic solution* of system (15.1) with the initial conditions $y_{10}, \ldots, y_{n0}$ for $t = t_0$.

We shall assume that the actual automatic control system is described by the system of equations

$$\frac{dy_s}{dt} = P_s(t, y_1, \ldots, y_n) \quad (s = 1, \ldots, n) \tag{19.3}$$

and is subjected to the action of random forces such that the coordinates $y_1, \ldots, y_n$, which describe its functioning, actually satisfy the system of equations

$$\frac{dy_s}{dt} = P_s(t, y_1, \ldots, y_n) + q_s(t, y_1, \ldots, y_n) \quad (s = 1, \ldots, n). \tag{19.4}$$

Later on we shall assume that the functions $P_s(t, y_1, \ldots, y_n)$ $(s = 1, \ldots, n)$ may be expressed in series of powers of $y_1, \ldots, y_n$, converging for $|y_s| < R$ for all $t \in [t_0, t_0 + T]$. Hence we shall consider that the expansion of P_s in series does not contain free terms, i.e. system (19.3) has a homogeneous solution.

We shall also assume that the realizations of the random functions $q_s(t, y_1, \ldots, y_n)$ with probability one may also be expanded in series, converging, for $|y_s| < R$ for all $t \in [t_0, t_0 + T]$.

We shall assume that the coefficients of these series form a process $X(t)$ with respect to which the complete system of correlation functions is known. The problem consists in giving a method of calculating the complete system of correlation functions of the stochastic solution (19.2) of system (19.4) for all sufficiently small initial deviations $y_{10}, \ldots, y_{n0}$.

For the sake of clarity of further exposition we shall indicate the way of finding the complete system of correlation functions for process (19.2). It consists in the following.

The stochastic solution (19.2) for system (19.4) may be represented in the form of two random processes

$$y_s = \bar{y}_s + z_s \quad (s = 1, \ldots, n), \tag{19.5}$$

so that $\bar{y}_s$ $(s = 1, \ldots, n)$ is a stochastic solution of system (19.4) with zero initial conditions. This stochastic solution may be found by the method of successive approximations. Then in system (19.4) one carries out a substitution of the sought functions according to formula (19.5), as result of which one obtains the system of equations

$$\frac{dz_s}{dt} = r_s(t, z_1, \ldots, z_n) \quad (s = 1, \ldots, n). \tag{19.6}$$

The stochastic solution of system (19.6) with initial conditions $y_{10}, \ldots, y_{n0}$ is found as a series in powers of $y_{10}, \ldots, y_{n0}$ with stochastic coefficients. After constructing this series, the stochastic solution of system (19.4) may be considered as established, since formula (19.5) holds.

After the stochastic solution is constructed, one may find the complete system of correlation functions of that solution, which is expressed by the complete system of correlation functions of the given process $q_s(t, y_1, \ldots, y_n)$.

We shall now carry out the sequence of operations indicated above.

We shall seek the stochastic solution of system (19.4) with zero initial conditions. As the zero-th approximation we shall take the numbers $y_1 = y_2 = \ldots = y_n = 0$. Then we shall obtain

$$\bar{y}_{s1} = \int_{t_0}^{t} q_s(t)dt \quad (s = 1, \ldots, n),$$

where the $q_s(t)$ are free terms in the expansion of the functions $q_s(t, y_1, \ldots, y_n)$ in powers of $y_1, \ldots, y_n$.

We shall set

$$\bar{y}_{sk} = \int_{t_0}^{t} [P_s(t, \bar{y}_{1\,k-1}, \ldots, \bar{y}_{n\,k-1}) + q_s(t, \bar{y}_{1\,k-1}, \ldots, \bar{y}_{n\,k-1})]\, dt.$$

It is known that the series

$$\bar{y}_s = y_{s1} + \sum_{k=2}^{\infty} (y_{sk} - y_{s\,k-1})$$

converges for a corresponding choice of a realization $q_s(t, y_1, \ldots, y_n)$ and, consequently, obtains a stochastic solution for system (19.4).

In system (19.4) we shall perform a substitution according to formula (19.5). Then to determine the new sought functions $z_1, \ldots, z_n$ we shall construct system (19.6).

System (19.6) has a homogeneous solution. We shall assume that

$$\frac{dz_s}{dt} = \sum_{i=1}^{n} p_{si}(t)z_i \quad (s = 1, \ldots, n) \tag{19.7}$$

represents a linear approximation of system (19.6).

It is clear that the functions $p_{si}(t)$ are, in general, random distributions which are obtained from the expansions of the coefficients of system (19.4). by applying the operations of addition, multiplication, and integration.

We shall find the fundamental system of solutions $Z(t)$ of system (19.7). For this, we shall write down system (19.7) in matrix form $dZ/dt = PZ$. If in this system we introduce a parameter ε, then we shall obtain the system $dZ/dt = \varepsilon PZ$, whose solution may be constructed in the form of the series

$$Z = E + \varepsilon \int_{t_0}^{t} P(t)dt + \varepsilon^2 \int_{t_0}^{t} P(\tau) \left[\int_{t_0}^{\tau} P(\theta)d\theta \right] d\tau + \ldots,$$

converging for all finite values of ε [2 & 21]. Consequently, for $\varepsilon = 1$ this series yields the fundamental system of solutions for the system of equations (19.7).

We shall write system (19.6) in vectorial form

$$\frac{dZ}{dt} = PZ + R(t, z_1, \ldots, z_n),$$ (19.8)

where $R(t, z_1, \ldots, z_n)$ is the set of nonlinear terms in system (19.6).

We shall seek the solution of system (19.8) in the form

$$Z = Z(t)C(t),$$ (19.9)

where $Z(t)$ is the matrix of the fundamental system of solutions for (19.7) and $C(t)$ is the vector sought.

Substituting (19.9) in (19.8) we shall obtain

$$C = \int_{t_0}^{t} Z^{-1}(\tau) R(\tau, z_1, \ldots, z_n) \, d\tau + Y_0.$$

Multiplying both members by $Z(t)$, we shall obtain

$$Z = \int_{t_0}^{t} Z(t, \tau) R(\tau, z_1, \ldots, z_n) \, d\tau + Z(t) Y_0,$$ (19.10)

where $Z(t, \tau) = Z(t) Z^{-1}(\tau)$ is a matrix obtained from the matrix of the fundamental system of solutions by replacing t_0 by τ, and Y_0 is the vector

$$Y_0 = \left\{ \begin{array}{c} y_{10} \\ \vdots \\ y_{n0} \end{array} \right\}.$$

We shall seek the solution of the integral equation (19.10) in the form of a series $Z = \sum_{m=1}^{\infty} Z^{(m)}$, where $Z^{(m)}$ is a homogeneous form of degree m in $y_{10}, \ldots, y_{n0}$ with vectorial coefficients.

We shall set $Z^{(1)} = Z(t) Y_0$, then $Z^{(2)}$ is uniquely determined by the relation

$$Z^{(2)} = \int_{t_0}^{t} Z(t, \tau) R_2(\tau) \, d\tau,$$

where $R_2(\tau)$ is the set of terms of second degree in $y_{10}, \ldots, y_{n0}$ in the function $R(\tau, z_1, \ldots, z_n)$, if instead of $z_1, \ldots, z_n$ one substitutes the components of vector $Z^{(1)}$.

The form $Z^{(3)}$ is defined by the relation

$$Z^{(3)} = \int_{t_0}^{t} Z(t, \tau) R_3(\tau) \, d\tau,$$

where $R_3(\tau)$ is the set of terms of the third degree in $y_{10}, \ldots, y_{n0}$ in the function $R(\tau, z_1, \ldots, z_n)$, if instead of $z_1, \ldots, z_n$ one substitutes the components of the vector $Z^{(1)} + Z^{(2)}$, etc.

From this it can be seen that all the forms $Z^{(m)}$ are uniquely determined. Thus, one obtains the stochastic solution (19.5) for the system of equations (19.4).

One should note the fact that all the forms $Z^{(m)}$ are defined in terms of the stochastic processes entering in the system, with the aid of three operations: multiplication, addition, and integration, and therefore all coefficients of the forms may be represented as multiple integrals of polynomials, which are formed from the processes entering in the system, and also of the functions $Z(t, \tau)$. Therefore all the correlation functions of the stochastic solution (19.2) of system (19.4) may be expressed in terms of the correlation functions of the original process in view of the fact that one may assume the transposability of mathematical expectation with integration with respect to the variable t.

The formulae for calculation of the correlation functions of the stochastic process (19.2) are considerably simplified, if one considers that the process $\bar{y}_s$ $(s = 1, ..., n)$ is given or, what amounts to the same, if one considers that the expansion of the functions q_s $(t, y_1, ..., y_n)$ in series of the variables $y_1, ..., y_n$ contains no free terms. In that case finding the complete system of correlation functions reduces to finding a series in powers of the initial conditions, satisfying the system of equations (19.10).

Finding the mathematical expectation from this series leads to the utilization of all the correlation functions of the process entering in system (19.4), and is represented by an infinite series. The correlation functions of second order are obtained also in the form of an infinite series of all the correlation functions of the process entering in system (19.4). In this connection, we recommend that as the stochastic solution of a system one take the stochastic process obtained by dispensing with the terms of the series which contain forms of a degree higher than m in $y_{10}, ..., y_{n0}$. The process obtained is an approximate stochastic solution of system (19.4), yet it allows one to find any correlation function expressed in terms of a finite number of correlation functions of the process entering in the right-hand member of system (19.4).

§ 20. A method of finding estimates for correlation functions of a stochastic solution in terms of the correlation functions of the given process

In the preceding section we have noted the difficulties which arise in finding the correlation functions of stochastic solutions of a system of equations.

In the present section a method is given which allows one to estimate these correlation functions in terms of the correlation functions of the random forces acting on a real system.

We shall assume that the coordinates $y_1, ..., y_n$ describe the transient process in the automatic control system upon which random forces are acting. It is known that in a wide class of cases these coordinates may be obtained as a stochastic solution of the system of equations

$$\frac{dy_s}{dt} = g_s(t, y_1, ..., y_n) + a_s(t); \qquad (s = 1, ..., n), \tag{20.1}$$

where $a_s(t)$ $(s = 1, ..., n)$ is the given stochastic process, i.e. for it one knows the complete system of correlation functions.

The functions $g_s(t, y_1, ..., y_n)$ possess the usual properties [see system (1.4)].

If we do not take into account the influence of random forces upon the system, then the transient process is described by the system of equations

$$\frac{dy_s}{dt} = g_s(t, y_1, ..., y_n) \qquad (s = 1, ..., n). \tag{20.2}$$

We shall consider that the steady-state motion is the homogeneous solution $y_1 = y_2 = ... = y_n = 0$.

THEOREM 38.   If one is given a quadratic form $V = \sum\limits_{i, j, = 1}^{n} a_{ij}(t) y_i y_j$ satisfying the following conditions:

1)   there exist two positive functions $\phi_1(t)$, $\phi_2(t)$, given for $t_0 \leqq t < t_0 + T$ and continuous there, such that

$$\phi_1(t) r^2 \leqq V \leqq \phi_2(t) r^2; \tag{20.3}$$

2)   the total derivative W of the function V, as based on system (20.2), satisfies the inequality

$$-\psi_1(t) r^2 \leqq W \leqq -\psi_2(t) r^2 \tag{20.4}$$

for $r < R$; the functions $\psi_1(t)$, $\psi_2(t)$ are continuous and given for $t \in [t_0, t_0 + T]$ —
then every solution of the system (16.1) satisfies the inequalities

$$\tag{20.5}$$

$$\sum_{i=1}^{n} y_i^2 \leqq \phi_1^{-1}(t) e^{-\int_{t_0}^{t} \frac{\tilde{\psi}_2}{\tilde{\phi}_2} d\tau} \left[\sum_{i=1}^{n} y_{i0}^2 \phi_2(t_0) + \int_{t_0}^{t} \mu^2 \sum_{s=1}^{n} a_s^2(\tau) e^{\int_{t_0}^{t} \frac{\tilde{\psi}_2(\theta)}{\tilde{\phi}_2(\theta)} d\theta} d\tau \right]$$

for $t \geq t_0$, $r(t, y_{10}, \ldots, y_{n0}, t_0) < R$;

$$\sum_{i=1}^{n} y_i^2 \geq \phi_2^{-1}(t) e^{-\int_{t_0}^{t} \frac{\tilde{\psi}_1}{\tilde{\phi}_1} d\tau} \left[\sum_{i=1}^{n} y_{i0}^2 \phi_1(t_0) - \int_{t_0}^{t} \mu^2 \sum_{s=1}^{n} a_s^2(\tau) e^{\int_{t_0}^{\tau} \frac{\tilde{\psi}_1(\theta)}{\tilde{\phi}_1(\theta)} d\theta} d\tau \right]$$

for $t \geq t_0$, $r(t, y_{10}, \ldots, y_{n0}) < R$;　　　(20.5′)

where $\tilde{\psi}_1 = \psi_1 + \mu^{-2} \phi_2^2$,

$\tilde{\psi}_2 = \psi_2 - \mu^{-2} \phi_2^2$,

$\tilde{\phi}_1 = \sigma_1 \phi_1 + \sigma_2 \phi_2$,

$\tilde{\phi}_2 = \sigma_3 \phi_1 + \sigma_4 \phi_2$.

Here

$$\sigma_1 = \frac{1 + \operatorname{sgn} \tilde{\psi}_1}{2}, \qquad \sigma_2 = \frac{1 - \operatorname{sgn} \tilde{\psi}_1}{2},$$

$$\sigma_3 = \frac{1 - \operatorname{sgn} \tilde{\psi}_2}{2}, \qquad \sigma_4 = \frac{1 + \operatorname{sgn} \tilde{\psi}_2}{2},$$

μ is any real number different from zero.

PROOF: We shall find the total derivative of the function V as based on system (16.1)

$$\frac{dV}{dt} = W + W_1, \text{ where } W_1 = 2 \sum_{s=1}^{n} a_s \sum_{i=1}^{n} a_{s_i}(t) y_i.$$

We shall estimate the function W_1 by applying the well known inequality $|2ab| \leq a^2/\mu^2 + \mu^2 b^2$; where μ is any real number different from zero.

Every component entering into the outer summation may be estimated in the following way:

$$2|a_s| \sum_{i=1}^{n} a_{si}(t) y_i \leq \mu^2 a_s(t) + \mu^{-2} \left[\sum_{i=1}^{n} a_{si}(t) y_i \right]^2. \qquad (20.6)$$

Hence it follows that

$$|W_1| \leq \mu^2 \sum_{s=1}^{n} a_s^2 + \mu^{-2} \sum_{s=1}^{n} \left[\sum_{i=1}^{n} a_{si}(t) y_i \right]^2. \qquad (20.7)$$

The second sum standing in the right-hand member of inequality (20.7) represents a quadratic form, whose matrix is the square of the matrix of the form A, and therefore there holds the inequality

$$|W_1| \leq \mu^2 \sum_{s=1}^{n} a_s^2 + \mu^{-2}\phi_2^2(t)r^2, \tag{20.8}$$

from which it follows that the total derivative of the form V, as based on system (20.1), will satisfy the inequality

$$-\mu^2 \sum_{s=1}^{n} a_s^2 - (\psi_1 + \mu^{-2}\phi_2^2)r^2 \leq \frac{dV}{dt} \leq \mu^2 \sum_{s=1}^{n} a_s^2 - (\psi^2 - \mu^{-2}\phi_2^2)r^2. \tag{20.9}$$

From inequality (20.9) we shall obtain

$$\frac{dV}{dt} \leq \mu^2 \sum_{s=1}^{n} a_s^2 - (\psi_2 - \mu^{-2}\phi_2^2)\frac{r^2}{V}V.$$

We shall estimate the function

$$(\psi_2 - \mu^{-2}\phi_2^2)\frac{r^2}{V} = -\tilde{\psi}_2\frac{r^2}{V}.$$

If $\tilde{\psi}_2 > 0$, then $-\tilde{\psi}_2\dfrac{r^2}{V} < -\dfrac{\tilde{\psi}_2}{\phi_2}$.

If $\tilde{\psi}_2 < 0$, then $-\tilde{\psi}_2\dfrac{r^2}{V} < -\dfrac{\tilde{\psi}_2}{\phi_1}$. Thus, we have

$$-(\psi_2 - \mu^{-2}\phi_2^2)\frac{r^2}{V^2} < -\frac{\tilde{\psi}_2}{\tilde{\phi}_2},$$

where $\tilde{\phi}_2 = \sigma_3\phi_1 + \sigma_4\phi_2$.

For the function V we have obtained the differential inequality

$$\frac{dV}{dt} \leq -\frac{\tilde{\psi}_2}{\tilde{\phi}_2}V + \mu^2 \sum_{s=1}^{n} a_s^2(t) \tag{20.10}$$

and correspondingly

$$-\mu^2 \sum_{s=1}^{n} a_s^2(t) - \frac{\tilde{\psi}_1}{\tilde{\phi}_1}V \leq \frac{dV}{dt}. \tag{20.11}$$

From these inequalities we have [50]

$$
e^{-\int_{t_0}^{t} \frac{\tilde{\psi}_1}{\tilde{\phi}_1} d\tau} \left[V(y_{10}, \ldots, y_{r0}, t_0) - \int_{t_0}^{t} \mu^2 \sum_{s=1}^{n} a_s^2(\tau) e^{\int_{t_0}^{\tau} \frac{\tilde{\psi}_1(\theta)}{\tilde{\phi}_1(\theta)} d\theta} d\tau \right] \leq V \leq
$$

$$
\leq e^{-\int_{t_0}^{t} \frac{\tilde{\psi}_2}{\tilde{\phi}_2} d\tau} \left[V(y_{10}, \ldots, y_{n0}, t_0) + \int_{t_0}^{t} \mu^2 \sum_{s=1}^{n} a_s^2(\tau) e^{\int_{t_0}^{\tau} \frac{\tilde{\psi}_2(\theta)}{\tilde{\phi}_1(\theta)} d\theta} d\tau \right]. \qquad (20.12)
$$

We shall apply inequalities (20.3) to both parts of (20.12), then we shall obtain

$$
r^2 \leq \phi_1^{-1}(t) e^{-\int_{t_0}^{t} \frac{\tilde{\psi}_2}{\tilde{\phi}_2} d\tau} \left[r_0^2 \phi_2(t_0) + \int_{t_0}^{t} \mu^2 \sum_{s=1}^{n} a_s^2(\tau) e^{\int_{t_0}^{\tau} \frac{\tilde{\psi}_2(\theta)}{\tilde{\phi}_1(\theta)} \theta} d\tau \right], \qquad (20.13)
$$

$$
r^2 \geq \phi_2^{-1}(t) e^{-\int_{t_0}^{t} \frac{\tilde{\psi}_1}{\tilde{\phi}_1} d\tau} \left[-r_0^2 \phi_1(t_0) - \int_{t_0}^{t} \mu^2 \sum_{s=1}^{n} a^2(\tau) e^{\int_{t_0}^{\tau} \frac{\tilde{\psi}_1(\theta)}{\tilde{\phi}_1(\theta)} d\theta} d\tau \right], \qquad (20.14)
$$

and then, *a fortiori*, inequalities (20.5) and (20.5′) hold.

Remark. Inequality (20.5′) is, in general, of interest only as long as its right-hand part is nonnegative.

We shall now describe a method of computing estimates for correlation functions of stochastic solutions of system (20.1) based on the application of inequalities (20.5) and (20.5′).

Say, for example, it is required to find the mathematical expectation of the quantity y_s. It is known that

$$My_s = \int_{-\infty}^{\infty} y_s dF,$$

where F is the distribution function of the quantity y_s.

Applying a known inequality, we shall obtain

$$|My_s| \leqq (My_s^2)^{\frac{1}{2}} \leqq \left\{ \phi_1^{-1}(t) e^{-\int_{t_0}^t \frac{\widetilde{\psi}_2}{\widetilde{\phi}_2} dt} \times \right.$$

$$\left. \times \left[\sum_{i=1}^n y_{i0}^2 \phi_2(t_0) + \int_{t_0}^t \mu^2 \sum_{s=1}^n Ma_s^2(\tau) e^{\int_{t_0}^\tau \frac{\widetilde{\psi}_2(\theta)}{\widetilde{\phi}_2(\theta)} d\theta} d\tau \right] \right\}^{\frac{1}{2}}$$

Analogously one computes the estimates for all remaining correlation functions of the stochastic solution of system (20.1).

We shall still compute the estimates for the correlation functions of the second order

$$My_s(t_1) y_l(t_2) \leqq \left(My_s^2(t_1) y_l^2(t_2) \right)^{\frac{1}{2}} \leqq$$

$$\leqq \left\{ \phi_1^{-\frac{1}{2}}(t_1) \phi_1^{-\frac{1}{2}}(t_2) e^{-\frac{1}{2}\left[\int_{t_0}^{t_1} \frac{\widetilde{\psi}_2}{\widetilde{\phi}_2} dt + \int_{t_0}^{t_2} \frac{\widetilde{\psi}_2}{\widetilde{\phi}_2} d\tau \right]} \right\}^{\frac{1}{2}} \times$$

$$\times \left\{ r_0^4 \phi_2^2(t_0) + r_0^2 \phi_2(t_0) \mu^2 \left[\int_{t_0}^{t_1} \sum_{s=1}^n Ma_s^2(\tau) e^{\int_{t_0}^\tau \frac{\widetilde{\psi}_2(\theta)}{\widetilde{\phi}_2(\theta)} d\theta} d\tau + \right.\right.$$

$$\left.\left. + \int_{t_0}^{t_2} \sum_{s=1}^n Ma_s^2(\tau) e^{\int_{t_0}^\tau \frac{\widetilde{\psi}_2(\theta)}{\widetilde{\phi}_2(\theta)} d\theta} d\tau \right] + \right.$$

$$\left. + \mu^4 \int_{t_0}^{t_1} \int_{t_0}^{t_2} e^{\int_{t_0}^{\tau_1} \frac{\widetilde{\psi}_2(\theta)}{\widetilde{\phi}_2(\theta)} d\theta + \int_{t_0}^{\tau_2} \frac{\widetilde{\psi}_2(\theta)}{\widetilde{\phi}_2(\theta)} d\theta} \sum_{i,j=1}^n Ma_i^2(\tau_1) a_j^2(\tau_2) d\tau_1 d\tau_2 \right\}^{\frac{1}{2}};$$

$$(s, l = 1, ..., n).$$

If the original system (20.2) is linear, then as the quadratic form V figuring in the Theorem one may take any quadratic form, taking positive values for $r \neq 0$. In the guise of such forms one may take, for example, those which are dealt with in §6. Moreover, these forms may be chosen in such a way that the estimates be highest.

In the case of linear systems, the estimates obtained above for the correlation functions hold for every choice of initial conditions $y_{10}, \ldots, y_{n0}$ defining the stochastic solution, and for all values of $t \in [t_0, t_0 + T]$.

In §20 the author has taken into account some considerations expressed by V. V. Khomenyuk.

CHAPTER VI

INVESTIGATION OF THE PROBLEM OF STABILITY IN DOUBTFUL CASES

§ 21. Formulation of the problem—Basic definitions

WE SHALL consider the system of n differential equations

$$\frac{dy_s}{dt} = \sum_{i=1}^{n} p_{si}y_i + f_s(t, y_1, ..., y_n) \quad (s = 1, ..., n), \tag{21.1}$$

where the p_{si} are real constants and $f_s(t, y_1, ..., y_n)$ are real functions representing the set of nonlinear terms in (21.1).

As has been noted above, the homogeneous solution of that system will be asymptotically stable for sufficiently broad assumptions relative to the functions f_s, provided that the real parts of the roots of the equation $|P - \lambda E| = 0$ are negative. If among these roots there exist such for which the real parts are zero, then the problem of stability may be solved by investigating the properties of the nonlinear terms entering into f_s.

It is well known that the solution of the problem of stability in that case is extremely difficult. In the theory of stability such cases are conventionally called doubtful or critical. A few such cases have been analysed in detail in works [2], [6], [9], [32–47].

Lyapunov has proposed a general method for investigating doubtful cases. This method consists in dividing the system of equations into two groups and clarifying the behaviour of the solutions depending on the properties of these groups of equations. In work [27] this method has first found its far-reaching development and extension. The problem, set in the present chapter, consists in formulating a general method allowing one to investigate the problem of stability in doubtful cases.

This method consists in investigating the problem of stability of the homogeneous solution separately for k and for n equations, obtained from the original system.

Let us consider a system of differential equations of the form

$$\left. \begin{array}{l} \dfrac{dy_s}{dt} = f_s(x_1, ..., x_n, y_1, ..., y_k, t), \\[2mm] \dfrac{dx_j}{dt} = g_j(x_1, ..., x_n, y_1, ..., y_k, t). \end{array} \right\} \tag{21.2}$$

177

We shall consider that the functions f_s and g_j are given in the region $|X| \leq H$; $|Y| \leq H$; $t \geq 0$ and are continuous there, where

$$|X| = \sqrt{\sum_{i=1}^{n} x_i^2} \; ; \quad |Y| = \sqrt{\sum_{s=1}^{k} y_s^2} \; .$$

We shall further assume that $f_s = 0$ for $Y = 0$; $g_j = 0$ for $X = Y = 0$ ($s = 1, \ldots, k$; $j = 1, \ldots, n$).

Let us recall the definition of stability.

The homogeneous solution of system (21.2) we shall call stable† in the sense of Lyapunov if for any $\varepsilon > 0$ there exists a $\delta(\varepsilon) > 0$ such that if $|X^{(0)}| < \delta(\varepsilon)$, $|Y^{(0)}| < \delta$ then

$$|X(t, X^{(0)}, Y^{(0)}, t_0)| < \varepsilon, \quad |Y(t, X^{(0)}, Y^{(0)}, t_0)| < \varepsilon$$

for $0 \leq t_0 \leq t$. Here by $X(t, X^{(0)}, Y^{(0)}, t_0)$, $Y(t, X^{(0)}, Y^{(0)}, t_0)$ is denoted the set of functions $x_1, \ldots, x_n, y_1, \ldots, y_k$ representing the solution of system (21.2) defined by the conditions $x_i = x_i^{(0)}$, $y_j = y_j^{(0)}$ for $t = t_0$ ($i = 1, \ldots, n; j = 1, \ldots, k$).

If the homogeneous solution of system (21.2) is stable and if

$$X(t, X^{(0)}, Y^{(0)}, t_0) \to 0, \quad Y(t, X^{(0)}, Y^{(0)}, t_0) \to 0$$

for $t \to +\infty$, then the homogeneous solution we shall call asymptotically stable. If in the first group of equations of system (21.2) the quantities $x_1, \ldots, x_n$ are replaced by continuously differentiable functions $x_1(t), \ldots, x_n(t)$, given for $t \geq 0$ and such that $|X(t)| < H$, then we shall obtain a system of k differential equations of the form

$$\frac{d\bar{y}_s}{dt} = f_s\left[t, x_1(t), \ldots, x_n(t), \bar{y}_1, \ldots, \bar{y}_k\right], \tag{21.3}$$

having a homogeneous solution.

DEFINITION 16. We shall call the homogeneous solution of system (21.3) strongly stable if there exists a number $H_1 > 0$ such that for every $\varepsilon_1 > 0$ there exists a $\delta_1 > 0$ possessing the property $|\bar{Y}(t, X^{(0)}, Y^{(0)}, t_0)| < \varepsilon_1$ for $0 \leq t_0 \leq t$ and $|Y^{(0)}| < \delta_1$, for all continuously differentiable functions $x_1(t), \ldots, x_n(t)$ given for $t \geq 0$ and $|X| < H_1$. If here $\bar{Y} \to 0$ as $t \to +\infty$, then the homogeneous solution of system (21.3) we shall call strongly asymptotically stable.

Let us consider the function $W(t, x_1, \ldots, x_n, y_1, \ldots, y_k)$.

---

† Here we shall be considering stability as being uniform with respect to t_0.

DEFINITION 17. We shall say that a function $W(t, x_1, ..., x_n, y_1, ..., y_k)$ is strictly negative-definite with respect to X if there exist functions $\phi_s(x_1, ..., x_n)$, $\phi_s(x_1, ..., x_n) = 0$ for $x_1 = ... = x_n = 0$ and $\phi_s(x_1, ..., x_n) > 0$ for $X \neq 0$, such the function $W[t, x_1, ..., x_n, y_1(x_1, ..., x_n), ..., y_k(x_1, ..., x_n)]$ will be negative-definite for any choice of continuous functions $y_s(x_1, ..., x_n)$ satisfying the condition $|y_s(x_1, ..., x_n)| < \phi_s(x_1, ..., x_n)$.

For example, the function $W = -x^2 + \sin ty$ will be strictly negative-definite, since here one may set $\phi = \frac{1}{2}x^2$.

§ 22. Fundamental theorems on the proposed method of investigating doubtful cases

In the theorems proposed here, the solution of the problem of stability is derived on the basis of utilizing the properties of the first and second groups of equations of system (21.2), taken separately.

THEOREM 39. If:

1) the homogeneous solution of system (21.3) is strongly stable (strongly asymptotically stable);

2) there exists a continuously differentiable positive-definite function $V(t, x_1, ..., x_n)$ uniformly continuous with respect to t for $X = 0$ i.e. $V(t, X) \to 0$ as $X \to 0$ uniformly with respect to $t \geq 0$;

3) the function

$$W(t, x_1, ..., x_n, y_1, ..., y_k) = \frac{\partial V}{\partial t} + \sum_{j=1}^{n} \frac{\partial V}{\partial x_j} g_j(t, X, Y)$$

is strongly negative-definite with respect to X —
then the homogeneous solution of system (21.2) will also be stable (asymptotically stable).

PROOF: By virtue of condition 2 there exists a number $h > 0$, $h < H$, such that for every $\varepsilon > 0$

$$\inf_{t > 0} V(X) = m_1(\varepsilon) > 0,$$

$$\varepsilon \leq |X| \leq h.$$

We shall fix some number $0 < \varepsilon < h$ and choose a positive number $m < m_1(\varepsilon)$.

By virtue of condition 2 of Theorem 1 there exists a number $\lambda < \varepsilon$ such that $V(t, X) < m$ for $|X| < \lambda$, $t \geq 0$. On the basis of condition 3 there exists a number $\varepsilon_1 \leq \varepsilon$ such that if $|Y| < \varepsilon_1$, then $W(t, X, Y) \leq 0$ for $t \geq 0$ and $\lambda \leq |X| \leq \varepsilon$. According to condition 1, for a number $\varepsilon_1 > 0$ there exists a number $\delta_1 > 0$ linked with ε by the relation indicated in Definition 16. Let $\delta = \min(\lambda, \delta_1)$.

We shall show that $\left| X(t, X^{(0)}, Y^{(0)}, t_0) \right| < \varepsilon$, $\left| Y(t, X^{(0)}, Y^{(0)}, t_0) \right| < \varepsilon$ for $t \geq t_0 \geq 0$, if $\left| X^{(0)} \right| < \delta, \left| Y^{(0)} \right| < \delta$.

Say this is not the case. Then there exists a number T such that

$$\left| X(t, X^{(0)}, Y^{(0)}, t_0) \right| < \varepsilon, \quad t \in [t_0, T] \text{ and } \left| X(t, X^{(0)}, Y^{(0)}, t_0) \right| = \varepsilon.$$

As follows from Definition 16, $\left| Y(t, X^{(0)}, Y^{(0)}, t_0) \right| < \varepsilon$ for $t \in [t_0, T]$, as the set of functions $Y(t, X^{(0)}, Y^{(0)}, t_0)$ may be considered as the solution of system (21.3) in the interval $[t_0, T]$, in which as the functions $x_j(t)$ we choose functions $x_j(t, X^{(0)}, Y^{(0)}, t_0)$.

By $V(t)$ we shall denote the value of the function $V(t, x)$ on the integral curve being studied. It is clear that $V(t_0) < m$ and $V(t) > m$. The function $V(t)$ is continuously differentiable, therefore there exists a number t_1 such that $V(t_1) = m$; $V(t) > m$ for $t_1 < t \leq T$. Then $\left. \dfrac{dV}{dt} \right|_{t=t_1} \geq 0$, while there holds the inequality $\lambda \leq \left| X(t_1, X^{(0)}, Y^{(0)}, t_0) \right| \leq \varepsilon$ and, consequently, $\left. \dfrac{dV}{dt} \right|_{t=t_1} < 0$. The contradiction obtained shows that $\left| X(t, X^{(0)}, Y^{(0)}, t_0) \right| < \varepsilon$ for $t \geq t_0 \geq 0$, provided that $\left| X^{(0)} \right| < \delta$, $\left| Y^{(0)} \right| < \delta$.

Then, as follows from condition 1 and Definition 16,

$$\left| Y(t, X^{(0)}, Y^{(0)}, t_0) \right| < \varepsilon_1 \leq \varepsilon \text{ for } t \geq t_0 \geq 0.$$

Thus, the homogeneous solution of system (21.2) is strongly stable.

If the homogeneous solution of system (21.3) is strong-asymptotically stable, then $Y(t, X^{(0)}, Y^{(0)}, t_0) \to 0$ as $t \to +\infty$. Let $\left| X(t, X^{(0)}, Y^{(0)}, t_0) \right| > \alpha > 0$ for $t \geq t_0$. Then there exists a number $\tau > t_0$ such that

$$W\left[t, X(t, X^{(0)}, Y^{(0)}. t_0), Y(t, X^{(0)}, Y^{(0)}, t_0) \right] < -\sigma < 0 \text{ for } t \geq \tau.$$

Consequently, $V(t) \leq V(\tau) - \sigma(t - \tau)$ for $t \geq \tau$, which is impossible. Hence,

$$X(t, X^{(0)}, Y^{(0)}, t_0) \to 0 \text{ for } t \to +\infty.$$

THEOREM 40. If there exists a nonempty set B in the $(k+1)$–dimensional space of points $(t_0, y_1^{(0)}, \ldots, y_k^{(0)})$ possessing the properties:

1) $\inf y^{(0)} = 0 \; (s = 1, \ldots, k), t_0 \geq 0$;

2) for some $\bar{\varepsilon} > 0$ and any $\delta > 0$ there exists a point $(t_0, y_1^{(0)}, \ldots, y_{(k)}^{0)}) \in B$ such that $\left| Y^{(0)} \right| < \delta$ and $\left| Y(t, X^{(0)}, Y^{(0)}, t_0) \right| < \varepsilon$ do not hold for all $t \geq t_0$ and for every choice of continuously differentiable functions $x_1(t), \ldots, x_n(t)$, $X(t)| \leq H_2$, where $0 < H_2 < \bar{\varepsilon}$ —

then the homogeneous solution of system (21.2) is unstable.

PROOF: We shall assume the contrary. Then for a number H_2 there exists, according to Definition 16, a number $\delta > 0$ such that

$$\left| X(t, X^{(0)}, Y^{(0)}, t_0) \right| < H_2 ; \quad \left| Y(t, X^{(0)}, Y^{(0)}, t_0) \right| < H_2 \qquad (22.1)$$

for $t \geqq t_0$ for all $X^{(0)}$ and $Y^{(0)}$ such that $\left| X^{(0)} \right| < \delta$, $\left| Y^{(0)} \right| < \delta$. We shall take a point $(t_0, y_1^{(0)}, ..., y_k^{(0)}) \in B$. The functions $y_s(t, x_1^{(0)}, ..., x_n^{(0)}, y_1^{(0)}, ..., y_k^{(0)}, t_0)$ may be considered as the solution of system (21.3), in which instead of $x_1(t), ..., x_n(t)$ one has substituted the functions $x_j(t, x_1^{(0)}, ..., x_n^{(0)}, y_1^{(0)}, ..., y_k^{(0)}, t_0)$, and then inequality (22.1), by virtue of condition 2 of the Theorem, cannot hold for all $t \geqq t_0$. The contradiction obtained shows that the homogeneous solution of system (21.2) is unstable.

We shall note a series of special cases of the Theorems formulated above.

THEOREM 41. If:

1) the homogeneous solution of system (21.3) is strongly stable (strong-asymptotically stable);

2) the homogeneous solution of the system

$$\frac{dx_j}{dt} = g_j(t, x_1, ..., x_n, 0, ..., 0) \quad (j = 1, ..., n) \qquad (22.2)$$

is uniform-asymptotically stable;

3) the functions $g_j(t, x_1, ..., x_n, y_1, ..., y_k)$ are continuously differentiable with respect to all their arguments in the region $t \geqq 0$, $\left| X \right| \leqq H$, $\left| Y \right| \leqq H$;

4) the partial derivatives with respect to all its arguments of the function $g_j(t, X, 0)$ $(j = 1, ..., n)$ are bounded, and the functions $g_j(t, X, Y) - g_j(t, X, 0)$ are uniformly continuous in the region $t \geqq 0$, $\left| X \right| < H$ at the point $Y = 0$ — then the homogeneous solution of system (21.2) will also be stable (asymptotically stable).

PROOF: When conditions $2, 3, 4$ are satisfied for system (22.2), there exists a Lyapunov function $V(t, x_1, ..., x_n)$ (see [12]). It is easily verified that the function

$$W(t, X, Y) = \frac{\partial V}{\partial t} + \sum_{j=1}^{n} \frac{\partial V}{\partial x_j} g_j$$

is in this case strictly negative-definite, and therefore with the satisfaction of conditions $2, 3, 4$, conditions $2, 3$ of Theorem 40 are also fulfilled. This concludes the proof.

Remark. Conditions $2, 3, 4$ of Theorem 41 may be weakened if one makes use of the results of work [2].

THEOREM 42. If there exists some number $\bar{\varepsilon} > 0$ such that the inequality $\left| \bar{Y}(t, X^{(0)}, Y^{(0)}, t_0) \right| < \bar{\varepsilon}$ does not hold for all $t \geq t_0 \geq 0$ and $\left| Y^{(0)} \right| \neq 0$ for any choice of continuously differentiable functions

$$x_j(t) \quad (j = 1, ..., n), \left| X(t) \right| < H_2, t \geq 0, H_2 > 0$$

sufficiently small, then the homogeneous solution of system (21.3) is unstable. Here, just as above, by $\bar{Y}(t, X^{(0)}, Y^{(0)}, t_0)$ we denote the set of functions $\bar{Y}_s$ representing the solution of system (21.3), which possesses the property $y_s = y_s^{(0)}$ for $t = t_0$.

PROOF: Let us take the region $t \geq 0$, $Y \leq \bar{\varepsilon}$. It is easy to see that it possesses all the properties of the region B formulated in Theorem 40. And then, according to Theorem 40, the homogeneous solution of system (21.2) is unstable.

§ 23. **Investigation of the problem of stability of systems of equations in the absence of linear terms in the expansion of their right-hand members**

In resolving the problem of stability in doubtful cases and particularly in applying the Theorem of the preceding section, it becomes necessary to solve the problem of stability of such systems of equations in which the expansion of the right-hand members into power series of the sought functions does not contain linear terms with respect to the latter.

In the present section, systems of equations are considered whose right-hand members are generalized-homogeneous functions, and various applications of the results obtained are given.

DEFINITION 18. A real function, given in E_n and continuous there, we shall call generalized-homogeneous of class $(m_1, ..., m_n)$ of order m, if for every $c \in (-\infty, +\infty)$ there holds the correlation

$$f(c^{m_1}x_1, ..., c^{m_n}x_n) = c^m f(x_1, ..., x_n), \tag{23.1}$$

where m_i $(i = 1, ..., n)$ are positive rational numbers; $m_i = P_i/q_i$, $m \geq 0$, $m = P/q$; the numbers q_i $(i = 1, ..., n)$ and q are odd.

Let us now derive the basic equation which is satisfied by all continuously differentiable generalized-homogeneous functions of class $(m_1, ..., m_n)$ of order m.

THEOREM 43. In order that a real function $f(x_1, ..., x_n)$ given and continuously differentiable in E_n, be generalized-homogeneous of class $(m_1, ..., m_n)$ of order m, it is necessary and sufficient that it satisfy the linear equation in partial derivatives

$$\sum_{i=1}^{n} m_i x_i \frac{\partial V}{\partial x_i} = mV. \qquad (23.2)$$

PROOF: The direct assertion of this Theorem follows from equality (23.1). In fact, differentiating both members of equality (23.1) with respect to c, we shall obtain

$$\sum_{i=1}^{n} m_i c^{m_i-1} x_i \frac{\partial f}{\partial y_i} = mc^{m-1} f(x_1, ..., x_n),$$

where $y_i = c^{m_i} x_i$. Multiplying that relation by c we shall obtain the required result.

The converse assertion of the Theorem may be obtained in the following way.

Let $f(x_1, ..., x_n)$ satisfy (23.2). Then substituting in (23.2) instead of V the function f, we shall obtain an identity. Upon the substitution $x_i = c^{m_i} y_i$ it turns into an identity of the form $c \, df/dc = mf$, which after integrating becomes $f(c^{m_1} y_1, ..., c^{m_n} y_n) = f_0 c^m$, whence follows that $f_0 = f(y_1, ..., y_n)$. Thus, the last equality is equivalent to (23.1).

We shall consider the system of differential equations of the form

$$\frac{dx_i}{dt} = X_i(x_1, ..., x_n) \qquad (i = 1, ..., n), \qquad (23.3)$$

whose right-hand members are given in E_n and continuous there. We shall assume that the functions x_i are generalized-homogeneous of class $(m_1, ..., m_n)$ of order $(\sigma + m_i)$, where σ is a rational number such that $\sigma + m_i \geqq 0$ $(i = 1, ..., n)$ and $\sigma = \bar{P}/\bar{q}$; $\bar{q}$ is odd.

From the assumptions made concerning the right-hand members of system (23.3), it follows that through any point $X^{(0)} = (x_1^{(0)}, ..., x_n^{(0)})$ of the space E_n passes an integral curve of system (23.3) $X = X(t, X^{(0)})$, $X = (x_1, ..., x_n)$ such that $X(t, X^{(0)}) = X^{(0)}$ for $t = 0$ and, besides, system (23.3) has a homogeneous solution.

By $A(c)$ we shall denote the diagonal matrix

$$\begin{bmatrix} c^{m_1} & ... & 0 \\ & \diagdown & \\ 0 & ... & c^{m_n} \end{bmatrix}$$

THEOREM 44. If the vector function $X = X(t, X^{(0)})$ is an integral curve of system (23.3), then the vector function $Y(t) = A(c) X(tc^{\sigma}, X^{(0)})$ represents the family of integral curves of system (23.3), so that $Y = A(c) X^{(0)}$ for $t = 0$; consequently, $Y = X[t, A(c) X^{(0)}]$.

PROOF: We shall show that the vector function $Y(t)$ satisfies system (23.3). Indeed, $y_i = c^{m_i} x_i(tc^{\sigma}, X^{(0)})$. We shall differentiate this relation through with respect to t, then we shall have

$$\frac{dy_i}{dt} = c^{\sigma + m_i} \frac{dx_i}{d\tau},$$

where

$$\tau = tc^{\sigma}.$$

Hence

$$\frac{dy_i}{dt} = c^{m_i + \sigma} X_i(x_1, ..., x_n) = X_i(y_1, ..., y_n).$$

This Theorem allows one to find the set of those systems for which asymptotic stability of the homogeneous solution is possible.

THEOREM 45.

1) The homogeneous solution of system (23.3) may be asymptotically stable for any complex perturbations only when $\sigma = 0$.

2) The homogeneous solution of system (23.3) may be asymptotically stable under real perturbations only when $\sigma = 2k/q$; k is an integer.

The proof of this Theorem may be obtained by the same method as is used in work [9], since system (23.3) is more general than the one which is considered there. Therefore we shall omit or give in abbreviated form all the demonstrations which may be further obtained from [9]. For subsequent use we shall note that from asymptotic stability of system (23.3) follows the asymptotic stability of the homogeneous solution on the whole, which ensues directly from Theorem 44.

We shall now propose that from asymptotic stability of the homogeneous solution of system (23.3) it follows that there exist two positive numbers a and b such that the inequality

$$|X(t, X^{(0)})| \leqq bt^{-a} \text{ holds for } t \geqq \tau \text{ and } |X^{(0)}| = 1. \qquad (23.4)$$

This proposition is true and may be demonstrated in a broad class of cases by formal proof following work [51]. In the general case, however, such a proof is still lacking and therefore, in what follows, we may simply view that we are considering the class of only those systems (23.3) for which the inequality (23.4) holds.

THEOREM 46. In order that the homogeneous solution of system (23.3) be asymptotically stable, it is necessary and sufficient that there exist continuous functions V and W given in E_n, possessing the following properties:

1) the function $W(x_1, \ldots, x_n)$ is negative-definite, the function $V(x_1, \ldots, x_n)$ is positive-definite;

2) the functions V and W are generalized-homogeneous of the class $(m_1, \ldots, m_n)$ of order $m - \sigma$ and m, respectively;

3) the function $V(x_1, \ldots, x_n)$ is continuously differentiable along the integral curves of system (23.3) and the correlation $d/Vdt = W$ holds.

If the functions x_i are continuously differentiable, then the functions V and W may be chosen also continuously differentiable, and then conditions 2 and 3 may be written in the form of a system of linear equations in partial derivatives

$$
\left.
\begin{aligned}
\sum_{i=1}^{n} x_i \frac{\partial V}{\partial x_i} &= W, \\
\sum_{i=1}^{n} m_i x_i \frac{\partial V}{\partial x_i} &= (m - \sigma) V, \\
\sum_{i=1}^{n} m_i x_i \frac{\partial W}{\partial x_i} &= m W.
\end{aligned}
\right\}
\qquad (23.5)
$$

and

PROOF: We shall take any continuous function W given in E_n, negative-definite and generalized-homogeneous of class $(m_1, \ldots, m_n)$ of order $m = 2l/q$. The function

$$
f(x_1, \ldots, x_n) = \frac{W(x_1, \ldots, x_n)}{\left(\sum_{i=1}^{n} |x_i|^{1/m_i} \right)^m}
$$

will be continuous everywhere in E_n with the possible exception of only the point $X = 0$. Besides, it satisfies the condition (23.1) for $c \neq 0$ and $m = 0$.

We shall set

$$
F_1 = \sup_{\sum_{i=1}^{n} |x_i|^{1/m_i} = 1} f(x_1, \ldots, x_n); \qquad F_2 = \inf_{\sum_{i=1}^{n} |x_i|^{1/m_i} = 1} f(x_1, \ldots, x_n)
$$

It is easily shown that in E_n holds the inequality

$$
F_1 r^m(X) \geq W \geq F_2 r^m(X), \qquad (23.6)
$$

where $r(X) = \sum_{i=1}^{n} |x_i|^{1/m_i}$.

And, moreover, let Y be some point of E_n. Then

$$W(Y) = r^m(Y) W(X),$$

where

$$x_i = \frac{y_i}{r^{m_i}(Y)} \; .$$

It may be considered that $m_1 \geqq m_2 \geqq \ldots \geqq m_n$. Let us choose a number m of the form $2l/q$ such that the inequality $ma \geqq 2m_1$ holds, where the number a is taken from inequality (23.4).

We shall set

$$V(X^{(0)}) = - \int_0^{+\infty} W[X(t, X^{(0)})] \, dt. \tag{23.7}$$

The integral standing in the right-hand member of equality (23.7) converges for every $X^{(0)}$ because of the choice of the number m and inequality (23.6). Therefore equality (23.7) defines a function V given in E_n. It may be shown that this function is continuous. We shall show that, in addition, it is generalized-homogeneous of the class $(m_1, \ldots, m_n)$ of the order $(m - \sigma)$. For this we shall perform a substitution under the integral sign

$$X^{(0)} = A(r_0) \varepsilon_0 \; ; \quad \tau = tr_0^\sigma,$$

where

$$r_0 = r(X^{(0)}).$$

Then we shall obtain

$$V[A(r_0) \varepsilon_0] = - \int_0^{+\infty} r_0^{-\sigma} W(X[\tau r_0^{-\sigma}, A(r_0) \varepsilon_0]) \, d\tau =$$

$$= - \int_0^{+\infty} W[A(r_0) X(\tau, \varepsilon_0)] r_0^{-\sigma} \, d\tau = -r_0^{m-\sigma} \int_0^{+\infty} W[x(\tau, \varepsilon_0)] \, d\tau \, .$$

Hence it is clear that $V[A_1(r_0) \varepsilon_0] = r_0^{m-\sigma} V(\varepsilon_0)$.

From this relation it follows that the function V is generalized-homogeneous of the class $(m_1, \ldots, m_n)$ of the order $m - \sigma$ and positive-definite. We shall note that for the transformation of the integral we have made use of Theorem 44 and of the generalized homogeneity of the function W. From the dynamicity of system (23.3) it follows that

$$V[X(t, X^{(0)})] = - \int_t^{+\infty} W[X(\tau, X^{(0)})] \, d\tau,$$

whence

$$\frac{dV}{dt} = W.$$

This completes the proof of necessity of the conditions of Theorem 46. The converse assertion of the Theorem may be obtained in the usual way, just as is done, for example, in work [9].

If the functions x_i are continuously differentiable, then the number m, which is the order of function W, may be chosen so large that the integral representing the formally calculated derivative of the function V with respect to the variable $x_j^{(0)}$

$$\frac{\partial V}{\partial x_j^{(0)}} = - \int_0^\infty \sum_{i=1}^n \frac{\partial W}{\partial x_i} \frac{\partial x_i}{\partial x_j^0} \, d\tau$$

will be uniformly convergent with respect to the parameters $x_1^{(0)}, \ldots, x_n^{(0)}$ from any bounded region of E_n.

Therefore the function V with such a choice of a continuously differentiable function W will also be continuously differentiable and will satisfy system (23.5).

COROLLARY. Theorem 46 shows that, in the presence of asymptotic stability of the homogeneous solution of system (23.3), the system of equations (23.5) will have a unique continuously differentiable solution $V(x)$ for any choice of a negative-definite generalized-homogeneous function W of class $(m_1, \ldots, m_n)$ of order $m > \sigma$, where m is a sufficiently large number of the form $2l/q$. This fact is advantageous, as it allows one to find the function V in finite form as solution of system (23.5) for any fixed n.

As a matter of fact we shall consider the case $n = 2$. Then system (23.5) has the form

$$x_1 \frac{\partial V}{\partial x_1} + x_2 \frac{\partial V}{\partial x_2} = W; \quad m_1 x_1 \frac{\partial V}{\partial x_1} + m_2 x_2 \frac{\partial V}{\partial x_2} = (m - \sigma) V. \quad (23.8)$$

Let us solve system (23.8) with respect to the quantities $\partial V/\partial x_1$, $\partial V/\partial x_2$. Then

$$\frac{\partial V}{\partial x_1} = a_1(x_1, x_2) V + a_2(x_1, x_2),$$

$$\frac{\partial V}{\partial x_2} = b_1(x_1, x_2) V + b_2(x_1, x_2). \quad (23.9)$$

The general solution of the first of these equations has the form

$$V(x_1, x_2) = e^{\int_{x_1^{(0)}}^{x_1} a_1(\varepsilon, x_2)\, d\varepsilon} \left[c(x_2) + \int_{x_1^{(0)}}^{x_1} e^{-\int_{x_1^{(0)}}^{\varepsilon} a_1(\eta, x_2)\, d\eta} a_2(\varepsilon, x_2)\, d\varepsilon \right].$$

This function should satisfy the second of equations (23.9), therefore for the function $c(x_2)$ we obtain the equation

$$\frac{dc}{dx_2} = c_1 c + c_2.$$

The general solution of this equation has the form

$$c(x_2) = e^{\int_{x_2^{(0)}}^{x_2} c_1(\varepsilon)\,d\varepsilon} \left[\gamma + \int_{x_2^{(0)}}^{x_2} e^{-\int_{x_2^{(0)}}^{\varepsilon} c_1(\eta)\,d\eta} c_2(\varepsilon)\,d\varepsilon \right].$$

The constant γ may be uniquely determined from the condition $V(0,0) = 0$.

The function V, found by means of quadratures, will be positive-definite if and only if (with the proper choice of the function W) the homogeneous solution of system (23.3) is asymptotically stable.

To conclude the proof of our assertion it still remains to be shown that finding the function V for $n = k + 1$ is reduced to finding the function for $n = k$.

We shall assume that a system of the form

$$\sum_{i=1}^{k} \bar{x}_i \frac{\partial V}{\partial x_i} = W \quad \text{and} \quad \sum_{i=1}^{k} m_i x_i \frac{\partial V}{\partial x_i} = (m - \sigma) V \qquad (23.10)$$

may be solved, where the function V is expressed in terms of quadratures of the known functions entering into it.

Then we shall show that the system

$$\sum_{i=1}^{k+1} x_i \frac{\partial V}{\partial x_i} = W \quad \text{and} \quad \sum_{i=1}^{k+1} m_i x_i \frac{\partial V}{\partial x_i} = (m - \sigma) V \qquad (23.11)$$

may be solved, and its solution is expressed in terms of the functions entering into it by means of quadratures.

Let the homogeneous solution of system (23.3) be asymptotically stable. Then system (23.11) has a unique continuously differentiable solution $V(x_1, \ldots, x_n)$ (with a proper choice of a negative-definite generalized-homogeneous function W of the class $(m_1, \ldots, m_n)$ of order $m > \sigma$).

We shall perform a substitution of the independent variable according to the formulae

$$x_i = \varepsilon_i; \quad i \leq k; \quad x_{k+1} = \sum_{i=1}^{k+1} c_i \varepsilon_i^{\frac{k+1}{m_i}}.$$

Then the function

$$V\left(\varepsilon_1, ..., \varepsilon_k, \sum_{i=1}^{k+1} c_i\varepsilon_i^{\frac{m_{k+1}}{m_i}}\right)$$

will be generalized-homogeneous of the class $(m_1, ..., m_{k+1})$ of order $(m - \sigma)$. Therefore it will satisfy the system of equations

$$\sum_{i=1}^{k+1} \Xi_i \frac{\partial V}{\partial \varepsilon_i} = W ; \quad \sum_{i=1}^{k+1} m_i\varepsilon_i \frac{\partial V}{\partial \varepsilon_i} = (m - \sigma)V, \qquad (23.12)$$

where

$$\Xi_i = X_i\left(x_1, ..., x_k, \sum_{i=1}^{k+1} c_i\varepsilon_i^{\frac{m_{k+1}}{m_i}}\right)$$

for $i \leqq k$,

$$\Xi_{k+1} = -\sum_{i=1}^{k+1} \frac{m_{k+1}}{m_ic_{k+1}} c_i\varepsilon_i^{\left(\frac{m_{k+1}}{m_i} - 1\right)} \Xi_i + \frac{1}{c_{k+1}} X_{k+1}\left(x_1, ..., x_k, \sum_{i=1}^{k+1} c_i\varepsilon_i^{\frac{m_{k+1}}{m_i}}\right).$$

The function V satisfies the second of equations (23.12) because of its generalized homogeneity (see Theorem 43).

We shall solve system (23.12) with respect to the quantities, for example, $\partial V/\partial\varepsilon_1$ and $\partial V/\partial\varepsilon_{k+1}$. Then we shall obtain

$$\frac{\partial V}{\partial \varepsilon_1} = \sum_{i=2}^{k} a_i(\varepsilon_1, ..., \varepsilon_{k+1}) \frac{\partial V}{\partial \varepsilon_i} + aV + b,$$

$$\frac{\partial V}{\partial \varepsilon_{k+1}} = \sum_{i=2}^{k} b_i \frac{\partial V}{\partial \varepsilon_i} + cV + d.$$

Setting $\varepsilon_{k+1} = 0$ in the first of these equations, we shall obtain that the function

$$V\left(\varepsilon_1, ..., \varepsilon_k, \sum_{i=1}^{k} c_i\varepsilon_i^{\frac{m_{k+1}}{m_i}}\right)$$

satisfies two equations of form (23.11):

$$\frac{\partial V}{\partial \varepsilon_1} = \sum_{i=2}^{k} a_1(\varepsilon_1, ..., \varepsilon_k, 0) \frac{\partial V}{\partial \varepsilon_i} + a(\varepsilon_1, ..., \varepsilon_k, 0)V + b(\varepsilon_1, ..., \varepsilon_{k0},),$$

$$\sum_{i=1}^{k} m_i\varepsilon_i \frac{\partial V}{\partial \varepsilon_i} = (m - \sigma)V.$$

Therefore, according to the assumption, it may be found by means of quadratures in terms of the known functions entering in the last system. Replacing in that function the arguments

$$\varepsilon_i = x_i, \quad \sum_{i=1}^{k} c_i \varepsilon_i^{\frac{m_k+1}{m_i}} = x_{k+1},$$

we shall obtain the solution of system (23.11) in closed form. The function found is positive-definite if and only if the homogeneous solution of system (23.3) is asymptotically stable.

The solution of the problem of asymptotic stability of the homogeneous solution of system (23.3) may also be carried out in another way, which is expounded in the following Theorem.

THEOREM 47. In order that the homogeneous solution of system (23.3) be asymptotically stable for $\sigma > 0$, it is necessary and sufficient that the region of asymptotic stability of the homogeneous solution of the system

$$\frac{dy_i}{d\tau} = - m_i y_i - X_i(y_1, \ldots, y_n) = F_i \quad (i = 1, \ldots, n) \tag{23.13}$$

be bounded.

PROOF: *Necessity.* Let the homogeneous solution of system (23.3) by asymptotically stable. Then there exist two functions V and W satisfying the conditions of Theorem 46; and then, according to the method of estimates expounded in chapter III, for any $X^{(0)}$ an estimate of the form

$$\frac{a_1 r(X^{(0)})}{\sqrt[\sigma]{1 + a_2 r^\sigma (X^{(0)})t}} \leq r[X(t, X^{(0)})] \leq \frac{b_1 r(X^{(0)})}{\sqrt[\sigma]{1 + b_2 r^\sigma (X^{(0)})t}} \quad \text{for all } t \geq 0$$

will hold, where a_i, b_i are positive constants. Hence it follows that the functions $x_i(t, X^{(0)})/z^{m_i}(t)$ are bounded for $t \in [0, +\infty]$, where $z(t)$ is some positive solution of the equation $dz/dt = -z^{\sigma+1}$.

Let $z = 1$ for $t = 0$ and $\tau = \ln z$. If $X(t, X^{(0)})$ is a solution of system (23.3), then the functions

$$y_i(\tau, X^{(0)}) = z^{-m_i}(t) x_i(t, X^{(0)}) \tag{23.14}$$

will be a solution of system (23.13). The homogeneous solution of system (23.13) is asymptotically stable, since $\sigma > 0$. Therefore any solution of that system starting in a sufficiently small neighbourhood of $y = 0$ will be bounded for $\tau \in [0, +\infty]$. This solution will be bounded for $\tau \in [-\infty, 0]$ by virtue of (23.14). Thus we have shown that the region of asymptotic stability of (23.13) is bounded.

Sufficiency. If the region of asymptotic stability of system (23.13) is bounded, then any solution $Y(\tau, X^{(0)})$ for sufficiently small $|X^{(0)}|$ is bounded by a vector function for $\tau \in [-\infty, +\infty]$. It may be shown that the vector function $X(t, X^{(0)}) = A[z(t)] Y(\ln z, X^{(0)})$ is a solution of the system (23.3). Therefore the homogeneous solution of system (23.3) is asymptotically stable.

COROLLARY.   If the functions X_i are continuously differentiable, then in order that the homogeneous solution of system (23.3) be asymptotically stable, it is necessary and sufficient that the equation

$$\sum_{i=1}^{n} \frac{\partial V}{dy_i} [- m_i y_i - X_i(y_1, ..., y_n)] = W,$$

where W is a positive-definite function, given in E_n, continuous, and such that $W > \alpha \sqrt{1 + \sum_{i=1}^{n} F_i^2} > 0$ for $|X| > p > 0$ and $W < l|X|^2$ for $|X| \leq \gamma$, have a solution in the form of a continuously differentiable negative-definite function such that the region of values of the argument containing the point $X = 0$, at which $V > -\infty$, be bounded.

The theory developed for system (23.3) may be applied in the solution of the problem of stability in the first approximation to the investigation of the critical cases, and also to the solution of the problem of distinguishing classes of systems, all the solutions of which are bounded as $t \to +\infty$.

We shall consider the system of equations

$$\frac{dx_i}{dt} = f_i(t, x_1, ..., x_n) + X_i(x_1, ..., x_n) \quad (i = 1, ..., n), \tag{23.15}$$

where the functions f_i are given for $t \geq 0, X \in E_n$ and are continuous there.

THEOREM 48.   If the homogeneous solution of system (23.3) is asymptotically stable, the functions X_i are continuously differentiable and

$$\frac{|f_i|}{r^{m_i + \sigma}(X)} \to 0 \text{ where } |X| \to 0, \ t \to +\infty,$$

or

$$|f_i| \leq \gamma r^{m_i + \sigma}(X) \text{ where } |X| \to 0, \ t \to \infty,$$

where γ is a sufficiently small positive number, then the homogeneous solution of system (23.15) is also asymptotically stable.

PROOF: Let the homogeneous solution of system (23.3) be asymptotically stable. Then there exist two continuously differentiable functions V and W satisfying the conditions of Theorem 46.

We shall set up the total derivative of the function V as based on system (23.15). Then we shall obtain

$$\frac{dV}{dt} = W + W_1,$$

where

$$W_1 = \sum_{i=1}^{n} \frac{\partial V}{\partial x_i} f_i.$$

The function $W + W_1$ is negative-definite, since the functions $\partial V/\partial x_i$ are generalized-homogeneous of the class $(m_1, ..., m_n)$ of order $m - \sigma - m_i$, and the function W satisfies inequality (23.6). Then, according to a theorem of Lyapunov[2], the homogeneous solution of system (23.15) is asymptotically stable.

THEOREM 49.   In order that every solution of system (23.15) $X = X(t, X^{(0)}, t_0)$ be bounded for $t \in [t_0, +\infty]$ with any choice of the functions f_i $(i = 1, ..., n)$ satisfying the condition

$$\frac{|f_i|}{r^{m_i+\sigma}(X)} \to 0 \text{ for } |X| \to +\infty, \; t \to +\infty$$

or

$$|f_i| \leq \gamma r^{m_i+\sigma}(X) \text{ for } |X| > R, \quad t > \tau,$$

where R and τ are sufficiently large positive constants and $\gamma > 0$ is sufficiently small, it is necessary and sufficient that the homogeneous solution of system (23.3) be asymptotically stable. Here X_i are continuously differentiable and $\sigma > 0$.

PROOF: *Necessity.* Let every solution of system (23.15) $X = X(t, X^{(0)}, t_0)$ be bounded for every choice of the function f_i and $t \geq t_0$. We shall set $f_i = m_i x_i$. Then, if $X(t, X^{(0)})$ is a solution of system (23.15), the function $A[z(t)] X[-\ln z(t), X^{(0)}]$ will be a solution of system (23.3), whence follows that the homogeneous solution of system (23.3) is asymptotically stable. Here $z(t)$ is a positive solution of the equation $dz/dt = -z^{\sigma+1}$.

Sufficiency. Let the homogeneous solution of system (23.3) be asymptotically stable. Then there exist two functions V and W satisfying all the conditions of Theorem 46.

We shall set up the total derivative of the function V, as based on system (23.15). Then we shall obtain $dV/dt = W + W_1$. It is clear that for $r(X) > R_1$ the function $W + W_1$ will satisfy the inequality $W + W_1 < -\delta r^m(X)$, $t > \tau$, where R_1, δ, and τ are some positive constants. Since the functions $\partial V/\partial x_i$ are generalized-homogeneous of class $(m_1, ..., m_n)$ of order $m - \sigma - m_i$, the function W satisfies inequality (23.6). From the properties of the functions V and W our assertion follows directly.

Remark. We shall consider a family of matrices $A(x_1, ..., x_n, C)$, dependent on a real parameter $C \in (-\infty, +\infty)$. Let $X(t, X^{(0)})$ be a vector function representing a solution of the system of equations

$$\frac{dX_i}{dt} = X_i(x_1, ..., x_n). \tag{23.16}$$

We form the vector function

$$Y(t) = A[X(C^\sigma t, X^{(0)})C]X(C^\sigma t, X^{(0)}).$$

We shall compute the derivative of that function with respect to t. Then

$$\frac{dY}{dt} = BC^\sigma \frac{dX}{dt},$$

where

$$B = B[X(C^\sigma t, X^{(0)}), C]$$

is the matrix obtained in a certain way from the matrix A.

We shall assume that the functions X_i standing in the right-hand member of system (23.16), possess the property

$$B(x_1, ..., x_n, C)C^\sigma F(X) = F[A(x_1, ..., x_n, C), X], \tag{23.17}$$

where F is the vector $[X_1(x_1, ..., x_n) ... X_n(x_1, ..., x_n)]$. Then the family of vector functions $Y(t)$ will be a family of solutions of system (23.16), so that

$$Y(t) = X[t, A(X^{(0)}, C), X^{(0)}].$$

Property (23.17), in particular, includes all the generalized-homogeneous systems of differential equations.

If one imposes certain requirements of a general nature upon the family of matrices B, then the theory developed above may be carried over to system (23.16), whose right-hand members satisfy condition (23.17).

§ 24. Stability in the first nonlinear approximation

In the present section we consider the case when one cannot judge the stability of the homogeneous solution of the system of differential equations on the basis of the linear terms, formed as result of expanding the right-hand members into series.

Let us consider again the system of equations dealt with in § 21. We shall assume that the functions $f_s(t, x_1, ..., x_n, y_1, ..., y_n)$ $(s = 1, ..., n)$ may be expanded in convergent series of integral positive powers in $x_1,...,x_n,y_1,...,y_n$ with real, continuous, bounded coefficients given for $t \geq 0$.

In Malkin's book [6] the following concept is proposed.

Say the system

$$\frac{dy_i}{dt} = Y_1^{(m)}(t, y_1, ..., y_r) + ... + Y_i^{(N)}(t, y_1, ..., y_r) + f_i(t, y_1, ..., y_r) \quad (i = 1, ..., r)$$
$$(24.1)$$

is given, and defined in the region

$$t \geq 0, \ |y_i| \leq H. \tag{24.2}$$

Here the $Y_i^{(l)}$ are forms of the l-th order in the variable $y_1, ..., y_r$, whose coefficients are continuous and bounded functions of time, and the f_i denote the totality of all terms of an order higher than N.

DEFINITION 19. A free motion $y_1 = y_2 = ... = y_r = 0$ is called stable outside the dependence on the form of the terms of order higher than N, if for every positive ε, no matter how small, there exists a positive number η (ε, A) such that for all solutions of equations (24.1), the initial values of y_{i0} which were chosen at the initial instant of time $t = 0$ according to the conditions $|y_{i0}| < \eta(\varepsilon, A)$, for all $t > 0$, the inequalities $|y_i| < \varepsilon$ are fulfilled for every choice of the functions $f_i(t, y_1, ..., y_r)$, satisfying in region (24.2) the conditions

$$|f_i(t, y_1, ..., y_r)| < A \{|y_1| + ... + |y_r|\}^{N+1} ,$$

where N is some constant.

We shall supplement this Definition by the condition that for system (21.2) the variables $x_1, ..., x_n$ have to be replaced by arbitrary continuous functions satisfying the inequalities $x_i < h_1$, where h_1 is a sufficiently small positive number.

THEOREM 50. If:

1) the homogeneous solution of the system (21.3) is stable (asymptotically stable) outside the dependence on the choice of terms of order n;

2) the functions $g_i(t, X, 0)$ are continuously differentiable with respect to all their arguments for $t \geqq 0, |X| < H$, and the homogeneous solution of the system

$$\frac{dx_i}{dt} = g_i(t, X, 0) \tag{24.3}$$

is uniform-asymptotically stable;

3) the partial derivatives with respect to all their arguments of the functions $g_j(t, X, 0)$ $(j = 1, ..., n)$ are bounded for $t \geqq 0$ and $|X| < H$, and the functions $g_j(t, X, Y) - g_j(t, X, 0)$ are uniformly continuous with respect to t and X for $t \geqq 0, |X| < H$ at the point $Y = 0$; —
then the homogeneous solution of system (24.2) is stable (asymptotically stable).

PROOF: The homogeneous solution of the system

$$\frac{dy_s}{dt} = f_s(t, X, Y) \quad (s = 1, ..., k) \tag{24.4}$$

will be strongly stable (asymptotically stable), and therefore the present Theorem holds, if one takes into account that with the satisfaction of the conditions of the Theorem there exists a function $V(t, x_1, ..., x_n)$ satisfying all the conditions of Theorem 41.

We shall assume that the expansion of the functions f_s has the form

$$f_s = \sum_{m=\mu}^{+\infty} f_s^{(m)}, \tag{24.5}$$

where $f_s^{(m)}$ is a form of the degree m in $y_1, ..., y_k$ with coefficients dependent on $t, x_1, ..., x_n$.

Further f_{s0}^{μ} $(s = 1, ..., k)$ be homogeneous forms of degree μ in $y_1, ..., y_k$ with constant coefficients, obtained from the forms f_s^{μ} with $x_1 = x_2 = ... = x_n = 0$. Then, for odd μ one may indicate a condition for the coefficients of these forms, necessary and sufficient to make the homogeneous solution of system (24.4) asymptotically stable outside the dependence on the choice of the forms of an order higher than μ.

This condition is obtained if one constructs the solution of the system of equations

$$\left.\begin{array}{l} \sum_{i=1}^{k} \dfrac{\partial V}{\partial y_i} f_{i0}^{(\mu)} = W, \\[3em] \sum_{i=1}^{k} \dfrac{\partial V}{\partial y_i} y_i = (m - \mu + 1) V, \end{array}\right\} \tag{24.6}$$

where W is a homogeneous negative-definite function of degree m.

The solution of system (24.6) may be constructed by the method which has been indicated in §23.

We shall assume that the functions $g_j(t, y_1, \ldots, y_k, x_1, \ldots, x_n)$, entering into the right-hand members of system (21.2), may be expanded in series

$$g_j = \sum_{m=0}^{+\infty} g_j^{(m)},$$

where $g_j^{(m)}$ is a homogeneous form of degree m in $x_1, \ldots, x_n$ whose coefficients represent series in $y_1, \ldots, y_k$ with real bounded coefficients dependent on t.

Let $g_j^{(v)}$ be the first form in the expansion of the functions $g_j(t, x_1, \ldots, x_n, 0, \ldots, 0)$.

We shall consider that the forms $g_j^{(v)}$ have constant coefficients and v is odd. On the basis of §23 one may derive the necessary and sufficient conditions to make the homogeneous solution of the system

$$\frac{dx_s}{dt} = g_s^{(v)} \qquad (s = 1, \ldots, n) \tag{24.7}$$

asymptotically stable.

This condition may be obtained by finding the solution of the system of equations

$$\left.\begin{array}{l} \sum_{s=1}^{n} \dfrac{\partial V}{\partial x_s} g_s^{(v)} = W, \\[3em] \sum_{s=1}^{n} \dfrac{\partial V}{\partial x_s} x_s = (m - v + 1) V, \end{array}\right\} \tag{24.8}$$

where W is a negative-definite function of the m-th degree in $x_1, \ldots, x_n$.

THEOREM 51. If:

1) the homogeneous solution of system (24.4) is stable (asymptotically stable) outside the dependence on the choice of terms of an order higher than N;

2) the homogeneous solution of (24.7) is asymptotically stable; —
then the homogeneous solution of system (21.2) is stable† (asymptotically
stable).

The proof of this Theorem follows from Theorem 41, as the function
$V(x_1, ..., x_n)$ in this case may be constructed in a finite form as a solution of the
system of equations (24.8) and, as it is a generalized-homogeneous function
of class $m_1 = m_2 = ... = m_n = 1$ of order $m - v + 1$ and differentiable for
sufficiently large m, its total derivative as based on the second group of
equations of the system (21.2) will be a negative-definite function of
$x_1, ..., x_n$. Such a function allows one to give the condition for asymptotic stability of the homogeneous solution in the case when the right-hand members
of the system of equations are single-valued analytic functions in the neighbourhood of the equilibrium position and the matrix of coefficients of the
linear approximation has k zero, or k pairs of purely imaginary characteristic values with simple elementary divisors, while the remaining characteristic values have negative real parts [9].

---

† The functions g_j for $\phi = 0$ are assumed to be uniformly continuous with respect to
t and $x_1, ..., x_n$.

CHAPTER VII

PERIODIC AND ALMOST-PERIODIC OSCILLATIONS IN NONLINEAR SYSTEMS

THE PRESENT chapter is devoted to one of the more important problems encountered in the analysis and synthesis of various systems.

In some nonlinear systems there arise basically new phenomena which are not observed in linear systems.

In § 25 a detailed investigation of self-oscillatory behaviour is carried out. Here we derive the necessary and sufficient conditions for the periodic behaviour to be a self-oscillation. In particular, we establish the property of stability of the characteristic diagram of the behaviour of integral curves in relation to constantly acting perturbations.

In § 26 of this chapter we study the rise of periodic behaviour under the action of an external perturbing force. In that section we have investigated the characteristic behaviour of integral curves in the case of the phenomenon of convergence and proposed a sufficient indication for the presence of a periodic behaviour asymptotically stable in the large.

In § 27 we study the case of the appearance of periodic and almost-periodic motions in the presence of k pairs of pure imaginary roots in the first approximation system.

In § 28 we bring the known methods of approximate determination of periodic behaviours. We shall note that in chapter VII we make use of the works of E. P. Popov, A. I. Lurye, I. G. Malkin, M. Zlamal, and others [13], [52], [6], [63].

§ 25. Self-oscillations

We shall consider a linear system of differential equations

$$\frac{dx_s}{dt} = \sum_{i=1}^{n} p_{si}x_i \qquad (s = 1, \ldots, n), \tag{25.1}$$

where the p_{si} are real constants.

We shall seek the solution of that system according to the rule in the form

$$x_s = e^{\lambda t}c_s \qquad (s = 1, \ldots, n), \tag{25.2}$$

where $\lambda, c_1, \ldots, c_n$ are arbitrary constants undergoing determination.

After substituting function (25.2) in system (25.1) and simplifying by the common factor $e^{\lambda t}$ in both members of the equality, we shall obtain a system of linear homogeneous algebraic equations of the form

$$\lambda c_s = \sum_{i=1}^{n} p_{si} c_i \quad (s = 1, ..., n). \tag{25.3}$$

For this system to have a nontrivial solution, it is necessary and sufficient that its determinant be equal to zero. This determinant is a polynomial in λ of the n-th degree,

$$p(\lambda) = \sum_{i=0}^{n} a_i \lambda^{n-i}, \tag{25.4}$$

and is called the characteristic polynomial of system (25.1).

To each root of this polynomial corresponds a system of numbers $c_1, ..., c_n$ obtained as the solution of the system of equations (25.3) when this root is substituted here.

Thus, to each root of polynomial (25.4) corresponds a solution of system (25.1), represented in form (25.2).

We shall assume that the polynomial (25.4) has a purely imaginary root. Then from formula (25.2) it follows that system (25.1) has a periodic solution which we shall denote as

$$x_s = \bar{x}_s(t) \quad (s = 1, ..., n). \tag{25.5}$$

In system (25.1) we shall perform a substitution of the sought functions according to the formulae:

$$\xi_s = x_s - \bar{x}_s(t) \quad (s = 1, ..., n); \tag{25.6}$$

then for the sought functions $\xi_1, ..., \xi_n$, which are deviations of the behaviour considered from the given periodic one, we shall obtain a system of exactly the same form as (25.1):

$$\frac{d\xi_s}{dt} = \sum_{i=1}^{n} p_{si} \xi_i \quad (s = 1, ..., n). \tag{25.7}$$

Among the roots of the characteristic polynomial (25.4) of system (25.7) there are roots with real parts equal to zero, and therefore the homogeneous solution of system (25.7), and consequently also the periodic solution (25.5) of system (25.1), cannot be asymptotically stable. Nevertheless, in the general case there exist two subspaces of the space of the variables $\xi_1, ..., \xi_n$ such that all the integral curves beginning with the first of them asymptotically approach the origin $\xi_1 = \xi_2 = ... = \xi_n = 0$ as $t \to +\infty$, and the integral curves in the remaining subspace asymptotically tend to the coordinate origin as $t \to -\infty$.

In fact, in system (25.6) we shall perform a transformation of the sought functions according to the formulae

$$\xi_s = \sum_{i=1}^{n} q_{si}\eta_i \quad (s = 1, ..., n), \tag{25.8}$$

where $\eta_1, ..., \eta_n$ are new sought functions.

It is known that the quantities q_{si} may be chosen so that the matrix of coefficients for the variables $\eta_1, ..., \eta_n$ will have a Jordan canonical form. Consequently, the system of these equations may be decomposed into several mutually disconnected groups, each of which corresponds to a definite box in the canonical structure of the matrix, namely

$$\left. \begin{aligned}
\dot{\eta}_1 &= \lambda_1\eta_1, \\
\dot{\eta}_2 &= \eta_1 + \lambda_1\eta_2, \\
\dot{\eta}_3 &= \lambda_3\eta_3, \\
\dot{\eta}_4 &= \eta_3 + \lambda_3\eta_4, \\
\dot{\eta}_5 &= \eta_4 + \lambda_4\eta_5, \\
&\cdots\cdots\cdots \\
\dot{\eta}_n &= \eta_{n-1} + \lambda_{n-1}\eta_n
\end{aligned} \right\} \tag{25.9}$$

(of course, system (25.9) represents a particular case of all possible ones of this kind).

We shall consider only those groups of equations in which the roots have a negative real part.

We shall consider that there turned out to be k such equations, and these equations may be numbered in such a way that they correspond to the first k equations of system (25.9). Consequently, any solution of system (25.9) corresponding to the initial conditions

$$\begin{aligned}
\eta_1 &= \eta_{10}, ..., \eta_k = \eta_{k0}, \\
\eta_{k+1} &= 0, ..., \eta_n = 0 \text{ for } t = 0
\end{aligned} \tag{25.10}$$

asymptotically tends to the coordinate origin $\eta_1 = ... = \eta_n = 0$ as $t \to +\infty$.

Taking into account transformation (25.8), we shall obtain that all the integral curves of system (25.7) tend to the coordinate origin $\xi_1 = ... = \xi_n = 0$ asymptotically as $t \to +\infty$, if only their initial conditions are defined by formulae

$$\xi_{s0} = \sum_{i=1}^{k} q_{si}\eta_{i0} \quad (s = 1, ..., n). \tag{25.11}$$

As the vectors forming the columns of the transformation matrix (25.8) are linearly independent, the initial conditions, defined by formulae (25.11), form a linear subspace of dimensionality k, which we shall denote as E_k.

If now in system (25.9) we distinguish all the equations corresponding to the roots with a positive real part, then, proceeding analogously in the space $\xi_1, ..., \xi_n$, one may construct a subspace E_l of dimensionality l such that all the integral curves of system (25.7) which start in that subspace tend asymptotically to the coordinate origin as $t \to -\infty$.

We shall now construct a set of dimensionality k in the original space $x_1, ..., x_n$, every point of which may be represented according to the formulae

$$x_s = \xi_s + \bar{x}_s \quad (s = 1, ..., n),$$

where $\xi_1, ..., \xi_n$ is any point of E_k, and $\bar{x}_1, ..., \bar{x}_n$ is any point lying on the periodic solution (25.5).

We shall denote the set obtained by R_k. Proceeding analogously, one may construct a set R_l. These sets possess the property that any integral curve of system (25.1), beginning in R_k, tends asymptotically to the periodic solution (25.5) as $t \to +\infty$. Any integral curve of system (25.1), beginning in R_l, tends asymptotically to the periodic solution (25.5) as $t \to -\infty$.

We shall note that some of the sets R_l and R_k may be empty. On the other hand, the dimensionality of each of them and the sum of their dimensionalities does not exceed $n-1$, and therefore there always exist integral curves of system (25.1) which have no common points with these sets and which do not tend to the periodic solution.

This is the state of affairs in the case when among roots (25.4) there are pure imaginary ones. If among those roots there are no pure imaginary ones, then system (25.1) cannot have periodic solutions (periodic behaviours).

Such is the complete characteristic of linear automatic control systems.

Phenomena connected with the presence of periodic behaviours in non-linear systems differ sharply from those which are intrinsic to linear systems and have been described above. This difference is characterized mainly by two factors:

1) the presence in the characteristic equation for the first approximation of roots with negative real parts does not guarantee the absence of periodic behaviours;

2) a periodic behaviour in nonlinear systems may be asymptotically stable.

To be more precise: say, one is given a system of equations

$$\frac{dx_s}{dt} = f_s(x_1, ..., x_n), \tag{25.12}$$

whose right-hand members are real functions given in the n-dimensional space.

We shall assume that system (25.12) has a periodic solution

$$x_s = \bar{x}_s(t) \tag{25.13}$$

with period T.

DEFINITION 20. A periodic solution (25.13) of system (25.12) is called *asymptotically stable* if for any $\varepsilon > 0$ there exists a $\delta > 0$ such that if $\rho(x_{10}, \ldots, x_{n0}) < \delta$ then $\rho[x_1(t), \ldots, x_n(t)] < \varepsilon$ for $t > 0$ and, besides, $\rho[x_1(t), \ldots, x_n(t)] \to 0$ as $t \to +\infty$.

Here by ρ we denote the distance from the transient process in the system (25.12) to the periodic behaviour

$$\rho(x_1, \ldots, x_n) = \inf_{t \in [0,T]} \sqrt{\sum_{i=1}^{n} [x_i - \bar{x}_i(t)]^2}.$$

Beginning with the works of Academician A. A. Andronov, asymptotically stable periodic behaviours are conventionally called self-oscillatory.

Thus, the nonlinear system (25.12) may have self-oscillations, while the linear system (25.1) never has them.

DEFINITION 21. The set A of all points $x_{10}, \ldots, x_{n0}$ of the n-dimensional space is called the *region of attraction of self-oscillation*, if from $(x_{10}, \ldots, x_{n0}) \in A$ it follows that $\rho[x_1(t), \ldots, x_n(t)] \to 0$ as $t \to +\infty$, where $x_1(t), \ldots, x_n(t)$ is the transient process in system (25.12), defined by the initial conditions $x_{10}, \ldots, x_{n0}$ for $t = 0$.

We shall further assume that to every point of the n-dimensional space $(x_{10}, \ldots, x_{n0})$ corresponds a solution of system (25.12)

$$x_s = x_s(t, x_{10}, \ldots, x_{n0}) \quad (s = 1, \ldots, n), \tag{25.14}$$

satisfying the initial conditions $x_s = x_{s0}$ for $t = 0$.

We shall consider that function (25.14) is continuous with respect to the set of its arguments.

THEOREM 52. In order that region A, consisting of entire trajectories of system (25.12) and containing the set $\rho(x_1, \ldots, x_n) < \delta$ for sufficiently small δ, be the region of attraction of self-oscillation (25.13) of system (25.12), it is necessary and sufficient that there exist two functions V and W satisfying the conditions:

1) the function $V(x_1, \ldots, x_n)$ is given in A and is continuous there; the function $W(x_1, \ldots, x_n)$ is given in the entire phase space E_n of the variables $x_1, \ldots, x_n$;

2) the functions V and W vanish at the points of curve (25.13);

3) the function V outside curve (25.13) takes negative values from the interval $(0, -1)$. The function W is positive and satisfies the inequality $W(x_1, ..., x_n) > \alpha > 0$ for $\rho(x_1, ..., x_n) > \beta > 0$;

4)
$$\frac{dV}{dt} = W(1 + V) \sqrt{1 + \sum_{i=1}^{n} f_i^2} \; ; \qquad (25.15)$$

5) the function $V(x_1, ..., x_n)$ tends to -1 as $x_s \to \tilde{x}_s$ $(s = 1, ..., n)$, where $\tilde{x}_s$ denotes a finite point of the boundary of the region A.

Before we pass to the proof of this Theorem, we shall analyse an example and shall make a series of remarks clarifying it.

We shall consider the system of equations

$$\begin{aligned} \dot{x} &= x + y - x(x^2 + y^2), \\ \dot{y} &= -x + y - y(x^2 + y^2), \\ \dot{z} &= -z. \end{aligned} \right\} \qquad (25.16)$$

System (25.16) has a periodic motion located in the plane $z = 0$ and describing a circle of unit radius $x^2 + y^2 = 1$.

We shall consider the equation in partial derivatives

$$\frac{\partial V}{\partial x} [x + y - x(x^2 + y^2)] + \frac{\partial V}{\partial y} [-x + y - y(x^2 + y^2)] - \frac{\partial V}{\partial z} z =$$
$$= \left[\frac{2[1 - (x^2 + y^2)]^2 [1 + x^2 + y^2]}{x^2 + y^2} + 2z^2 \right] (1 + V). \qquad (25.17)$$

Equation (25.17) is obtained from equation (25.15) by a special choice of the function W and by finding the total derivative dV/dt as based on (25.16).

In this equation we shall perform a substitution of the sought function according to the formula

$$V_1 = \ln(1 + V); \qquad (25.18)$$

then for the function V_1 we shall obtain the equation

$$\frac{\partial V_1}{\partial x} [x + y - x(x^2 + y^2)] + \frac{\partial V_1}{\partial y} [-x + y - y(x^2 + y^2)] - \frac{\partial V_1}{\partial z} z =$$
$$= \frac{2[1 - (x^2 + y^2)]^2 [1 + x^2 + y^2]}{x^2 + y^2} + 2z^2.$$

The solution of the latter equation will have the form

$$V_1 = - \frac{[1 - (x^2 + y^2)]^2}{x^2 + y^2} - z^2. \qquad (25.19)$$

It is easy to see that the function V_1 will be defined at all points of the phase space not lying on the axis. From (25.19) and substitution (25.18) it follows that the function V satisfies all the conditions of the Theorem in the region A, obtained from the phase space by excluding the z-axis. Consequently, the periodic solution of system (25.16) is a self-oscillation, the region of attraction of which coincides with the whole phase space, if from it we exclude the z-axis.

We shall take a numerical negative parameter μ and consider the set of all points defined by the equality

$$V_1 = \mu. \tag{25.20}$$

This equality may be rewritten otherwise, namely:

$$(x^2 + y^2 - \gamma)^2 + z^2(x^2 + y^2) = \gamma^2 - 1,$$

where

$$\gamma = 1 - \tfrac{1}{2}\mu,$$

or in the form

$$(x^2 + y^2 - \phi)^2 = \phi^2 - 1,$$

where

$$\phi = 1 - \tfrac{1}{2}\mu - \tfrac{1}{2}z^2.$$

The section made by the plane $z = c$, $c \in [-\sqrt{\mu}, +\sqrt{\mu}]$ shows that the surface defined by (25.20) represents a torus. As $\mu \to -\infty$ that surface divides in such a way that the region of attraction of periodic solution of system (25.16) may be considered as the limit of the surfaces of the tori as $\mu \to -\infty$.

All the integral curves of system (25.16) intersect the surfaces of the tori from outside inward and, with $t \to -\infty$, asymptotically approach the periodic solution of system (25.16).

This example is indubitably one of the primitive examples of such kind, nevertheless it contains that generality which is characteristic of the behaviour of integral curves in nonlinear systems in the presence of self-oscillations. A specific feature inherent in system (25.16) consists in that the region of attraction of the self-oscillation fills the entire phase space with the exception of the z-axis, while in the general case the region of attraction of the self-oscillation in a nonlinear system may be located in a bounded portion of the space.

We shall now make a series of comments whose sense of becomes obvious in relation to the example analysed above.

Remark 1. In equation (25.15) one may perform a substitution for the function V according to the formula $V_1 = \ln(1 + V)$. As a result of this substitution equation (25.15) will take the form

$$\frac{dV_1}{dt} = W\sqrt{1 + \sum_{i=1}^{n} f_i^2}.$$

Here, the function V_1 in the region A, apart from the self-oscillations, will take negative values from the segment $(0, -\infty)$. Here the function $V_1 \to -\infty$ as one approaches a finite or infinite point of the boundary of A.

If the function V_1 is continuously differentiable with respect to its arguments, then the last equation may be written in the form

$$\sum_{i=1}^{n} \frac{\partial V_1}{\partial x_i} f_i = W \sqrt{1 + \sum_{i=1}^{n} f_i^2}. \tag{25.21}$$

Remark 2. If system (25.12) has self-oscillations, then it may be shown that the region of its attraction is an open and connected set, i.e. a region in the mathematical sense of the word. It may be shown also that on the boundary of the region A are situated entire trajectories of system (25.12), i.e. if the integral curve of system (25.12) begins on the boundary of the region A, then it remains on it with increasing and decreasing time.

We shall consider the set of points defined by the equation $V_1 = \mu$. It may be shown that this set of points represents the surface of a torus which is intersected by all integral curves of system (25.12) beginning on that torus, from the outside in, if time is increasing.

If $\mu \to 0$, then the surfaces of these tori are drawn into self-oscillations. If $\mu \to -\infty$, then the surfaces of these tori expand, in the limit approaching the boundary of the region A. It should be noted that no pair of tori from the family described above has common points.

The last remark allows us to give a geometric formulation of the Theorem having a very lucid meaning.

We shall now pass to the proof of the Theorem.

PROOF: *Necessity.* Let system (25.12) have a self-oscillation (25.13). Then one may show that it is a uniform-asymptotically stable and uniformly attracting motion. Consequently, there exists a positive function $l(t)$ strictly monotonically decreasing from $-\infty$ to 0, given for $t \in (-\infty, \infty)$ and such that $\rho[x_1(t), \ldots, x_n(t)] < l(t)$ for $t > 0$ and $\rho(x_{10}, \ldots, x_{n0}) < \delta$.

By virtue of uniform attractingness, for a number $h > 0$ there exist two numbers T, α such that $\rho[x_1(t), \ldots, x_n(t)] > \alpha > 0$ for $t \in [0, T_1]$ and $\rho(x_{10}, \ldots, x_{n0}) > h$. We shall take the function W in the form

$$W = \rho(x_1, \ldots, x_n)e^{-k(\rho)},$$

where $k(\rho)$ is a function inverse to $l(t)$. The function $V_1(x_{10}, \ldots, x_{n0})$ we shall define by the formula

$$V_1 = \int_{0}^{+\infty} -W\,dt.$$

Because of uniform asymptotic stability and uniform attractingness, this function will possess all the properties indicated in the Theorem (at any rate, when all the solutions of system (25.12) are defined for all values of $t \in (-\infty, \infty)$). If this is not the case, then by a substitution of the independent variable according to the formula

$$d\tau = dt \sqrt{1 + \sum_{i=1}^{n} f_i^2}$$

we shall obtain from (25.12) a system such that all its solutions are defined for $\tau \in (-\infty, \infty)$.

Sufficiency. Say there exist functions V_1 and W satisfying all the conditions of the Theorem. We shall then show that the periodic solution (25.13) is a self-oscillation in the system (25.12) and that the region A is a region of attraction of that self-oscillation.

We shall take $\varepsilon > 0$. For it we shall find a number $\mu(\varepsilon) = \sup\limits_{\rho(x_1, \ldots, x_n) = \varepsilon} V_1$.

(It is clear, that ε may be considered as not exceeding δ, which is dealt with in the theorem.) Because of continuity of the function V_1, for a number M there exists a number $\gamma(\varepsilon)$ such that if $\rho(x_1, \ldots, x_n) < \gamma(\varepsilon)$, then $V_1 < M$.

All the integral curves beginning in the region $\rho(x_1, \ldots, x_n) < \gamma(\varepsilon)$ of the periodic motion (25.13) remain in the ε-neighbourhood, since, on the one hand, we have $V_1(x_{10}, \ldots, x_{n0}) < V_1[x_1(t), \ldots, x_n(t)]$ for $t > 0$, and on the other hand, with the exit of an integral curve from the ε-neighbourhood, there would hold $V_1[x_1(T^*), \ldots, x_n(T^*)] \leqq M < V_1(x_{10}, \ldots, x_{n0})$, where T^* is the instant of exit of the integral curve from the ε-neighbourhood.

The contradiction of these inequalities demonstrates the correctness of our assertions.

It now remains to be shown that the integral curves beginning in a $\gamma(\varepsilon)$-neighbourhood, asymptotically approach the periodic solution. This is demonstrated by the same method as the corresponding Theorem in Chapter I.

In conclusion, it remains to be shown that the region A is the region of attraction of the periodic solution. This follows directly from the fact that A consists of entire trajectories of system (25.12) and contains a sufficiently small region of the periodic solution (25.13).

We shall note that from the Theorem proved follow the necessary and sufficient conditions for asymptotic stability of the periodic solution in the small. Say the system (25.12) has a periodic solution (25.13). Then for this periodic solution to be a self-oscillation, it is necessary and sufficient that there exist two functions V and W satisfying the following conditions:

1) the functions V and W are given in the neighbourhood of the periodic motion (25.13) $\rho(x_1,...,x_n) < l$ and are continuous there;

2) the functions V and W satisfy the inequalities $V < -\gamma_1$, $W > \gamma_2$ for $\rho(x_1,...,x_n) > \beta > 0$, where γ_1, γ_2, and β are positive constants, $V = W = 0$ for $\rho = 0$;

3) the total derivative of the function V as based on system (25.12) satisfies the equality $dV/dt = W$.

By L we shall denote a closed curve in the phase space of the variables $x_1,...,x_n$, which is described by a point corresponding to the periodic solution (25.13). We shall call Condition 2, to which the functions V and W are subject, the property of negative-definiteness and positive-definiteness of a function, respectively.

The proof of the assertion formulated above may be established in the same way in which the proof of the preceding Theorem was carried out.

In fact, the necessity of these conditions may be considered as established since, in the first part of the proof of the Theorem, functions V and W have been constructed so as to satisfy these conditions. The second part of the proof of the Theorem contains the sufficiency of these conditions for self-oscillation of the periodic solution (25.13). The Theorem given above allows one to find the dependence of the right-hand members of system (25.13) on the form of the region A and on the periodic curve

$$x_s = \bar{x}_s(t) \qquad (s = 1,...,n), \tag{25.22}$$

initially given and located in that region, in the sense that from this data one may construct a system of differential equations for which the region A will be the region of attraction of the self-oscillation (25.22).

Let L be a closed non-self intersecting curve described by the periodic vector (25.22). We shall find the general form of the systems of differential equations having a self-oscillation, whose trajectory coincides with L. For this purpose we shal construct two functions V and W satisfying the conditions:

1) $V(x_1,...,x_n)$, $W_1(x,...,x_n)$ are given in the neighbourhood of the curve L, $\rho(x_1,...,x_n) < l$;

2) the function V is negative-definite and W is positive-definite in the neighbourhood of L;

3) the function W is continuous, V is continuously differentiable with respect to all its arguments.

We shall consider the system of differential equations

$$\frac{dx_s}{dt} = g_s(x_1,...,x_n) \qquad s=1,...,n). \tag{25.23}$$

whose right-hand members are defined by the formula

$$
\left.
\begin{aligned}
g_1 &= \frac{\dfrac{dV}{dx_1}W}{\displaystyle\sum_{i=1}^{n}\left(\frac{\partial V}{\partial x_i}\right)^2} - \sum_{i=2}^{n}\gamma_i\frac{\partial V}{\partial x_i}, \\[3ex]
g_i &= \frac{\gamma_i\dfrac{\partial V}{\partial x_1} + \dfrac{\partial V}{\partial x_i}W}{\displaystyle\sum_{i=1}^{n}\left(\frac{\partial V}{\partial x_i}\right)^2} \qquad (i = 2, ..., n).
\end{aligned}
\right\}
\tag{25.24}
$$

The quantities γ_i in (25.24) are arbitrary functions of the variables $x_1, ..., x_n$, subject to two conditions:

1) system (25.23) satisfies in the phase space the conditions for existence of a continuous solution, i.e. for any point $x_{10}, ..., x_{n0}$ there exist continuous functions $x_i = x_i(t, x_{10}, ..., x_{n0})$ $(i = 1, ..., n)$ satisfying the initial conditions $x_i = x_{i0}$ for $t = 0$; V and W may be considered as continuous over the whole space;

2) the sum $\displaystyle\sum_{i=1}^{n} g_i^2 > 0$ on the curve L and in a sufficiently small neighbourhood of it.

We shall show that with the satisfaction of conditions 1 and 2, system (25.23) has a periodic solution of a self-oscillatory type whose trajectory coincides with L.

Indeed, we shall take the point $(x_{10}, ..., x_{n0})$, located on the curve L and from it we shall extend an integral curve of system (25.23); then there are two possibilities:

1) the integral curve $x_i = x_i(t, x_{10}, ..., x_{n0})$ $(i = 1, ..., n)$ remains for all $t > 0$ on the closed curve L;

2) the integral curve leaves at some instant the closed curve L.

We shall show that in actuality the second possibility is not realized.

We shall assume the contrary. Then there exists a number $T_1 > 0$ such that $\rho[x_1(T_1), ..., x_n(T_1)] = \varepsilon > 0$, where ρ denotes the distance considered from the integral curve to the closed curve L.

We shall set $m = \sup\limits_{\rho\,(x_1, ..., x_n)\,\varepsilon} V(x_1, ..., x_n)$.

We shall take a number δ such that if $\rho(x_1, ..., x_n) < \delta$ then $V(x_1, ..., x_n) > m$.

Then all the integral curves of system (25.23) beginning in a δ-neighbourhood of the curve L $\rho(x_1, ..., x_n) < \delta$ remain in the ε-neighbourhood, i.e. $dV/dt = W \geq 0$, $\rho(x_1, ..., x_n) < \varepsilon$, while the considered integral curve leaves the curve L

and its δ-neighbourhood and at the instant T_1 it reaches the boundaries of the ε-neighbourhood, which is impossible.

Thus, the integral curve beginning on L remains there for $t > 0$.

Because of condition 2, on the curve L there are no equilibrium positions of system (25.23). Therefore after the lapse of time T the integral curve under consideration will return to the initial point, and then by virtue of the autonomicity of system (25.23) this integral curve will be periodic (since the property of autonomicity denotes that system (25.23) together with the solution $x_i = x_i(t, x_{10}, ..., x_{n0})$ $(i = 1, ..., n)$ has also a solution $x_i = x_i(t + h, x_{10}, ..., x_{n0})$ for all real h, $-\infty < h < +\infty$).

We shall now show that this periodic solution of system (25.23) will be a self-oscillation.

In fact, we shall find the total derivative of the function V as based on that system. Then we shall obtain

$$\frac{dV}{dt} = \sum_{i=1}^{n} g_i \frac{\partial V}{\partial x_i} = W,$$

which shows the correctness of the assertion made.

During its performance, an automatic control system is subjected to the influence of constantly acting perturbations. We shall clarify the effect of these perturbations on the self-oscillations.

Let system (25.12) have a self-oscillation (25.13) of period T, whose trajectory coincides with a closed non-self intersecting curve L situated in the phase space $x_1, ..., x_n$. Then, according to the above, one may construct two functions V and W satisfying the three conditions mentioned earlier.

We shall consider the system of equations

$$\frac{dx_s}{dt} = f_s(x_1, ..., x_n) + r_s(x_1, ..., x_n). \tag{25.25}$$

If the constantly acting perturbations $r_s(x_1, ..., x_n)$ satisfy the conditions:

1) there exist $n-1$ functions $\gamma_2, ..., \gamma_n$ and a positive-definite function W_1 in the neighbourhood of the curve L such that

$$\left. \begin{aligned} r_1(x_1, ..., x_n) &= \frac{\dfrac{dV}{dx_1}(W_1 - W)}{\displaystyle\sum_{i=1}^{n}\left(\dfrac{\partial V}{\partial x_i}\right)^2} - \sum_{i=2}^{n} \gamma_i \frac{\partial V}{\partial x_i}, \\[2em] r_i(x_1, ..., x_n) &= \frac{\gamma_i \dfrac{\partial V}{\partial x_1} + \dfrac{\partial V}{\partial x_i}(W_1 - W)}{\displaystyle\sum_{i=1}^{n}\left(\dfrac{\partial V}{\partial x_i}\right)^2} \quad (i = 2, ..., n); \end{aligned} \right\} \tag{25.26}$$

2) the functions $f_i + r_i$ do not vanish simultaneously at any point situated on the curve L, and are continuous in its neighbourhood —
then system (25.25) has a self-oscillation whose trajectory coincides with the curve L.

In fact, the total derivative of the function V calculated on the basis of system (25.25) coincides with the function W_1, which is positive-definite in the neighbourhood of the curve L. Consequently, from the preceding considerations one may conclude that the integral curve of system (25.25), beginning on the closed curve L, is periodic, and its trajectory coincides with L. Here this periodic solution is asymptotically stable. Thus, system (25.25) has self-oscillations.

We shall note that with constantly acting perturbations of this kind, the self-oscillations, as a rule, change their period. We shall clarify this with the aid of an example.

Let us take the system

$$\left.\begin{aligned}
\dot{x} &= \quad x + y - x(x^2 + y^2) + r_1, \\
\dot{y} &= -x + y - y(x^2 + y^2) + r_2, \\
\dot{z} &= -z + r_3,
\end{aligned}\right\} \tag{25.27}$$

where

$$\begin{aligned}
r_1 &= ay(x^2 + y^2), \\
r_2 &= -ax(x^2 + y^2), \\
r_3 &= 0.
\end{aligned}$$

Making use of the same functions V and W as in the preceding example, it may be established that for any $a > 0$ system (25.27) has a self-oscillation whose trajectory is located on a circumference of unit radius with its centre at the coordinate origin, situated in the plane $z = 0$.

In system (25.16) the self-oscillations are described by the functions $x = \sin t$, $y = \cos t$, $z = 0$.

In system (25.27) the self-oscillations are described by the functions $a = \sin(a + 1)t$, $y = \cos(a + 1)t$, $z = 0$.

Thus perturbations, insignificant in quantity, may change the period of the self-oscillation.

We shall also note that the property of a self-oscillation is stable under constantly acting perturbations.

DEFINITION 22. Self-oscillations (25.13) of system (25.12) are called *stable under constantly acting perturbations* if for every $\varepsilon > 0$ there exist two numbers $\delta_1 > 0$ and $\delta_2 > 0$ such that for every possible choice of the functions $r_s(x_1, \ldots, x_n) < \delta_2$ for $\rho(x_1, \ldots, x_n) < \varepsilon$, the integral curves of system (25.25) beginning in the δ_1-neighbourhood of the curve L, remain in an ε-neighbourhood of the curve L for all $t \geq 0$.

THEOREM 53. Self-oscillations are stable under constantly acting perturbations.

PROOF: We shall take $\varepsilon > 0$. Without limiting its generality, it may be chosen so small that the functions V and W be given in a closed ε-neighbourhood of the curve L (here we are dealing with those functions V and W which exist because of the presence of the self-oscillation (25.13) of system (25.12) and satisfy the three conditions given earlier).

We shall set $m = \sup V(x_1, ..., x_n)$ for $\rho(x_1, ..., x_n) = \varepsilon$. By virtue of continuity of the function V, for the found number m there exists a number δ_1 such that if $\rho(x_1, ..., x_n) < \delta_1$ then $V > m$.

We shall further choose a number δ_2 so that the inequality

$$W - \delta_2 \sum_{i=1}^{n} \left| \frac{\partial V}{\partial x_i} \right| < 0 \text{ for } \delta_1 \leq \rho(x_1, ..., x_n) \leq \varepsilon$$

hold.

We shall show that with such a choice of the quantities δ_1 and δ_2, the integral curves of the system

$$\frac{dx_s}{dt} = f_s(x_1, ..., x_n) + r_s(x_1, ..., x_n) \qquad (s = 1, ..., n), \qquad (25.28)$$

beginning at $t = 0$ in the region $\rho(x_1, ..., x_n) < \delta_1$, remain in the region $\rho(x_1, ..., x_n) < \varepsilon$ of the curve L.

In fact, we shall let an integral curve out from the point $(x_{10}, ..., x_{n0}) \in$ $\in \rho(x_1, ..., x_n) < \delta_1$; then we shall have $V(x_{10}, ..., x_{n0}) > m$. Let us assume that this curve, as time increases, at the instant t_1 has reached first the surface $r(x_1, ..., x_n) = \varepsilon$; then at that point $V[x_1(t_1), ..., x_n(t_1)] \leq m$.

The function $V[x_1(t), ..., x_n(t)]$ of the variable t, given in the interval $[0, t_1]$, has points at which it decreases. Therefore $dV/dt < 0$ must hold at those points of the integral curve situated within the set $\delta_1 < \rho(x_1, ..., x_n) \leq \varepsilon$.

However, the total derivative of the function V as based on system (25.28) remains positive in that set. The contradiction obtained proves the Theorem.

Remark. We shall note that the functions r_i, which are being dealt with in the definition of stability under constantly acting perturbations, are arbitrary functions entering into the right-hand members of the equations of system (25.28), but such that the right-hand members of system (25.28) satisfy the conditions for the existence of solutions.

The method of proving Theorem 53 requires that the right-hand members of system (25.12) be continuously differentiable. Then the function V may be chosen as continuously differentiable.

With constantly acting perturbations, the self-oscillation may completely disappear or be deformed in such a way that its trajectory will not coincide with the curve L. Nevertheless, the characteristic diagram of the behaviour of the integral curves of system (25.28) in the first approximation remains the same as in system (25.12).

Let us again consider the system (25.27), but functions r_i $(i = 1, ..., n)$, describing the constantly acting perturbations, we shall choose in another way:

$$\left.\begin{array}{l} r_1 = - x(\alpha x^2 + \beta y^2) + \beta y, \\ r_2 = - y(\alpha x^2 + \beta y^2) - \alpha x, \\ r_3 = 0, \end{array}\right\} \text{ where } \alpha \text{ and } \beta > 0.$$

Then one obtains a system having a self-oscillation, whose trajectory is situated on the ellipse $(\alpha + 1)x^2 - (\beta + 1)y^2 = 1$, lying in the plane $z = 0$.

Thus, constantly acting perturbations, small in absolute value (α and β are sufficiently small), produce a displacement of the self-oscillation in the phase space.

Neither is it hard to give examples when the self-oscillations vanish altogether, but the diagram of the behaviour of the transient processes in the system remains the same as in the presence of self-oscillations. This may occur, for example, when in a sufficiently small neighbourhood of the old self-oscillation there appear points of equilibrium of system (25.28). The stability of the characteristic diagram in the presence of self-oscillation may be explained in the following way:

1) with constantly acting perturbations there exist trajectories, stable in the sense of Lagrange, i.e. such, as beginning in $\rho(x_1, ..., x_n) < \delta_1$-neighbourhood of the curve, remain in an ε-neighbourhood of that curve; and then in that neighbourhood exists a closed set consisting of entire trajectories which are ω-bounded for the trajectories, stable in the sense of Lagrange;

2) it is known that a closed bounded set, consisting of entire trajectories, contains a minimal set which, by definition, is a closed nonempty set consisting of entire trajectories having no real subset with the same properties;

3) it is known that every trajectory of the minimal bounded set is recurrent. We shall recall that a trajectory is called recurrent, if for any $\varepsilon > 0$ there exists $T(\varepsilon) > 0$ such that every trajectory is located in an

ε-neighbourhood of an arc previously chosen for it, of temporal length T. Thus, in an ε-neighbourhood of the curve L there exists a minimal set and, consequently, recurrent motions exist.

§ 26. Periodic forced oscillations appearing under the action of external force

We shall consider a state of affairs appearing in a linear system under the action of an external periodic driving force. It is clear that all such states are described by means of systems of linear differential equations of the form

$$\frac{dx_s}{dt} = \sum_{i=1}^{n} a_{si} x_i + p_s(t) \quad (s = 1, ..., n). \tag{26.1}$$

We shall consider that the quantities a_{si} in system (26.1) are real constants and the characteristic values of the matrix of these quantities have negative real parts. The non-homogeneous parts in system (26.1) are real continuous periodic functions of period T.

By Y we shall denote the matrix of the fundamental system of solutions of the system of equations

$$\frac{dx_s}{dt} = \sum_{i=1}^{n} a_{si} x_i \quad (s = 1, ..., n); \tag{26.2}$$

$$Y = \{y_{si}(t)\},$$

where s is the number of the solution function, and i is the number of the solution. Consequently, the columns of the matrix Y are solutions of (26.2). The matrix Y may always be chosen in such a way that $Y = E$ for $t = 0$, where E is the unit matrix.

Any solution of system (26.1) may be written with the aid of matrix Y in the following form

$$x_s = \sum_{i=1}^{n} y_{si}(t) x_{i0} + \int_0^t \sum_{i=1}^{n} y_{si}(t - \tau) P_i(\tau) d\tau \quad (s = 1, ..., n), \tag{26.3}$$

where $x_{10}, ..., x_{n0}$ are arbitrary real constants, which are the initial conditions for the system (26.3).

We shall show that the linear system (26.1) has a unique periodic solution $x_s = \phi_s(t)$ $(s = 1, ..., n)$. Indeed, we shall assume that the quantities $x_{10}, ..., x_{n0}$ in equality (26.3) are chosen so that the functions $x_1, ..., x_n$ defined by these equalities come out periodic with period T. Taking this fact into account, we shall have the equalities

$$x_s(t) = x_s(t + T) \quad (s = 1, ..., n). \tag{26.4}$$

To abbreviate the calculations we shall write equality (26.3) in matrix form. Then we shall obtain

$$X(t) = Y(t) X_0 + \int\limits_0^t Y(t - \tau) P(\tau) d\tau, \qquad (26.5)$$

where

$$X = \begin{bmatrix} x_1 \\ \vdots \\ \dot{x}_n \end{bmatrix}, \quad X_0 = \begin{bmatrix} x_{10} \\ \vdots \\ x_{n0} \end{bmatrix}, \quad P = \begin{bmatrix} P_1 \\ \vdots \\ P_n \end{bmatrix}.$$

Taking the conditions of periodicity into account, we shall find

$$[Y(t + T) - Y(t)] X_0 + \int\limits_0^{t+T} Y(t + T - \tau) P(\tau) d\tau - \int\limits_0^t Y(t - \tau) P(\tau) d\tau = 0$$

whence

$$X_0 = [E - Y(T)]^{-1} \int\limits_{-T}^0 Y(-\tau) P(\tau) d\tau. \qquad (26.6)$$

Substituting (26.6) in (26.3), we shall find the expression for the periodic solution of the system (26.1)

$$\phi(t) = Y(t) [E - Y(t)]^{-1} \int\limits_{-T}^0 Y(-\tau) P(\tau) d\tau + \int\limits_0^t Y(t - \tau) P(\tau) d\tau. \qquad (26.7)$$

Functions (26.7) are a particular solution of system (26.1), and therefore, after replacing the sought functions according to the formulae $x_s = z_s + \phi_s(t)$ for the sought functions $z_1, \ldots, z_s$, we shall obtain the homogeneous system of equations

$$\frac{dz_s}{dt} = \sum_{i=1}^n a_{si} z_i .$$

In view of the fact that the roots of the characteristic equation of this system have negative real parts, its homogeneous solution is asymptotically stable. Consequently, the periodic solution (26.7) of system (26.1) will be asymptotically stable as a whole.

Thus, the linear system (26.1) has a unique periodic solution, asymptotically stable as a whole. Such a property of the rise of periodic behaviours under the action of an external periodic driving force is observed also in some nonlinear systems. For the sake of clarity of further exposition, we shall define this phenomenon more precisely. We shall consider the system of equations

$$\frac{dx_s}{dt} = f_s(x_1, \ldots, x_n) + p_s(t) \qquad (s = 1, \ldots, n). \qquad (26.8)$$

We shall assume that the right-hand members of system (26.8) are given for all $x_1, ..., x_n, t$ and are real and continuous. Besides, the functions $p_s(t)$ $(s = 1, ..., n)$ are periodic with period T.

DEFINITION 23. If system (26.8) has a unique periodic solution asymptotically stable as a whole, then the system is termed as possessing the property of *convergence*.

We shall give a general theorem containing the characteristic feature of the behaviour of integral curves of system (26.8) in the presence of convergence.

For the sake of clarity of the following exposition, by $X(t, X_0)$ we shall denote the solution of system (26.8) satisfying the initial conditions $X(0, X_0) = X_0$. We shall consider, further, that the vector function $X(t, X_0)$ is continuous with respect to the totality of its arguments. Here:

$$X = \{x_1, ..., x_n\};$$
$$X(0, X_0) = \{x_{10}, ..., x_{n0}\}.$$

THEOREM 54. In order that system (26.8) possess the property of convergence, it is necessary and sufficient that the following conditions be fulfilled:

1) every solution of system (26.8) is bounded for $t > 0$;

2) the difference between any two solutions tends to zero as $t \to \infty$; here for any $\varepsilon > 0$ and arbitrarily large number $R > 0$ there exists a number $\delta(\varepsilon, R) > 0$ such that if $|X_0 - \bar{X}_0| < \delta$ then

$$|X(t, X_0) - X(t, \bar{X}_0)| < \varepsilon \tag{26.9}$$

for all

$$t \geqq 0 \text{ and } |\bar{X}_0| < R, |X_0| < R; \text{ here } |X| = \sqrt{\sum_{i=1}^{n} x_i^2}$$

PROOF: *Sufficiency.* We shall assume that conditions 1 and 2 of Theorem 54 are satisfied. We shall then show that in system (26.8) the phenomenon of convergence is present.

The functions $f_s(x_1, ..., x_n)$ do not depend explicitly on the variable t. Therefore, together with the solution $X(t, X_0)$, system (26.8) has the solution $X = X(t + T, X_0)$. Then, by virtue of condition 2, $|X(t + T, X_0) - X(t, X_0)| \to 0$ will hold as $t \to +\infty$.

Because of condition 1, the solution $X(t, X_0)$ is bounded for $t > 0$, and therefore according to the Bolzano–Cauchy theorem there exists a sequence of instants $T_1, T_2, \ldots, T_k, \ldots$ tending to $+ \infty$, so that $X(t_k, X_0) \rightarrow V_0$ as $k \rightarrow + \infty$; $t_k = T_{n_k}$, n_k are integers.

We shall construct the solution of system (26.8), issuing at the instant $t = 0$ from the point Y_0, and we shall denote it by $\Phi(t)$, so that $\Phi(0) = Y_0$. We shall show that the function $X = \Phi(t)$ is a periodic solution of system (26.8) with period T.

In fact, by X_k we shall denote the point $X_k = X(t_k, X_0)$ and shall consider the sequence of integral curves $X(t, X_k)$. Because of continuity, for $t = T$ $X(T, X_k) \rightarrow \Phi(T)$ will hold, while $X(t, X_k) = X(t_k + T, X_0)$; consequently, $X(t, X_k) \rightarrow Y_0$ for $k \rightarrow + \infty$, and therefore $\Phi(T) = Y_0$.

In view of the periodicity of the right-hand member of system (26.8) with respect to t with a period T, it may easily be established that the solution $X = \Phi(t)$ will be periodic of period T. It now remains to be shown that the periodic solution $X = \Phi(t)$ is asymptotically stable as a whole. For this we shall choose $\varepsilon > 0$. According to condition 2, there exist quantities $R > 0$ and $\delta > 0$ connected with ε by inequalities (26.9).

As the point $\bar{X}_0$ we shall take Y_0. Then we shall obtain $\left| X(t) - \Phi(t) \right| < \varepsilon$ for $t > 0$ and $\left| X_0 - Y_0 \right| < \delta$. Besides, $\left| X(t) - \Phi(t) \right| \rightarrow 0$ as $t \rightarrow + \infty$, which indicates the presence of asymptotic stability. In view of condition 2 this asymptotic stability will hold in the large, i.e. the initial vector X_0 may be an arbitrary finite vector, while the relation $\left| X(t) - \Phi(t) \right| \rightarrow 0$ as $t \rightarrow + \infty$ remains unchanged.

Necessity. Let us assume that the system (26.8) possesses convergence. We shall then show that all the conditions of Theorem 54 are fulfilled.

According to the assumption, all the integral curves of system (26.8) approach the unique periodic solution and, consequently, each of these integral curves is bounded and, besides, the difference between any two solutions tends to zero as $t \rightarrow + \infty$.

To conclude the proof, we shall take a number $\varepsilon > 0$ and an arbitrarily large positive number R. We shall further take a number ε_1 such that $\varepsilon_1 > 0$, $\varepsilon_1 \leqq \varepsilon/2$. For the indicated number ε_1 one can find a number $\delta(\varepsilon_1)$ such that if $\left| X_0 - Y_0 \right| < \delta(\varepsilon_1)$ then $\left| X(t) - \Phi(t) \right| < \varepsilon_1$ for $t > 0$.

It may be shown that there exists a number t_1 such that all the integral curves which begin in the region $\left| X_0 \right| \leqq R$, for $t \geqq t_1$ will satisfy the inequality $\left| X(t, X_0) - \Phi(t) \right| < \varepsilon_1$, as each of these curves will reach the δ-neighbourhood of the periodic curve $\Phi(t)$.

The function $X(t, X_0)$ will be uniformly continuous for $|X_0| \leq R$, $t \in [0, t_1]$. Therefore there exists a $\delta > 0$ such that if $|X_0 - \bar{X}_0| < \delta$ then $|X(t, X_0) - \Phi(t)| < \varepsilon$ for $t \in [0, t_1]$.

On the strength of the above reasoning, the last equation will hold also for $t \geq t_1$.

In conclusion of the proof, it remains to be shown that the quantity t_1, possessing the indicated properties, exists. Say this is not the case. Then one can indicate a sequence of quantities $T_1, T_2, ..., T_k, ...$ tending to $+\infty$ as $k \to +\infty$, and a sequence of points $X_1, X_2, ..., X_k, ..., |X_k| \leq R$, such that $|X(t, X_k) - \Phi(t)| > \delta(\varepsilon_1)$ for $t \in [0, T_k]$. Then one can indicate a sequence of points $X_1, X_2, ...$ such that it will have a limiting point X^*. This point will possess the property $|X(t, X^*) - \Phi(t)| \geq \delta(\varepsilon_1)$ for $t \geq 0$, which contradicts the presence of convergence in system (26.8).

This completes the proof of the Theorem.

We shall now pass to the finding of the concrete sufficient conditions for the presence of the phenomenon of convergence in system (26.8).

By a_i we denote the values of the functions $f_i(x_1, ..., x_n)$ at the coordinate origin.

We shall set

$$g_i(x_1, ..., x_n) = f_i - a_i,$$
$$q_i = p_i + a_i \qquad (i = 1, ..., n).$$

With these notations system (26.8) will take the form

$$\frac{dx_s}{dt} = g_s(x_1, ..., x_n) + q_s(t).$$

From the function $g_s(x_1, ..., x_n)$ we shall choose the terms linear in $x_1, ..., x_n$, and the remainder of the function we shall denote as $h_s(x_1, ..., x_n)$. Then system (26.8) may be written also in the form

$$\frac{dx_s}{dt} = \sum_{i=1}^{n} a_{si} x_i + h_s(x_1, ..., x_n) + q_s(t) \quad (s = 1, ..., n). \qquad (26.10)$$

THEOREM 55. If the right-hand members of system (26.10) satisfy the conditions:

1) the real parts of the roots of the matrix $A = \{a_{si}\}$ are negative, i.e.

$$\lambda < 0; \; \lambda = \max_{i=1, ..., n} \operatorname{Re} \lambda_i;$$

2) the functions $h_s(x_1, ..., x_n)$ satisfy the inequalities

$$|h_s(x_1, ..., x_n) - h_s(y_1, ..., y_n)| \leq \sum_{i=1}^{n} b_{si} |x_i - y_i| \qquad (s = 1, ..., n), \qquad (26.11)$$

where b_{si} are nonnegative constants;

3) the number μ satisfies the inequality $\mu < |\bar{\lambda}|$, where μ is the largest real part of the roots of the matrix $M \times B$, where $M = \{m_{si}\}$; $B = \{b_{si}\}$ —
then

$$m_{si} = \sup y_{si}(t - \tau)e^{-\bar{\lambda}(t-\tau)},$$

for $0 < \tau < t$; $t > 0$.

Here, just as above, we denote by $y_{si}(t)$ the function entering in the fundamental system of solutions Y of system (26.2), and by $\bar{\lambda}$ we denote some negative constant satisfying the inequality $\bar{\lambda} > \lambda$.

PROOF: If in system (26.10) the functions $h_s(x_1, ..., x_n)$ are considered as known functions of time, then, making use of the fundamental system Y, one can find every solution of that system satisfying the initial conditions $x_s = x_{s0}$ for $t = 0$, according to the formula

$$x_s = \sum_{i=1}^{n} y_{si}(t)x_{i0} + \int_0^t \sum_{i=1}^{n} y_{si}(t - \tau)h_i[x_1(\tau), ..., x_n(\tau)]\,d\tau +$$

$$+ \int_0^t \sum_{i=1}^{n} y_{si}(t - \tau)p_i(\tau)\,d\tau \quad (s = 1, ..., n). \quad (26.12)$$

If we now note that the functions h depend in reality on the sought functions, which have as yet not been found, equality (26.12) may be considered as a system of integral equations serving to define the solutions of system (26.10). Applying equalities (26.12), we shall show first that every solution of system (26.10) is bounded for $t \geq 0$.

Indeed, from (26.12) we have

$$|x_s| \leq \sum_{i=1}^{n} |y_{si}(t)||x_{i0}| + \int_0^t \sum_{i=1}^{n} |y_{si}(t - \tau)||h_i[x_1(\tau) ... x_n(\tau)]|\,d\tau +$$

$$+ \int_0^t \sum_{i=1}^{n} |y_{si}(t - \tau)||p_i(\tau)|\,d\tau \quad (s = 1, ..., n). \quad (26.13)$$

We shall now make use of the inequalities (26.11) for $y_1 = y_2 = ... = y_n = 0$, and also of the inequalities $|y_{si}(t - \tau)e^{-\bar{\lambda}(t-\tau)}| \leq m_s$ for $t \geq \tau \geq 0$. Then we shall obtain

$$|x_s| \leq \sum_{i=1}^{n} |y_{si}(t)||x_{i0}| + \int_0^t e^{\bar{\lambda}(t-\tau)} \sum_{i=1}^{n} h_{si}|x_i(\tau)|\,d\tau + \int_0^t e^{\bar{\lambda}(t-\tau)} \sum_{i=1}^{n} m_{si}n_i\,d\tau, \quad (26.14)$$

where by m_{si} are denoted the elements of the matrix $M \times B$, and by $n_1, ..., n_n$ the largest values of the functions $|q_1(t)|, ..., |q_n(t)|$.

Multiplying both members of (26.14) by $e^{-\bar{\lambda}t}$ and introducing new functions defined by means of the formulae

$$y_s(t) = \int_0^t e^{-\bar{\lambda}\tau} |x_s(\tau)| d\tau,$$

we shall obtain

$$\frac{dy_s}{dt} \leqq \sum_{i=1}^n h_{si}y_i + \sum_{i=1}^n |y_{si}(t)| |x_{i0}| e^{-\bar{\lambda}t} + (e^{-\bar{\lambda}t} - 1)c_s, \qquad (26.15)$$

where

$$c_s = \sum_{i=1}^n \frac{m_{si}n_i}{|\bar{\lambda}|}.$$

Relations (26.15) may be otherwise represented in the form of linear differential equations

$$\frac{dy_s}{dt} = \sum_{i=1}^n h_{si}y_i + \sum_{i=1}^n |y_{si}(t)| |x_{i0}| e^{-\bar{\lambda}t} + c_s(e^{-\bar{\lambda}t} - 1) - R_s(t), \qquad (26.16)$$

where R_s are some positive functions of time, given for $t > 0$.

We shall seek the solution of system (26.15) satisfying the conditions $y_s = 0$ for $t = 0$. With this aim we shall introduce into the argument the matrix $Z(t)$ of the fundamental system of solutions of the system of equations

$$\frac{dy_s}{dt} = \sum_{i=1}^n h_{si}y_i.$$

Then the solution sought for may be represented in the form

$$y_s = \int_0^t \sum_{i=1}^n z_{si}(t-\tau) \left(\sum_{k=1}^n |y_{ik}| |x_{k0}| e^{-\bar{\lambda}\tau} + c_i(e^{-\bar{\lambda}\tau} - 1) - R_i \right) d\tau. \qquad (26.17)$$

Here, by $z_{si}(\tau)$ we denote functions entering in the fundamental system of solutions Z. It is easy to convince oneself that every one of the functions $z_{si}(t-\tau)$; $t \geqq \tau \geqq 0$ is nonnegative. Therefore from the equalities (26.17) one may obtain an inequality by cancelling out the unknown nonnegative functions $R_i(t)$, as a result of which we shall obtain

$$y_s \leqq \int_0^t \sum_{i=1}^n z_{si}(t-\tau) \left(\sum_{k=1}^n |y_{ik}| |x_{k0}| e^{-\bar{\lambda}\tau} + c_i(e^{-\bar{\lambda}\tau} - 1) \right) d\tau. \qquad (26.18)$$

We shall choose a positive number $\bar{\mu}$ so that $\bar{\mu} > \mu$, $\bar{\mu} + \bar{\lambda} < 0$. Then the functions $z_{si}(t-\tau)e^{-\bar{\mu}(t-\tau)}$ are bounded for all $t \geqq \tau \geqq 0$. We shall denote their common upper bound by a. The functions $|y_{si}(t)| e^{-\bar{\lambda}t}$ are also bounded for $t > 0$. We shall denote their common upper bound by b.

Taking these estimates into account, we shall obtain

$$y_s \leqq \int_0^t \left[e^{+\bar{\mu}(t-\tau)} nab \sum_{i=1}^n |x_{i0}| + e^{\bar{\mu}(t-\tau)} a \sum_{i=1}^n c_i(e^{-\bar{\lambda}\tau} - 1) \right] d\tau,$$

whence finally

$$y_s \leqq \frac{nab}{\bar{\mu}} \sum_{i=1}^n |x_{i0}|(e^{\bar{\mu}t} - 1) + \frac{a}{\bar{\mu}+\bar{\lambda}} \sum_{i=1}^n c_i(e^{-\bar{\lambda}t} - e^{\bar{\mu}t}). \qquad (26.19)$$

Making use of (26.19), we shall eliminate the quantities $y_1, ..., y_n$ from the right-hand members of inequalities (26.15). Then we shall obtain the inequalities

$$|x_s| e^{-\bar{\lambda}t} \leqq \sum_{i=1}^n h_{si} \frac{nab}{\bar{\mu}} \sum_{i=1}^n |x_{i0}|(e^{+\bar{\mu}t} - 1) + \frac{a}{|\bar{\mu} + \bar{\lambda}|} \sum_{i=1}^n c_i(e^{-\bar{\lambda}t} - e^{\bar{\mu}t}) +$$

$$+ \sum_{i=1}^n |y_{si}(t)||x_{i0}|e^{-\bar{\lambda}t} + c_s(e^{-\bar{\lambda}t} - 1). \qquad (26.20)$$

Multiplying both members of the inequalities obtained by $e^{\bar{\lambda}t}$ and taking into account the relations $\bar{\lambda} + \bar{\mu} < 0$, we shall obtain that every solution of system (26.10) is bounded for $t > 0$.

We shall note that the quantities bounding the functions x_s, for $t = 0$ are linear forms in the quantities $|x_{10}|, ..., |x_{n0}|, ..., |x_{n1}|, ..., |x_{nn}|$. Here, from the last inequality (26.20) follows that $|x_s(t)| \to 0$ as $t \to +\infty$, if only $n_1 = n_2 = ... = n_n = 0$. We shall now show that the difference between any two solutions of system (26.10) satisfies conditions 2 of Theorem 54.

We shall denote one of the solutions by $x_1, ..., x_n$, another by $y_1, ..., y_n$. Both solutions satisfy (26.12) identically. Subtracting the above-mentioned identities term by term, we shall obtain

$$x_s - y_s = \sum_{i=1}^n y_{si}(t)(x_{i0} - y_{i0}) + \int_0^t \left[\sum_{i=1}^n y_{si}(t - \tau) \left\{ h_i[x_1(\tau), ..., x_n(\tau)] - \right. \right.$$

$$\left. \left. - h_i[y_1(\tau), ..., y_n(\tau)] \right\} d\tau \quad (s = 1, ..., n).$$

We shall make use of condition 2 of Theorem 55. Then

$$|x_s - y_s| \leqq \sum_{i=1}^n |y_{si}(t)||x_{i0} - y_{i0}| + \int_0^t \sum_{i=1}^n |y_{si}(t - \tau)| \times$$

$$\times \left(\sum_{k=1}^n b_{ik}|x_k(\tau) - y_k(\tau)| \right) d\tau. \qquad (26.21)$$

We shall note that in the last inequality the quantities $|x_s - y_s|$ are again denoted as $|x_s|$, and the quantities $|x_{s0} - y_{s0}|$ are denoted as x_{s0}. Then it will be clearly apparent that inequalities (26.21) in no way differ from those considered earlier, if in them we have set $n_1 = n_2 = ... = n_n = 0$.

Thus, the arguments given above show that $|x_s - y_s| \to 0$ as $t \to +\infty$. Here for every number $\varepsilon > 0$ there exists a number $\delta(\varepsilon) > 0$ such that if $|x_{s0} - y_{s0}| < \delta(\varepsilon)$ then $|x_s(t) - y_s(t)| < \varepsilon$ for $t \geq 0$.

Thus, it has been shown that if the conditions of Theorem 55 are satisfied then both conditions of Theorem 54 are fulfilled, and therefore system (26.10) possesses convergence.

Theorem 55, just proved, is an existence theorem and does not contain a method of finding the periodic solution. We shall construct the system of integral equations for the sought periodic solution.

Let us assume that system (26.10) has a periodic solution of period T, determined by the initial conditions $x_{10}, \ldots, x_{n0}$ at $t = 0$. By substituting that solution into equality (26.12), we shall obtain the system of n identities

$$x_s(t) = \sum_{i=1}^{n} y_{si}(t) x_{i0} + \int_0^t \sum_{i=1}^{n} y_{si}(t - \tau) h_i [x_1(\tau), \ldots, x_n(\tau)] d\tau +$$

$$+ \int_0^t \sum_{i=1}^{n} y_{si}(t - \tau) p_i(\tau) d\tau \quad (s = 1, \ldots, n). \quad (26.22)$$

To shorten the following calculations we shall rewrite identity (26.22) in matrix form

$$X = Y(t)X_0 + \int_0^t Y(t - \tau) H [X(\tau)] d\tau + \int_0^t Y(t - \tau) P(\tau) d\tau,$$

where H is an n-dimensional vector whose components are the functions $h_1, \ldots, h_n$, P is an n-dimensional vector whose components are the functions $p_1, \ldots, p_n$.

In the last identity we shall perform a change of argument, displacing it by the period of the function P.

If in the identity thus obtained one performs a change of variable of integration according to the formula $\tau = \theta + T$ and makes use of the periodicity of the functions $X(t)$ and $P(t)$, one obtains

$$X(t + T) = Y(t + T) X_0 + \int_{-T}^t Y(t - \theta) H [X(\theta)] d\theta + \int_{-T}^t Y(t - \theta) P(\theta) d\theta.$$

Subtracting from the last identity the preceding one and setting $t = 0$, we shall obtain

$$[Y(T) - E]X_0 - \int_{-T}^t Y(-\theta) \{H [X(\theta)] + P(\theta)\} d\theta = 0.$$

Solving the last equality for vector X_0, we shall find

$$X_0 = [E - Y(T)]^{-1} \int_{-T}^0 Y(-\theta) \{H[X(\theta)] + P(\theta)\} d\theta. \quad (26.23)$$

Thus, the initial conditions determining the periodic solution necessarily satisfy relation (26.23). Utilizing that relation, we shall eliminate the quantities $x_{10}, \ldots, x_{n0}$ from equalities (26.12). Then we shall obtain a system of integral equations for determining the periodic solutions of system (26.10)

$$X = Y(t)[E - Y(t)]^{-1} \int_{-T}^{0} Y(-\theta)\{H[X(\theta)] + P(\theta)\}\, d\theta +$$

$$+ \int_{0}^{t} Y(t - \tau)\ \{H[X(\tau)] + P(\tau)\}\, d\tau. \qquad (26.24)$$

Let us study the possibility of applying the method of successive approximations for finding the periodic solutions of system (26.10). We shall denote the right-hand member of equalities (26.25) by $R(X)$. We shall show first that for any periodic function $X(t)$ of period T, the operator R will give also a corresponding periodic function of period T. Indeed,

$$R[X(t + T)] - R[X(t)] = Y(t)\{Y(t)[E - Y(t)]\}^{-1} \int_{-T}^{0} Y(-\theta)\{H[X(\theta)] +$$

$$P(\theta)\}\, d\theta + \int_{0}^{t+T} Y(-\tau + T)\ \{H[X(\tau)] + P(\tau)\}d\tau - \int_{0}^{t} Y(-\tau)\ \{H[X(\tau)] +$$

$$+ P(\tau)\}\, d\tau - [E - Y(T)]^{-1} \int_{-T}^{0} Y(-\theta)\ \{H[X(\theta)] + P(\theta)\}d\theta \equiv 0.$$

We form the sequence of periodic vector functions defined by the following formulae

$$X_1 \equiv 0;\ X^{k+1} = R(X^k)k \geq 0. \qquad (26.25)$$

Into the investigation we shall introduce constant vectors F^k, whose components represent the upper limits of the moduli of the corresponding components of the vector

$$X^{k+1} - X^k,\ \text{i.e. } f^k = \sup_{0 \leq t \leq T}|x_s^{k+1} - x_s^k|.$$

By N_1 we shall denote the matrix obtained from $[E - Y(T)]^{-1}$ by replacing its elements by their absolute values. By N_2 we shall denote the matrix obtained from the matrix $Y(t-\theta)$ by replacing its arguments with the upper bounds of their moduli in the interval $-T \leq \theta \leq 0$ and in the interval $0 \leq t \leq T$.

By N_3 we shall denote the matrix whose elements are the upper bounds of the moduli of the corresponding elements of the matrix $Y(t-\tau)$ in the interval $0 \leq \tau \leq t \leq T$.

Let us construct the matrix N

$$N = (N_1 N_2 + N_3) B. \tag{26.26}$$

THEOREM 56.   If the following conditions are satisfied:

1)   the matrix $[E - Y(T)]$ is nonsingular;

2)   condition 2 of Theorem 55 is fulfilled;

3)   the roots of the characteristic polynomial of the matrix N (26.26) lie within a circle of radius $1/T$ centred at the coordinate origin —
then the system (26.10) has a periodic solution which is the uniform limit of the sequence $X^k(t)$.

PROOF: We shall show that the sequence $x^0, \dots, x^k$ converges uniformly for $0 \leq t \leq T$.

For this we shall estimate the difference between two vectors $X^{k+1}(T)$ and $X^k(T)$.

Let us adopt the convention to denote in what follows by $[X^{k+1}(T) - X^k(T)]$ the vector obtained from the vector $X^{k+1}(T) - X^k(T)$ by replacing its coordinates by their moduli. Then we shall have the inequality

$$[X^{k+1}(T) - X^k(T)] \leq [E - Y(T)]^{-1} \int_{-T}^{0} Y(t - \theta) \{ H[X^k(\theta)] -$$

$$- H[X^{k-1}(\theta)]\} \, d\theta + \int_{0}^{t} Y(t - \tau)\{H[X^k(\tau)] - H[X^{k-1}(\tau)]\} \, d\tau. \tag{26.27}$$

Applying the notations introduced above, we shall obtain

$$F^k \leq (N_1 N_2 + N_3) BTF^{k-1} \leq NTF^{k-1}; \quad k \geq 1. \tag{26.28}$$

From (26.28) we have

$$F^k \leq T^k N^k F^0.$$

The last estimate shows that the series

$$X^0 + (X^1 - X^0) + (X^2 - X^1) + (X^3 - X^2) + \dots + (X^{k+1} - X^k) + \dots$$

converges uniformly in the interval $0 \leq t \leq T$, as it has a majorant in the converging series

$$\sum_{k=1}^{\infty} T^k N^k F^0. \tag{26.29}$$

Series (26.29) converges in view of the fact that the roots of the characteristic polynomial of the matrix NT lie within the unit circle. Thus, there exists a continuous periodic function $X(T)$ which is the uniform limit of the sequence $X^k(t)$. In view of the fact that in both members of the equality $X^{k+1} = R(X^k)$ we shall admit a limiting process, we shall obtain that the periodic function found satisfies the integral equation $X(t) = R[X(t)]$.

Term by term differentiation of this identity shows that the periodic function $X(T)$ found is the solution of system (26.10).

In conclusion we shall give two sets of examples of applying Theorems 55 and 56 to a system of two equations.

EXAMPLES

Example 1.   Let us consider the system

$$\dot{x} = \lambda_1 x + h_1(xy) + p_1(t),$$

$$\dot{y} = \lambda_2 y + h_2(xy) + p_2(t),$$

where $\lambda_1 < 0$; $\lambda_2 \leq \lambda_1$.

We shall consider that the functions p_1 and p_2 are continuous periodic with period T, and the functions $h_1(xy)$ and $h_2(xy)$ satisfy the inequalities

$$\left| h_i(xy) - h_i(\bar{x}\,\bar{y}) \right| \leq b_{i1} \left| x - \bar{x} \right| + b_{i2} \left| y - \bar{y} \right|, \quad b_{ij} \geq 0. \qquad (26.30)$$

If the quantities λ_1 and b_{ij} $(i,j = 1,2)$ are related by the inequality

$$2\lambda_1 + b_{11} + b_{22} + \sqrt{(b_{11} - b_{22})^2 + 4b_{12}b_{21}} < 0,$$

then the original system possesses the property of convergence.

Indeed, in this example one may take as λ the quantity λ_1. Then the matrix M will be a unit matrix. As $\bar{\mu}$ one may take a number equal to the largest real root of the matrix B. Following such a choice of the quantities $\bar{\lambda}$ and $\bar{\mu}$, the application of Theorem 55 leads to the assertion formulated above.

Example 2.   Let us consider the system of equations

$$\dot{x} = \lambda x + \omega y + h_1(xy) + p_1(t),$$

$$\dot{y} = \lambda - \omega x + \lambda y + h_2(xy) + p_2(t). \qquad (26.31)$$

The fundamental system of solutions Y in that case has the form

$$e^{\lambda t} \begin{Vmatrix} \sin \omega t & -\cos \omega t \\ \cos \omega t & \sin \omega t \end{Vmatrix}.$$

We shall consider that $\lambda < 0$, the functions p_1 and p_2 are periodic with period T, and the functions h_1 and h_2 satisfy condition (26.30).

As $\bar{\lambda}$ one may take here the quantity λ. Then the elements of matrix M will be defined by the equalities $m_{ij} = 1$. If the quantities λ and b_{ij} $(i, j = 1, 2)$ are related by the inequality

$$2\lambda + \sum b_{ij} + \sqrt{(b_{11} + b_{21}) - (b_{12} - b_{22})^2 + 4(b_{11} + b_{12})(b_{21} + b_{22})} < 0,$$

then the system (26.31) possesses the property of convergence.

Example 3.   We shall consider the system of equations

$$\left.\begin{aligned}
\dot{x} &= (\lambda - \varepsilon)x + h_1(xy) + p_1(t), \\
\dot{y} &= x + (\lambda - \varepsilon)y + h_2(xy) + p_2(t),
\end{aligned}\right\} \qquad (26.32)$$

where $\lambda - \varepsilon < 0$, $\varepsilon > 0$, $\lambda < 0$.

The fundamental system of solutions Y in that case has the form

$$Y(t) = \begin{Vmatrix} e^{(\lambda - \varepsilon)t} & 0 \\ te^{(\lambda - \varepsilon)t} & e^{(\lambda - \varepsilon)t} \end{Vmatrix}.$$

We shall set $\bar{\lambda} = \lambda$. Then the elements of the matrix M may be chosen in the following way

$$m_{11} = 1, \quad m_{22} = 1,$$
$$m_{12} = 0 \quad m_{21} = \frac{1}{e\varepsilon}.$$

We shall assume that the functions h_1 and h_2 satisfy condition (26.30), and the functions p_1 and p_2 are continuous periodic with period T. We shall find the elements of the matrix H

$$h_{11} = b_{11}, \; h_{21} = \frac{b_{11}}{e\varepsilon} + b_{21},$$

$$h_{12} = b_{12}, \; h_{22} = \frac{b_{12}}{e\varepsilon} + b_{22}.$$

If the quantities $\lambda, \varepsilon, b_{ij}$ are related by the inequality

$$2\lambda + h_{11} + h_{22} + \sqrt{(h_{11} - h_{22})^2 + 4(h_{21} + h_{12})} < 0,$$

then system (26.32) possesses the property of convergence.

Example 4.   We shall consider the system

$$\left.\begin{aligned}
\dot{x} &= \lambda_1 x + h_1(xy) + P_1(t), \\
\dot{y} &= \lambda_2 y + h_2(xy) + P_2(t),
\end{aligned}\right\} \qquad (26.33)$$

where $\lambda_1 > 0$, $\lambda_2 < 0$.

The fundamental system of solutions Y has the form

$$Y(t) = \begin{Vmatrix} e^{\lambda_1 t} & 0 \\ 0 & e^{\lambda_2 t} \end{Vmatrix}.$$

We shall assume that the functions P_1 and P_2 are periodic with period T, and the functions h_1 and h_2 satisfy conditions (26.30).

Then the matrix N_1 will be diagonal

$$N_1 = \begin{Vmatrix} \dfrac{1}{e^{\lambda_2 T}} - 1 & 0 \\ 0 & \dfrac{1}{1 - e^{\lambda_2 T}} \end{Vmatrix}.$$

The matrix N_2 has the form

$$N_2 = \begin{Vmatrix} e^{2T\lambda_1} & 0 \\ 0 & 1 \end{Vmatrix}.$$

The matrix N_3 has the form

$$N_3 = \begin{Vmatrix} e^{\lambda_1 T} & 0 \\ 0 & 1 \end{Vmatrix}.$$

The matrix $N_1 N_2 + N_3$ will therefore be diagonal

$$N_1 N_2 + N_3 = \begin{Vmatrix} a & 0 \\ 0 & b \end{Vmatrix}.$$

The elements of the matrix N are calculated from known functions, so that

$$N = \begin{Vmatrix} ab_{11} & ab_{12} \\ bb_{21} & bb_{22} \end{Vmatrix}.$$

If the quantities λ_1 and λ_2 are subject to the inequality

$$ab_{11} + bb_{22} + \sqrt{(ab_{11} - bb_{22})^2 + 4abb_{12}b_{21}} < \frac{2}{T},$$

then system (26.33) has a periodic solution, which may be obtained as the limit of the sequence indicated earlier.

We shall note that the method of finding the periodic solution indicated in Theorem 56, as follows from example 4, may be applied even in those cases when the original system does not possess the property of convergence. However, one should not think that the method of successive approximations for the construction of periodic solutions, indicated in Theorem 56, is suitable in all those cases when the original system possesses the property of convergence. In fact, we shall consider the equation $\dot{x} = -2x + p(t)$, where $p(t)$ is a continuous periodic functions with period T. It is easy to see that this equation possesses the property of convergence.

Let us write this equation in the form

$$\dot{x} = -x + h(x) + p(t), \quad h(x) = -x.$$

For the periodic solution we shall construct the integral equation

$$x = (1 - e^T)^{-1} \int_{-T}^{0} e^{t-\theta} [-x + p(\theta)]d\theta + \int_{0}^{t} e^{t-\tau}[-x + p(\tau)]d\tau.$$

For definiteness we shall set $p = 1$, and determine the sequence of approximations $x_0, x_1, \ldots, x_k, \ldots$. For $x_0 = 0$ we shall obtain $x_1 = 1$, $x_2 = 0$, $x_3 = 1, \ldots$. The sequence found does not converge; nevertheless, the original equation has a unique periodic solution. This remark would not be complete if we did not note that the sequence found nevertheless converged in the Cesaro sense to the known periodic solution $x = \frac{1}{2}$.

§ 27. Periodic and almost-periodic oscillations in nonlinear autonomic systems

We shall consider the system of homogeneous differential equations

$$\frac{dx_s}{dt} = \sum_{i=1}^{n} a_{si}x_i \quad (s = 1, \ldots, n).$$

If the characteristic equation of that system has pure imaginary roots then in the system there exist periodic oscillations. If there exist several pure imaginary roots, among which there are at least two ($i\omega_1$ and $i\omega_2$) which are incommensurate, then in the system together with the periodic oscillations one also observes almost-periodic oscillations appearing from the super-position of some periodic oscillations with incommensurate periods.

A similar phenomenon is observed in some nonlinear autonomic systems. In what follows, we consider a system of $n + 2k$ equations whose linear approximation has k pairs of pure imaginary roots, among which there are no multiple ones. This investigation is carried out mainly in two directions. First, we investigate the stability properties of the equilibrium position. Secondly, we investigate the analytic properties of these periodic and almost-periodic solutions depending on the choice of the initial conditions determining them.

Let us consider the system

$$
\left.
\begin{aligned}
\frac{dx_s}{dt} &= -\ \lambda_s y_s + \bar{X}_s(x_1,\ldots,x_k,\ y_1,\ldots,y_k,\ z_1,\ldots,z_n) \quad (s=1,\ldots,k); \\
\frac{dy_s}{dt} &= \quad \lambda_s x_s + \bar{Y}_s(x_1,\ldots,x_k,\ y_1,\ldots,y_k,\ z_1,\ldots,z_n); \\
\frac{dz_j}{dt} &= \sum_{i=1}^{n} r_{ji} z_i + Z_j(x_1,\ldots,x_k,\ y_1,\ldots,y_k,\ z_1,\ldots,z_n) \quad (j=1,\ldots,n).
\end{aligned}
\right\} \quad (27.1)
$$

We shall assume that the functions $\bar{X}_s, \bar{Y}_s, Z_j$ may be expanded in convergent power series in $x_1,\ldots,x_k;\ y_1,\ldots,y_k;\ z_1,\ldots,z_n$, containing no linear terms. We shall consider the right-hand members of system (27.1) as real. The quantities $\lambda_1,\ldots,\lambda_k$ are positive and such that

$$
\left.
\begin{aligned}
\sum_{i=1}^{k} \mu_i \lambda_i &\neq 0, \\
\sum_{i=1}^{k} |\mu_i| &\neq 0,
\end{aligned}
\right\} \quad (27.2)
$$

for any integers $\mu_1,\ldots,\mu_k$.

The system

$$
\left.
\begin{aligned}
\sum_{j=1}^{n} \frac{\partial x_s}{\partial z_j}\left(\sum_{i=1}^{n} r_{ji} z_i + Z_j\right) &= -\ \lambda_s y_s + \bar{X}_s, \\
\sum_{j=1}^{n} \frac{\partial y_s}{\partial z_j}\left(\sum_{i=1}^{n} r_{ji} z_i + Z_j\right) &= \quad \lambda_s x_s + \bar{Y}_s \quad (s=1,\ldots,k),
\end{aligned}
\right\} \quad (27.3)
$$

has the solution

$$
x_s = U_s(\bar{z}_1,\ldots,\bar{z}_n),
$$
$$
y_s = V_s(\bar{z}_1,\ldots,\bar{z}_n),
$$

holomorphic in the neighbourhood of the point $z_1 = \ldots = z_n = 0$. We shall perform the transformation

$$
x_s = \bar{x}_s + U_s,\ y_s = \bar{y}_s + V_s,\ldots \quad (27.4)
$$

in system (27.1). Then we shall obtain

$$
\left.
\begin{aligned}
\frac{d\bar{x}_s}{dt} &= -\ \lambda_s \bar{y}_s + \bar{X}_s(\bar{x}_1,\ldots,\bar{x}_k,\ \bar{y}_1,\ldots,\bar{y}_k,\ \bar{z}_1,\ldots,\bar{z}_n), \\
\frac{d\bar{y}_s}{dt} &= \quad \lambda_s \bar{x}_s + \bar{Y}_s, \\
\frac{d\bar{z}_j}{dt} &= \sum_{i=1}^{n} r_{ji} Z_i + Z_j.
\end{aligned}
\right\} \quad (27.5)
$$

It is clear that $\bar{X}_s, \bar{Y}_s, \bar{Z}_j$ possess the same properties as the original X_s, Y_s, Z_j. Besides, $\bar{X}_s = \bar{Y}_s = 0$ when all the $\bar{x}_s = \bar{y}_s = 0 \ (s = 1, \ldots, k)$.

Further, in system (27.5) we shall perform the substitution

$$\left.\begin{aligned} \bar{x}_s &= r_s \cos \theta_s , \\ \bar{y}_s &= r_s \sin \theta_s , \end{aligned}\right\} \tag{27.6}$$

as a result of which we shall obtain the system

$$\left.\begin{aligned} \frac{dr_s}{dt} &= R_s \qquad (s = 1, \ldots, k); \\[2ex] \frac{d\theta_s}{dt} &= \lambda_s + \Theta_s; \\[2ex] \frac{d\bar{z}_j}{dt} &= \sum_{i=1}^{n} r_{ji} \bar{z}_i + P_j(r_1, \ldots, r_k, \ \theta_1, \ldots, \theta_k, \ \bar{z}_1, \ldots, \bar{z}_n), \end{aligned}\right\} \tag{27.7}$$

where

$$R_s = \cos \theta_s \, \bar{X}_s (r_1 \cos \theta_1, \ldots, r_k \cos \theta_k, \ r_1 \sin \theta_1, \ldots, r_k \sin \theta_k, \ \bar{z}_1, \ldots, \bar{z}_n) +$$
$$+ \ \sin \theta_s \bar{Y}_s (r_1 \cos \theta_1, \ldots, r_k \sin \theta_k, \ \bar{z}_1, \ldots, \bar{z}_n);$$

$$\Theta_s = \frac{\cos \theta_s \bar{Y}_s - \sin \theta_s \bar{X}_s}{r_s} \ ;$$

$$P_j = \bar{Z}_j(r_1 \cos \theta_1, \ldots, \bar{z}_1, \ldots, \bar{z}_n).$$

It is easy to see that the functions R_s and P_j are holomorphic in the neighbourhood of $r_1 = \ldots = r_k = \bar{z}_1 = \ldots = \bar{z}_n = 0$. Here $R = 0$ for $r_1 = \ldots = r_k = 0$. The coefficients in the expansions of the functions R_s and P_j are periodic functions in $\theta_i \ (i = 1, \ldots, k)$. We shall further assume that the functions Θ_s possess the same properties as R_s and P_j. We shall note that conditions (27.2) allow one to carry out a transformation of system (27.5), after which the functions Θ_s will be formally expanded in series in powers of $r_1, \ldots, r_k$, $\bar{z}_1, \ldots, \bar{z}_n$.

We shall seek the solution of system (27.7) in the form of series

$$\left.\begin{aligned} r_s &= c_s + \sum_{m=2}^{\infty} \bar{r}_s^{(m)} (\theta_1, \ldots, \theta_k, \ c_1, \ldots, c_k); \\[2ex] \bar{z}_j &= \sum_{m=1}^{\infty} \bar{z}_j^{(m)} (\theta_1, \ldots, \theta_k, \ c_1, \ldots, c_k). \end{aligned}\right\} \tag{27.8}$$

The functions $\bar{r}_s^{(m)}$ and $\bar{z}_j^{(m)}$ are homogeneous forms in $c_1, \ldots, c_k$ of the m-th degree with periodic coefficients in $\theta_1, \ldots, \theta_k$ undergoing determination.

We shall set up the equations for finding the solutions of system (27.7) in the form (27.8),

$$\left.\begin{aligned} \sum_{i=1}^{k} \frac{\partial r_s}{\partial \theta_i} (\lambda_i + \Theta_i) &= R_s \qquad (s = 1, \ldots, k); \\ \sum_{i=1}^{k} \frac{\partial \bar{z}_j}{\partial \theta_i} (\lambda_i + \Theta_i) &= \sum_{i=1}^{n} r_{ji} \bar{z}_i + P_j \qquad (j = 1, \ldots, n). \end{aligned}\right\}$$ (27.9)

Substituting series (27.8) in system (27.9) and equating the forms of the same degree in the quantities $c_1, \ldots, c_k$, we shall obtain the system of equations

$$\left.\begin{aligned} \sum_{i=1}^{k} \frac{\partial r_s^{(m)}}{\partial \theta_i} \lambda_i &= R_s^{(m)} \qquad (s = 1, \ldots, k); \\ \sum_{i=1}^{k} \lambda_i \frac{\partial \bar{z}_j^{(m)}}{\partial \theta_i} &= \sum_{i=1}^{n} r_{ji} \bar{z}_i^{(m)} + P^{(m)} \qquad (j = 1, \ldots, n). \end{aligned}\right\}$$ (27.10)

The forms $R_s^{(m)}$ and $P_j^{(m-1)}$ are determined if one finds the functions $r_s^{(m_1)}$ and $\bar{z}_j^{(m_2)}$; $m_1 < m$, $m_2 < m - 1$.

We shall assume that functions (27.9) were determined from system (27.10) as periodic in $\theta_1, \ldots, \theta_k$ and for sufficiently small $|c_s|$ they supply the solution of system (27.9). Say the construction of series (27.8) was realized, so that $\mathrm{r}_s^{(m)} = 0$ for $\theta_1 = \ldots = \theta_k = 0$ $(m \geqq 2)$.

In this special case we shall investigate the problem of stability of the homogeneous solution of system (27.1). In system (27.7) we shall perform the substitution

$$r_s = \rho_s + \sum_{m=2}^{\infty} r_s^{(m)} (\theta_1, \ldots, \theta_k, \rho_1, \ldots, \rho_k),$$ (27.11)

$$\bar{z}_j = z_j + \sum_{m=2}^{\infty} z_j^{(m)} (\theta_1, \ldots, \theta_k, \rho_1, \ldots, \rho_k),$$

where $\rho_1, \ldots, \rho_k$ are new sought functions.

Then we shall obtain

$$\left.\begin{aligned} \frac{d\rho_s}{dt} &= \bar{R}_s; \\ \frac{d\theta_s}{dt} &= \lambda_s + \bar{\Theta}_s; \\ \frac{dz_j}{dt} &= \sum_{i=1}^{n} r_{ji} z_i + \bar{P}_j. \end{aligned}\right\}$$ (27.12)

System (27.12) has the family of solutions $\rho_s = c_s$ $(s = 1, ..., k)$, $z_j = 0$
$(j = 1, ..., n)$.

Further it may be shown that the system

$$\sum_{j=1}^{n} \frac{\partial \rho_s}{\partial \bar{z}_j} \left(\sum_{i=1}^{n} r_{ji} z_i + P_j \right) + \sum_{i=1}^{k} \frac{\partial \rho_s}{\partial \theta_i} (\lambda_i + \bar{\Theta}_i) = \bar{R}_s \qquad (27.13)$$

has a family of solutions

$$\rho_s = c_s + F_s(z_1, ..., z_n, \ \theta_1, ..., \theta_k, \ c_1, ..., c_k) \quad (s = 1, ..., k). \qquad (27.14)$$

The functions F_s may be expanded in converging power series in $z_1, ..., z_n$, $c_1, ..., c_k$ for sufficiently small $|z_j|$ and $|c_s|$. Here $F_s = 0$ for $z_1 = ... = z_n = 0$. Making use of equalities (27.14), we shall eliminate the quantities ρ_s from the third group of equations (27.12). Then we shall obtain a system for determining the functions $\bar{z}_j$, from which it follows that for all sufficiently small $|c_s|$ and for any choice of continuous real functions $\theta_1(t), ..., \theta_k(t), \bar{z}_j(t) \to 0$ as $t \to +\infty$ uniformly with respect to $c_1, ..., c_k$, if only $|\bar{z}_j(0)|$ are sufficiently small. Hence also from (27.14) it follows that $\rho_s \to c_s$ as $t \to +\infty$. In other words the homogeneous solution of system (27.1) is stable. Thus, the Theorem is proved.

THEOREM 57. If system (27.7) has a family of bounded solutions (27.8), then the homogeneous solution of system (27.1) is stable in the sense of Lyapunov.

We shall solve equalities (27.14) with respect to the quantities $c_1, ..., c_k$. Then

$$c_s = \rho_s + \Phi_s(\theta_1, ..., \theta_k, \ \rho_1, ..., \rho_k, \ \bar{z}_1, ..., \bar{z}_n) \quad (s = 1, ..., k). \qquad (27.15)$$

In equalities (27.15) we shall pass to quantities $r_1, ..., r_k$ and, applying (27.6), we shall obtain

$$c_s^2 = \bar{x}_s^2 + \bar{y}_s^2 + \psi_s \ (\bar{x}_1, ..., \bar{x}_k, \ \bar{y}_1, ..., \bar{y}_k, \ \bar{z}_1, ..., \bar{z}_n) \quad (s = 1, ..., k). \qquad (27.16)$$

It can be shown that the functions ψ_s may be expanded in converging series in integral positive powers of the quantities $\bar{x}_s, \bar{y}_s, \bar{z}_j$. Thus, equalities (27.16) give k holomorphic integrals of system (27.5). Here

$$\sqrt{\bar{x}_s^2 + \bar{y}_s^2 + \psi_s} = r_s + \bar{\psi}_s(\theta_1, ..., \theta_k, \ r_1, ..., r_k, \ \bar{z}_1, ..., \bar{z}_n), \qquad (27.17)$$

where ψ_s is holomorphic in the neighbourhood of the point

$$r_1 = ... = r_k = \bar{z}_1 = ... = \bar{z}_n = 0.$$

THEOREM 58. In order that system (27.7) have a family of bounded solutions (27.8), it is necessary and sufficient that there exist k holomorphic integrals of system (27.5) of form (27.16), possessing property (27.17).

PROOF: The necessity of the condition is established above, and the sufficiency of the condition may be derived by carrying out the inverse transformations upon integrals (27.17).

We shall consider in greater detail the case when all the functions $r_s^{(m)}$ and $z_j^{(m)}$ are periodic. Making use of functions (27.8), we shall eliminate the variables $r_1, ..., r_k, z_1, ..., z_n$ from the second group of equations of system (27.7). Then for the determination of the functions $\theta_1, ..., \theta_k$ we shall obtain the system of equations

$$\frac{d\theta_s}{dt} = \lambda_s + \Phi_s(\theta_1, ..., \theta_k, c_1, ..., c_k) \qquad (s = 1, ..., k). \qquad (27.18)$$

The functions Φ_s entering in the right-hand members of system (27.18) may be expanded in series, distributed over the integral positive powers of the quantities $c_1, ..., c_k$ not containing free terms in the latter. The coefficients in these series are finite trigonometric polynomials in $\theta_1, ..., \theta_k$. We shall introduce into the investigation new independent variables according to the formulae $\tau_s = t h_s$, where h_s represent series of the form $h_s = \dot\lambda_s + + \sum_{m=1}^{\infty} h_s^{(m)}$, and $h_s^{(m)}$ are homogeneous forms in the quantities $c_1, ..., c_k$ of the order m with coefficients to be determined

System (27.18) has a solution defined by the conditions $\theta_s = \theta_s^0$ for $t = 0 \ (s = 1, ..., k)$.

This solution is represented in the form of a series in powers of the variables $t, c_1, ..., c_k$; the coefficients of these series are determined as known trigonometric polynomials in the quantities $\theta_1^0, ..., \theta_k^0$.

We shall define the coefficients of the forms $h_s^{(m)}$ in such a way that the quantities θ_s be dependent on t only through the intermediary of the variables $\tau_1, ..., \tau_k$. We shall show that the functions $h_1, ..., h_k$ may always be chosen so that the indicated dependence holds. Indeed, we shall consider the system of equations in partial derivatives

$$\sum_{i=1}^{k} \frac{\partial \theta_s}{\partial \tau_i} h_i = \lambda_s + \Phi_s \qquad (s = 1, ..., k). \qquad (27.19)$$

We shall seek the solution of these equations in the form

$$\theta_s = \theta_s^0 + \tau_s + T_s. \qquad (27.20)$$

Substituting functions (27.20) in system (27.19), we shall find

$$\sum_{i=1}^{k} \frac{\partial T_s}{\partial \tau_i} h_i = \lambda_s - h_s + \bar{\Phi}_s. \tag{27.21}$$

In equations (27.21) by $\bar{\Phi}_s$ we denote functions obtained from Φ_s by replacing the quantities $\theta_1, \ldots, \theta_k$ according to formulae (27.20). We shall show, that the functions h_s may be chosen so that one may be able to define the functions T_s from system (27.21) in a unique way in the form of series in $c_1, \ldots, c_k$, and so that their coefficients be trigonometric polynomials in $\tau_1, \ldots, \tau_k$. We shall seek the solution of system (27.21) in the form of series $T_s = \sum_{m=1}^{\infty} T_s^{(m)}$, where $T_s^{(m)}$ represents a form of the m-th degree in $c_1, \ldots, c_k$ with the coefficients undergoing determination in the form of trigonometric polynomials in $\tau_1, \ldots, \tau_k$.

We shall substitute these series in equations (27.21) and, equating on the left and right the forms in $c_1, \ldots, c_k$ of the same degree, we shall obtain

$$\sum_{i=1}^{k} \frac{\partial T_s^{(m)}}{\partial \tau_i} \lambda_i = - h_s^{(m)} + \bar{\Phi}_s^{(m)} \quad (s = 1, \ldots, k), \tag{27.22}$$

where the $\bar{\Phi}_s^{(m)}$ represent a known form of the m-th degree in $c_1, \ldots, c_k$ whose coefficients are trigonometric polynomials in $\tau_1, \ldots, \tau_k$, if one finds all the forms $T_s^{(m_1)}$ $(m_1 < m)$ in the aspect mentioned earlier.

We shall consider the system of equations (27.22) in detail. The functions $\bar{\Phi}_s^{(m)}$ are represented in the form

$$\bar{\Phi}_s^{(m)} = \sum_{l_1 + \ldots + l_k = m} c_1^{l_1} c_2^{l_2}, \ldots, c_k^{l_k} R^{(m) l_1, \ldots, l_k}. \tag{27.23}$$

The functions $R^{(m) l_1, \ldots, l_k}$ represent the trigonometric polynomials

$$R_s^{(m) l_1, \ldots, l_k} = \sum R_s^{(m) l_1, \ldots, l_k, p_1, \ldots, p_k} e^{i \sum_{t=1}^{k} p_t \tau_t} + R_{s0}^{(m) l_1, \ldots, l_k}. \tag{27.24}$$

The summation in formula (27.24) is extended over all integers $p_1, \ldots, p_k$ not equal to zero and not exceeding some finite limit $N(m)$ in absolute value. We shall seek the solution of equations (27.22) in the form

$$T_s^{(m)} = \sum_{l_1 + \ldots + l_k = m} c_1^{l_1} c_2^{l_2}, \ldots, c_k^{l_k} \sum_{\sum_{i=1}^{k} |p_i| \leq N(m)} T_s^{(m) l_1, \ldots, l_k, p_1, \ldots, p_k} e^{i \sum_{i=1}^{k} p_i \tau_i} \tag{27.25}$$

Substituting series (27.25) in system (27.22), for defining the coefficients we shall find equations of the form

$$i \sum_{i=1}^{k} P_i \lambda_i T_s^{(m) \, l_1, \, \ldots, \, l_k, \, p_1, \, \ldots, \, p_k} = R_s^{(m) l \, 1, \ldots, l_k, \, p_1, \, \ldots, \, p_k},$$

whence, in view of the rational independence of the quantities $\lambda_1, \ldots, \lambda_k$, the coefficients of the forms $T_s^{(m)}$ are defined uniquely. Thus, in order that system (27.22) have a solution of form (27.25), it is necessary and sufficient that the forms $h_s^{(m)}$ satisfy the relation

$$-h_s^{(m)} + \sum_{l_1 + \ldots + l_k = m} c_1^{l_1}, \ldots, c_k^{l_k} R_{s0}^{(m) l_1, \, \ldots, l_k} \equiv 0.$$

The last relation for $m \geq 1$ allows one to determine uniquely the functions $h_1^{(m)}, \ldots, h_k^{(m)}$. Here it should be noted that $h_s^{(1)} \equiv 0$. Thus there exists a unique system of functions $h_s = \lambda_s + \sum_{m=2}^{\infty} h_s^{(m)}$ such that the functions θ_s are represented in the form $\theta_s = \theta_s^0 + \tau_s + T_s$.

We shall eliminate from functions (27.6) the variables $\theta_1, \ldots, \theta_k$, making use of formulae (27.20), and shall return to the original variables x_s, y_s, and z_j. Then we shall obtain that these functions may be represented in the form of series in powers of the quantities $c_1, \ldots, c_k$, whose coefficients are trigonometric polynomials in $\tau_1, \ldots, \tau_k$. We shall introduce into the argument the quantities

$$b_1 = \frac{h_2}{h_1}, \ldots, b_{k-1} = \frac{h_k}{h_1}.$$

If the quantities $c_1, \ldots, c_k, \theta_1^{(0)}, \ldots, \theta_k^{(0)}$ are chosen so that $b_1, \ldots, b_{k-1}$ are rational, then the functions x_s, y_s, z_j just constructed supply a periodic solution of the original system. If among them there exists an irrational number, then the original system has an almost-periodic solution defined by these quantities.

In fact, the functions x_s, y_s, z_j may be expanded in series in powers of the quantities $c_1, \ldots, c_k$, whose coefficients are trigonometric polynomials in $\tau_1, \ldots, \tau_k, \tau_s = th_s$. In the first case these polynomials have one common period. and in the second case there is no such common period. Therefore to the first case correspond periodic solutions and to the second, almost-periodic ones, if then one does not observe a cancelling out of the terms with incommensurate frequencies.

Of course, the same properties will be possessed by the functions $\bar{x}_s, \bar{y}_s, \bar{z}_j$, which are a solution of system (27.5), if they are defined by formulae (27.6).

We shall set $t = 0$ and denote by x_s^0, y_s^0, z_j^0 the series obtained from these functions. It is clear that these quantities are series in $c_1, \ldots, c_k$ whose coefficients are trigonometric polynomials in $\theta_1^0, \ldots, \theta_k^0$.

Making use of the first two series, we shall eliminate from the series h_s and z_j the quantities $c_1, \ldots, c_k$, $\theta_1^0, \ldots, \theta_k^0$, and the newly obtained functions we shall denote as h_s and $\tilde{z}_j$.

It may be shown that these functions may be expanded in series in powers of the quantities $x_1^0, \ldots, x_k^0, y_1^0, \ldots, y_k^0$. Here the functions are the solution of the system of equations in partial derivatives

$$\sum_{i=1}^{k} \frac{\partial z_j}{\partial \bar{x}_i}(-\lambda_i \bar{y}_i + \bar{X}_i) + \sum_{i=1}^{k} \frac{\partial z_j}{\partial \bar{y}_i}(\lambda_i \bar{x}_i + \bar{Y}_i) = \sum_{i=1}^{n} r_{ji} z_i + Z_j \quad (j = 1, \ldots, n).$$
(27.26)

We shall substitute the functions $\tilde{z}_j$, which are the solution of system (26.27), in the first two groups of equations (27.5) instead of the quantities $\bar{z}_1, \ldots, \bar{z}_n$. Then we shall obtain the system of equations:

$$\frac{dx_s}{dt} = -\lambda_s y_s + \tilde{X}_s(x_1, \ldots, x_k, y_1, \ldots, y_k),$$
$$\frac{dy_s}{dt} = -\lambda_s x_s + \tilde{Y}_s(x_1, \ldots, x_k, y_1, \ldots, y_k) \quad (s = 1, \ldots, k).$$
(27.27)

It may be shown that the functions $\tilde{h}_s$ $(s = 1, \ldots, k)$ are integrals of that system.

Summing up the above, we shall note that those and only those integral curves of system (27.5) enter in the family of periodic and almost-periodic solutions for which the initial conditions for the functions $\tilde{z}_j$ are functions of $x_{10}, \ldots, x_{k0}, y_{10}, \ldots, y_{k0}$, defined by system (27.26).

We shall consider the $(\Delta - 1)$-dimensional space, in which we shall choose two sets: A of points $a_1, \ldots, a_{k-1}$ such that all the coordinates are rational, and C of points $c_1, \ldots, c_{k-1}$ such that among their coordinates there is at least a single irrational one. The functions $b_1, \ldots, b_{k-1}$, after the quantities $c_1, \ldots, c_k$, $\theta_1^0, \ldots, \theta_k^0$ are eliminated from them, are represented in the form of series in the quantities $x_1^0, \ldots, x_k^0, y_1^0, \ldots, y_k^0$.

By $F(a_1, \ldots, a_{k-1})$ we shall denote the set of points of the sphere of radius r

$$\sum_{i=1}^{k} x_i^2 + \sum_{i=1}^{k} y_i^2 \leqq r^2,$$
(27.28)

such that $b_1 = a_1, \ldots, b_{k-1} = a_{k-1}$. It is known that the set $F(a_1, \ldots, a_{k-1})$ is closed.

By F we shall denote the sum of all such closed sets extending over all the points of the set A. As the set A is denumerable, the set F is a set of the class F_σ. By G we shall denote a set complementing F to the closed sphere (27.28). We shall show that the set G is a set of the class G_δ.

Indeed, we shall consider the open sphere of radius $r_1 > r$ and the system of open sets which is the intersection of that sphere with $F(a_1, ..., a_{k-1})$. Then the set G may be obtained as the intersection of a denumerable number of these open sets and the closed sphere (27.28), and therefore is a set of the type G_δ.

THEOREM 59   If system (27.7) has a family of bounded solutions (27.8), then any integral curve of system (27.5) defined by the initial conditions $x_{10}, ..., x_{k0}, y_{10}, ..., y_{k0} \in F$; $z_{j0} = \tilde{z}_j(x_{10}, ..., x_{k0}, y_{10}, ..., y_{k0})$ $(j = 1, ..., n)$ is periodic, and any integral curve defined by the initial conditions $x_{10}, ..., x_{k0}, y_{10}, ..., y_{k0} \in G$; $z_{j0} = \tilde{z}_j(x_{10}, ..., x_{k0}, y_{10}, ..., y_{k0})$ is almost periodic, where the set F does not have interior points and the set G may also have no interior points. Here the set G is known not to have interior points for $k = 2$ and $b_1 \neq \lambda_2/\lambda_1$.

PROOF: Periodicity or almost-periodicity of the integral curves of system (27.5), as has been established above, depends on the values of the integrals $\tilde{h}_s$ $(s = 1, ..., k)$ of system (27.27). This dependence is such that the integral curve will be periodic if the quantities $b_1, ..., b_{k-1}$ are rational, or almost-periodic if among these quantities there exists at least one irrational quantity. This condition, in its turn, is related to the "belongingness" of the initial conditions to the set F or G, which demonstrates the correctness of the first part of the Theorem.

We shall now show that the set F has no interior points. Say this is not the case. Say there exists a point a, which is a point of the set F. Then there exists a sphere of sufficiently small radius at that point which lies completely in the set F. At least one of the functions $b_1, ..., b_{k-1}$ has to take at least two values (in the contrary case all these functions will be constant), and consequently $b_i = \lambda_i/\lambda_1$, which is impossible, as among these quantities there are irrational ones. Then, according to the Weierstrass theorem, the function which takes two different rational values will take irrational values, which contradicts the assumption made. Thus, F has no interior points.

In the case $k = 2$ it is proved analogously that the set G cannot have interior points, with the exception of those cases when $b_1 = \lambda_2/\lambda_1$.

In conclusion, we shall give an example.

Let us consider the system

$$\dot{x}_1 = -\lambda_1 y_1 - y_1(x_1^2 + y_1^2 + x_2^2 + y_2^2);$$
$$\dot{y}_1 = \lambda_1 x_1 + x_1(x_1^2 + y_1^2 + x_2^2 + y_2^2);$$
$$\dot{x}_2 = -\lambda_2 y_2 - y_2(x_1^2 + y_1^2);$$
$$\dot{y}_2 = \lambda_2 x_2 + x_2(x_1^2 + y_1^2);$$
$$\dot{z} = -z + x_1(x_2^2 + y_2^2).$$

This system has a family of bounded solutions

$$x_1 = x_1^0 \cos\tau_1 - y_1^0 \sin\tau_1;$$
$$y_1 = x_1^0 \sin\tau_1 + y_1^0 \cos\tau_1,$$

where

$$\tau_1 = t(\lambda_1 + x_1^{02} + y_1^{02} + x_2^{02} + y_2^{02});$$
$$x_2 = x_1^0 \cos\tau_2 - y_1^0 \sin\tau_2,$$

where

$$\tau_2 = t(\lambda_2 + x_1^{02} + y_1^{02});$$
$$y_2 = x_1^0 \sin\tau_2 + y_1^0 \cos\tau_2;$$

$$z = \frac{y_1^0(x_1^{02} + y_1^{02}) + (\lambda_1 + x_1^{02} + y_1^{02} + y_2^{02} + x_2^{02})\, x_1^0(x_1^{02} + y_1^{02})}{[1 + (\lambda_1 + x_1^{02} + y_1^{02} + y_2^{02} + x_2^{02})]^2} \cos\tau_1 +$$

$$+ \frac{x_1^0(x_1^{02} + y_1^{02}) + (\lambda_1 + x_1^{02} + y_1^{02} + x_2^{02} + y_2^{02})\, y_1^0(x_1^{02} + y_1^{02})}{[1 + (\lambda_1 + x_1^{02} + y_1^{02} + y_2^{02} + x_2^{02})]^2} \sin\tau_1 \ .$$

It is easy to see that the quantities τ_1/t and τ_2/t are integrals of the first four equations. At the points where the function

$$b_1 = \frac{\lambda_2 + x_1^{02} + y_1^{02}}{\lambda_1 + x_1^{02} + y_1^{02} + x_2^{02} + y_2^{02}}$$

takes a rational value, the solution is periodic. If the function takes an irrational value, the solution is almost-periodic.

In this case the entire four-dimensional space is divided into two sets F and G, each of which has no interior points, which denotes the presence of an almost-periodic solution in an arbitrarily small neighbourhood of a point corresponding to the periodic solution, and conversely: in an arbitrarily small neighbourhood of a point corresponding to an almost-periodic solution, periodic solutions begin.

We shall note that one can give examples of such systems in which the functions $h_1, \ldots, h_k$ are dependant, and even such in which only one integral participates in the formation of the series describing the bounded family of solutions.

§ 28.   Methods of approximate construction of periodic behaviours

Important problems of the approximate construction of periodic behaviours are touched upon in various widely diffused publications. In the present section we shall formulate briefly the basic content of these methods, referring for details to the above-mentioned publications.

I.   The method of a small parameter. We shall consider the system of equations

$$\frac{dx_s}{dt} = X_s(t, x_1, \ldots, x_n) + \mu F_s(t, x_1, \ldots, x_n, \mu) \qquad (s = 1, \ldots, n), \quad (28.1)$$

whose right-hand members are analytic functions in $x_1, \ldots, x_n, \mu$ and periodic continuous functions in t with period T. We shall assume that the system

$$\frac{dx_s}{dt} = X_s(t, x_1, \ldots, x_n) \qquad (s = 1, \ldots, n) \qquad (28.2)$$

has a periodic solution $x_s = x_s^0(t)$.

The question arises: does there exist a periodic solution $x_s = x_s(t, \mu)$ of system (28.1) such that

$$x_s(t, \mu) \to x_s^0(t) \text{ for } \mu \to 0. \tag{28.3}$$

To solve this problem we shall consider the function

$$x_s(T, \mu) - x_s(0, \mu) = g_s(\mu, b_1, \ldots, b_n), \tag{28.4}$$

where $b_s = x_s(0, \mu) - x_s^0(0)$.

It is clear that the function g_s vanishes for $\mu = b_1 = \ldots = b_n = 0$. Therefore, if the functional determinant

$$\begin{vmatrix} \dfrac{\partial g_1}{\partial b_1} & \cdots & \dfrac{\partial g_1}{\partial b_n} \\ \cdots\cdots\cdots \\ \dfrac{\partial g_n}{\partial b_1} & \cdots & \dfrac{\partial g_n}{\partial b_n} \end{vmatrix} \tag{28.5}$$

at the above-mentioned point differs from zero, then there exists a unique system of analytic functions $b_1(\mu), \ldots, b_n(\mu)$ such that the solution of system (28.1) with the initial conditions $X_s^0(0) + b_s(\mu)$ $(s = 1, \ldots, n)$ will have property (28.3). This solution will be analytic in μ and therefore may be found by successive integration of linear inhomogeneous systems obtained from system (28.1) with the substitution of the series defining that solution, and by equating on the left and right the terms containing the same powers of μ.

If system (28.2) has a family of periodic solutions dependent on one parameter $x_s = x_s^0(t, h)$, then the functional determinant (28.4) necessarily vanishes at the point $\mu = b_1 = \ldots = b_n = 0$, since for $\mu = 0$, the relation

$$g_s = 0 \qquad (28.6)$$

will be satisfied not only by the quantities $b_1 = b_2 = \ldots = b_n = 0$, but also by the quantities $b_s = x_s^0(0, h_1) - x_s^0(0, h_0)$, where h_1 is the value of the parameter taken as the basis in constructing determinant (28.5).

We shall eliminate $b_1, \ldots, b_{n-1}$ from the relation (28.6). Then we shall obtain the equality

$$g(\mu, b_1, \ldots, b_n) = 0. \qquad (28.7)$$

Relation (28.7), for $\mu = 0$, is fulfilled identically. In view of the "analyticity" of function $g(0, b_1, \ldots, b_n)$, the relation reduces to a formula of the form

$$P(h_1) + Q(h_1) b_n + \mu r + \sum_{i+k=2}^{\infty} g_{ik} \mu^i b_n^k = 0.$$

In order that there exist a solution of that equation possessing the property $b_n = 0$ for $\mu = 0$, it is necessary that $P(h_1) = 0$, and sufficient if also $Q(h_1) \neq 0$. To such values of the parameter correspond solutions of system (28.1) possessing property (28.3). Here the matter dealt with solutions for one and the same period T. Analogous results are obtained when system (28.1) is dependent on several small parameters, and system (28.2) has a family of periodic solutions dependent also on several parameters. In applying that method to autonomic systems for finding the solutions possessing property (28.3), one finds not only its initial conditions as analytic functions of the parameter μ, but also the period as an analytic function of this parameter. The originator of that method is H. Poincaré, while variants of the application and development of that method are ascribed to various scientists, in particular to B. V. Bulgakov, I. G. Malkin, and A. A. Andronov.

II.   The Academicians N. M. Krylov and N. N. Bogolyubov were the original discoverers of another method of approximate construction of periodic behaviours, which has been applied to the theory of automatic control, and has obtained its further development in the works of L. C. Goldfarb, A. I. Lurye, Ye. P. Popov, and others.

We shall give a short characterization of that method as applied to finding self-oscillations in a system of direct control with a single control organ.

Let us consider the system of equations

$$x_s = \sum_{i=1}^{n} p_{si} x_i + P_s f(\sigma), \quad \sigma = \sum_{i=1}^{n} r_i x_i \quad (s = 1, ..., n). \quad (28.8)$$

We shall seek the solutions of that system in the form of trigonometric series with no free terms. Substituting these series in the function $f(\sigma)$, we shall choose the terms corresponding only to the first harmonic, and instead of the complete system (28.8) we shall consider the system in which the nonlinear function is replaced by the function $h(a)\cos \omega t + s(a)\sin \omega t$.

We shall seek the solutions of the newly obtained system in the form

$$\sigma = a \sin \omega t; \quad x_s = a_s \cos \omega t + b_s \sin \omega t.$$

We shall substitute these functions in the system of the first n equations and shall find the quantities a_s and b_s, which are expressed in terms of the coefficients of the system p_{si}, P_s, and also in terms of the functions $h(a)$, $s(a)$. Substituting the expressions found in the equations of the system and equating on the left and on the right the coefficients of sin ωt and cos ωt, we shall obtain two equalities relating the quantities a and ω: $f_1(a, \omega) = 0$ and $f_2(a, \omega) = 0$. The real roots of these equations correspond to the possible self-oscillatory trajectories in the system.

It is obvious that the example proposed here is a simple application of the method of harmonic balancing which gives effective results when applied to various problems but at the same time remains just a system of practical rules whose sphere of application is not theoretically established.

III.   For the construction of the periodic trajectories, one also makes use of various methods connected with the finding of successive approximations. It is usual to reduce the original system of differential equations to a system of integral equations which include the initial conditions $x_1^0, ..., x_n^0$. Further, taking into account that to these initial conditions corresponds a periodic trajectory, one seeks a special system of integral equations for the periodic trajectories

$$x_s = r_s(x_1, ..., x_n, t) \quad (s = 1, ..., n).$$

In the right-hand member of that system, there usually stand operators which transform sets of continuous periodic functions into themselves. Then, one applies some theorem on the existence of a fixed point. That existence theorem, as a rule, allows one to carry out an approximate construction of the periodic trajectories. The realization of such an approach is contained, for example, in § 26.

IV. Results of unparalleled profundity are obtained with the application of the theory of periodic solutions of A. M. Lyapunov. The development of these ideas as applied to the case of several pairs of pure imaginary roots is given in § 27. The series constructed in that section give an apparatus for the approximate representation of periodic and almost-periodic oscillations in autonomic systems.

In view of the fact that only such periodic trajectories as are asymptotically stable are physically realizeable, much attention in the theory of periodic solutions is given to the problem of their stability. This is all the more necessary in order that the approximate representation of the periodic trajectories have a firm basis. Let the system of equations

$$\frac{dx_s}{dt} = f_s(x_1, \ldots, x_n, t) \quad (s = 1, \ldots, n), \tag{28.9}$$

whose right-hand members are functions continuous in $x_1, \ldots, x_n, t$ and simultaneously periodic in t with period T, have a periodic solution

$$x_s = x_s(t) \quad (s = 1, \ldots, n). \tag{28.10}$$

In this system we shall perform a substitution of the sought functions according to the formulae

$$x_s = y_s + x_s(t) \quad (s = 1, \ldots, n),$$

where $y_1, \ldots, y_n$ are new sought functions.

For their determination we shall obtain the system of differential equations

$$\frac{dy_s}{dt} = g_s(t, y_1, \ldots, y_n) \quad (s = 1, \ldots, n).$$

In the functions g_s we shall distinguish the terms linear in $y_1, \ldots, y_n$, and the remainder of the functions we shall denote by $h_1, \ldots, h_n$. Then we shall obtain the system

$$\dot{y}_s = \sum_{i=1}^{n} p_{si}(t) y_i + h_s(y_1, \ldots, y_n, t) \quad (s = 1, \ldots, n). \tag{28.11}$$

Thus, the problem of stability of the periodic solution (28.10) of system (28.9) is reduced to that of the stability of the homogeneous solution of system (28.11), and finally (with sufficiently broad assumptions as to the functions $h_1, \ldots, h_n$) to the solution of the stability of the homogeneous solution of the linear system

$$\frac{dy_s}{dt} = \sum_{i=1}^{n} p_{si}(t) y_i \quad (s = 1, \ldots, n) \tag{28.12}$$

with periodic coefficients.

242 MATHEMATICS OF AUTOMATIC-CONTROL SYSTEMS

Say $Y(t)$ is the fundamental system of solutions of this system. If $Y^{(0)} = E$, then $Y(t + T)$ will also be a fundamental system of solutions of this system.

Consequently,

$$\left. \begin{array}{l} Y(t + T) \ = Y(t)\,A, \\ Y(t + nT) = Y(t)\,A^n. \end{array} \right\} \tag{28.13}$$

It is easy to see that $A = Y(T)$ and that the homogeneous solution of system (28.12) will be asymptotically stable if and only if all the elements of the matrix A_n vanish as $n \to \infty$. Therefore, for asymptotic stability of the homogeneous solution of system (28.12), it is necessary and sufficient that all the roots of the equation $(A - \lambda E) = 0$ (28.14) lie within the unit circle centred at the coordinate origin. The construction of the matrix A is equivalent in a precise sense to the integration of the system (28.12). However, one may indicate the series [16] suitable for the creation of an apparatus for the approximate construction of such matrices.

CHAPTER VIII

APPLICATION OF ELECTRONIC COMPUTING MACHINES TO THE ANALYSIS AND SYNTHESIS OF AUTOMATIC-CONTROL SYSTEMS

§ 29. General features of computing machines and devices†

THE RAPID development of science and technology in the twentieth century brought about the extensive application of mathematical methods of investigation to the study of the flow of manufacturing processes with the aim of controlling them in optimum schedules, and also for building high-speed aircraft, guided missiles, and rockets, for the study of processes occurring in atomic fission, for the design of high-precision automatic control systems, for weather-forecast analysis, etc.

Of special interest is the penetration of mathematical methods into biology, the planning investigation of surgical operations. A characteristic feature of the investigation of natural phenomena by means of mathematical methods is the reduction of the problem under investigation to the carrying out in definite succession of a series of mathematical operations upon functions or numbers, such as integration, differentiation, multiplication, division, addition, subtraction, etc.

Assuredly, such an extensive penetration of mathematical methods into other disciplines was a consequence of the far-reaching development of these sciences, which have passed at this stage of their development from descriptive and qualitative methods to quantitative methods of investigation, and is explained by a high level of development of mathematics itself, which creates methods easily applicable to the requirements of the various sciences. However, the reduction of a problem under investigation to some mathematical problem does not as yet make for the solution of that problem. One has to indicate the method of solution of that problem or, as they say, one has to indicate the algorithm of the solution of a given problem.

Since mathematical operations, such as integration, differentiation, the taking of a nonlinear function, and others, reduce to the carrying out in definite succession, in the general case, of the four arithmetical operations (multiplication, division, addition, subtraction), then to indicate the algorithm for a

---

†   § 29 has been written by V. I. Chernetskiy.

given problem means to reduce the solution of that problem to the carrying out of some number of basic arithmetical operations in a definite succession.

For the solution of the majority of problems encountered in technology, such algorithms have been found by mathematicians a very long time ago. However, for the solution of some problems by such algorithms, it is necessary to carry out a very large number of arithmetical operations.

If one takes into account that with the penetration of mathematical methods into other sciences, it was necessary to bring to computation an ever increasing number of problems, and that with improved methods of economic activity the requirements in accounting and statistical analyses also grew continuously, it will become clear that office calculators, the slide rule, and Odner's arithmometer, available as they were, could not completely fulfill the requirements of management.

For the mechanization of accounting and statistical methods, computing and analysing machines are designed — computers which operate on an electromechanical principle and are utilized by mathematicians for the solution of mathematical problems applicable to other domains of science. Arithmometers equipped with an electric drive, as well as keyboard calculating machines, are made convenient for computation by virtue of an arrangement for the setting of numbers and carrying out of the arithmetical operations involved.

For the solution of some frequently occurring problems, computing machines and devices, operating on the principle of physical or mathematical analogies, are produced. Thus, for solving systems of differential equations, Academician A. N. Krylov created in 1903 a special continuous-action computer based on a mechanical principle.

However, computation-analysis machines, keyboard calculating machines, devices and machines with continuous action, by virtue of their structural peculiarities cannot, in general, ensure the necessary speed of computation. This has occasioned the appearance of electronic computers with discrete action, creating a revolution in computer engineering. Whereas an experienced computer could carry out during one second, on the average, one arithmetical operation with the aid of a keyboard machine, and ten operations, with a numerical analysis machine, a digital electronic computer carries out in one second a number of operations counted in the thousands and even in the tens of thousands. A particularly rapid adaptation of electronic computers in various engineering investigations has been apparent since 1945.

At the present time, the pace and scale of operations in the domain of electronic computers may be compared only with the pace of work in the fields of atomic energy and rocket technology.

The development of methods of mathematical modelling has led to the appearance of electronic computing machines with continuous action [analogue computers].

The appearance of electronic computing machines has not only permitted the solution of mathematical problems unsolvable earlier because of the enormous volume of computations, but has also fundamentally changed the view as to the domain of applicability of mathematical methods and has allowed one to consider computers as machines which mechanize the mental labour of man.

As a matter of fact, from the point of view of the theory of information, man's mental labour consists in the transformation of one form of information into some other forms of it, and the same we observe in computing machines. The principal novelty in the electronic digital computer, in contradistinction to other machines, is the fact that it can also solve problems of logic, hence these machines now determine the general trend in the development of computer engineering.

It should be noted that the electronic computer, just as any other machine, is a tool of production, created by man for his needs, and therefore it can solve only those problems which, as a result of long-range efforts of mankind, are reduced to mathematical form, for which the algorithms for the solution have been found, and whose premises, together with the solution algorithm, are introduced into the machine.

In contemporary computers, the work of processing the information is fully automatic. Only the operation of information input remains non-automatic. It is entirely obvious that it is impossible to automate completely the operation of information input for the solution of every mathematical problem since in some way one has to "communicate" to the machine the premises of the problem and the algorithm of its solution which, as a rule, are stated on paper by a man.

Concurrently, for the solution of a specific problem under physically realizable conditions, one may construct a specialized computer operating to one and the same algorithm and obtaining information as to the premises of the problem from special transducers — sensory elements reacting to the variation in the premises under which the given phenomenon proceeds.

Specialized computers are utilized for automatic control of production processes and for carrying out calculations according to a given algorithm.

The application of specialized computing machines, in many cases, permits the complete automation of the computation process, with a considerable saving in time. Besides, such machines do not require a staff of mathematician-programmers to service them, as they operate on fixed programs built into the machine during its construction. Because of the narrow specialization, the structure of the machines is very simple. This leads to a sharp reduction in the cost of specialized machines as against universal ones. It goes without saying that a general-purpose computing machine may be applied to the automatic control of a given process, but a cursory comparison, even for that case, shows the enormous advantages of specialized computers.

We shall note that in many applications of mathematics to technology, one must reduce to numerical computation an enormous number of problems of the same type, and therefore there is a sharp need for the design of specialized machines for the solution of problems of a definite type. For example, for the requirements of the theory of automatic control, it is necessary to design a machine that determines automatically the optimum trajectories for the functioning of automatic-control systems.

The mathematical scheme of one of the variants of a specialized machine for the determination of optimum trajectories for automatic-control systems will be expounded in § 31.

One of the essential advantages of such a specialized machine is the fact that it is adapted to the analysis of the solution and to the change in the direction of the computational process in dependence on the result obtained.

The analysis of the solution and the change in the control of the computational process in dependence on the result obtained, in the case of a general purpose machine, requires considerable labour for the construction of a cumbersome programme and considerable machine-time for its realization.

Of late there began being made electronic machines of a combination type, containing in their design elements of both the continuous and the discrete action.

Abroad, computing machines have a wide application also in the domain of military engineering, where they are employed along two main lines:

1. The carrying out of complex mathematical calculations in the construction and planning of various weapon models with the aim of designing, or of investigating the possibility of designing, weapon models with prespecified tactical characteristics.

2. The utilization of specialized computers in the automatic application of the weapon and in the analysis of battle environment and also for purposes of army training.

The carrying out of an extensive programme of analysis in constructing a model ensures considerable economy of means, since then the experimental testing of an expensive model is reduced to a minimum. Physical experiments are carried out for obtaining the input data only.

Electronic computers are widely applied in the work of scientific and research institutes, design offices, and laboratories, hence the study and mastery of the methods of using such machines is a must for every engineer.

The appearance of high-speed electronic computing machines has changed fundamentally the mathematician's views as to the applicability and expediency of bringing mathematical methods to the solution of an existing problem.

Thus, many methods applied earlier in theoretical arguments only, since they require a large number of arithmetical operations, have now turned out to be more effective with the solution of problems by means of high-speed machines, by virtue of the simplicity of computational schemes, allowing the construction of simpler programmes.

The most effective methods in the applications to the solution of problems with the aid of electronic digital computers are iteration methods, with their inherent cyclicity of the computational process and the self-correction of the result, which eliminates the necessity for additional control computations. Besides, in utilizing iteration methods to realize one step, actions are carried out with a small set of numbers, which takes a considerable load off the machine memory. One also uses extensively other methods of successive approximations, with their cyclicity of the computational process, regardless of the fact that in these the self-correction of the result is not always present.

For methods of successive approximations, a special case of which are iteration methods, one does not know in advance the number of arithmetical operations which have to be carried out to obtain the result with a given accuracy. Therefore, in applying such methods it is necessary to have error estimates for the halting of computations at a given step so as to determine approximately the number of arithmetical operations necessary to obtain the result with a given accuracy, and to draw conclusions as to the expediency of applying one or another method of successive approximations to the solution of a given problem.

Attention should be drawn to the fact that for the solution of many problems there exist methods which give an exact result with a previously known number of arithmetical operations. However, very often one encounters a case when the method of successive approximations gives a result with sufficient accuracy by means of a smaller number of arithmetical operations. Of late, for the solution of problems by machine, probabilistic methods are elaborated increasingly.

It is possible to formulate the fundamental requirements imposed upon mathematical methods meant for the solution of problems with the aid of electronic digital computers. These methods should:

1) permit a relatively simple programme structure;

2) allow the location of the initial numerical material in the memory unit of the machine;

3) give the result with the required accuracy over a relatively small operating time of the machine;

4) have a well-designed control system over the results of the computations, or else to be self-correcting.

Undoubtedly, for the solution of a given problem it is difficult to indicate a method possessing such properties in full measure. Therefore, it is necessary either to choose from the existing methods that which most fully satisfies the requirements formulated, or to design a new one.

The appearance of high-speed digital computers has called forth in mathematics an extensive development of numerical methods for solution of problems. However, for the solution of many technological problems of today, we are still short on well advanced machine methods (for example, for the solution of the problem of optimization of automatic-control systems).

An electronic computing machine is called a continuous (analogue) computer if the mathematical operations in the machine are carried out on continuously varying quantities.

An electronic computing machine is of discrete action (digital electronic computer) if the mathematical operations in the machine are carried out upon discretely varying quantities.

The basic assemblies of every digital electronic computer are the following units:

1) arithmetic;

2) memory;

3) control;

4) input and output.

The memory function is carried out mainly by means of cathode-ray tubes with a capacity of 1024 or 2048 binary numbers, by means of magnetic tapes or drums, by means of mercury delay lines, etc.†

Arithmetic units are produced with electron tubes ordinarily used in radio technology. Extensive work is being carried out on the application of semiconductor devices (germanium triodes, etc.) to replace the cumbersome electron tubes.

---

† [This was written in 1959. In present large-scale machines (U.S.A.), magnetic cores are predominantly used for the internal memory, and the trend is to magnetic films and superconductive elements such as cryotrons — Transl.]

Input of the intial data into the digital computers is realized as a rule by means of punched tapes or cards.

The input speed of numbers fed into the machine by means of punched cards approximates 1200 numbers per minute, by means of punched tapes 4000 numbers per minute (in this estimate we do not take into account the time required to punch the cards or the tapes).

In the U.S.S.R. the best known digital machines are the "BESM", "Strela", and "Ural".

The "BESM" has a speed of carrying out arithmetical and logical operations of about 10000 per second with a capacity of the fast memory unit (working memory) of 1024 words and of the external (slow) memory unit (external memory) of 100000 words. In order to give some idea of the size of the machine, we shall note that it has about 8000 electron tubes, weighs 20 tons, and occupies an area of 200 square metres.

The machine "Strela", somewhat below the "BESM" in speed of operation, is more convenient and reliable in use.

The main characteristics of universal digital electronic computers (average for the present† level of development) are the following:

Speed of computation, number of operations per second	2000–8000
Number of decimal digits for representing numbers in the machine	8–12
Memory capacity (number of words):	
operating memory	1024–2048
external memory (storage)	100000–1000000
Number of electron tubes	3000–5000
Area occupied, square metres	100–200
Power required, kilowatts	50–100
Staff of service personnel per shift, men:	
engineers	2–4
technicians	3–5
Staff of mathematicians for formulating problems	50–150
Mean "effective time" per 24 hrs, hrs	10–16

† [These figures are no longer valid in 1961. For example, the IBM 7090 operational in 1959 had a single-address speed of 250,000 operations per second and up to 200,000 of directly addressable words in the memory—Transl.]

The machine "Strela" has an arrangement for long-term storing of standard subroutines for typical computational processes frequently encountered in practice.

In comparing the machine "Strela" with the most widely used American digital machine, the "IBM 701", it turns out that despite the superiority of the IBM 701 in maximal speed of operation (up to 14000 operations per second), it is inferior to the "Strela" in mathematical and performance capabilities, and in practise its speed of computation is reduced to 3000 to 4000 operations per second.

In the U.S.S.R. considerable work is being done in the design of specialized digital electronic computing machines. For example, a machine is being developed for computing weather forecasts, for automatic running of railway trains, for automatic control of blast-furnace processes, etc.

The small-size electronic computing machine "Ural" is used extensively. This machine, mass-produced by Soviet industry, belongs to the type of small automatic univeral digital electronic computers. The machine "Ural", as well as the larger computing machines, allows one to carry out arithmetical operations on numbers and a whole series of logical operations. These capabilities determine its designation as "universal".

The electronic computing machine "Ural" is designated for use in computation centres, scientific and research institutes, design and project offices, and other establishments for the solution of the most variegated engineering and mathematical problems.

We shall dwell briefly upon the principle of operation of that machine, consisting of three groups of units:

1) the machine proper;
2) output units;
3) external units.

All the arithmetical and logical operations on numbers are carried out in the machine by special electronic computing devices joined in a common block, called the arithmetic unit.

The numbers upon which the operations are carried out in the machine, and the intermediate results of the calculations necessary for utilization in subsequent operations, are stored in the so-called working memory of the machine — storage on a magnetic drum. The numbers are written into the operating memory in the form of combinations of respectively magnetized sections of the ferromagnetic coating of the drum. To each number corresponds its combination of such sections. For allocating the numbers, the operating store is divided into a series of cells, the number of which defines the capacity of the store. In every such cell there can be one number. Reading a number from the store, carrying out the corresponding operation upon it, and writing the result back in the store are carried out by means of signals from the control unit of the machine.

The control unit directs the computational process and the functioning of the machine as a whole under the action of commands, preconstructed and introduced into the machine in coded form. In carrying out the command, the control unit switches the electronic relays for the choice of the required number and sets the arithmetic unit for the carrying out of the corresponding operation on that number. To each command corresponds one operation.

The machine can carry out a limited number of operations on numbers. Besides purely arithmetical and logical commands, the machine "Ural" has also a whole series of others, by means of which, for example, at a desired instant one may stop the machine, give out the results of the solution, etc., i.e. ensure the total automation of the computational process.

The preparation of the problem for its solution by the machine consists in a preliminary representation of the computational process in the form of a sequence of these operations. The sequence of operations of the computational process, coded in the form of numbers, is called a programme for the solution of the problem. The preparation of the programme for solution of the problem and of the numerical material for input into the machine is carried out on external units consisting of an input punch, a keyboard unit, and a control reading unit, not electrically connected with the machine proper.

Every number and command of the programme set by the programmer for the solution of a specific problem is set on the keyboard of the keyboard unit, and is perforated by the input punch on the usual blackened film (punched tape) in the form of some combination of holes. To every number or command corresponds its own combination of holes. This coding of the programme material is carried out by means of automatic switching of electric relays when the keys are pressed. The control reading unit is meant for the control and duplication (repunching) of the perforated tapes struck on the punch.

The direct input of the programme material from the punched tape into the machine is realized by means of an input unit—stored on punched tape. Reading of the coded numbers and commands is carried out by means of photodiodes "scanning" the combination of holes in the punched tape. The number thus read is written into the operating store. For the purpose of expanding the operating memory, in the "Ural" machine there is also a slow-speed store on magnetic tape. The utilization of numbers written on the magnetic tape is realized after rewriting them into the operating store.

For manual control of the performance of the machine and a visual check on its operation, the "Ural" computing machine has a control desk and a signal-light panel.

The results of the solutions on the machine are carried from the arithmetic unit to the printing unit and are printed on a paper tape in the form of tables. The printing of results is also carried out upon orders proceeding from the control unit. All material located in the operating store may be punched on the perforated tape by means of the output punch.

In operation, the arithmetic unit produces not only the results of the computation, but also certain indications as to the results, proceeding in the form of corresponding signals to the control unit. These indications, by means of corresponding commands, make it possible to change the order of the computations, repeat the carrying out of separate portions of the programme, etc., which is a very important factor, ensuring as it does the automation of the computational process. We shall cite some technical characteristics of the "Ural" computing machine:

Speed of computation, number of operations per second   100

Number of decimal digits   9

Capacity (quantity of numbers) in the memory:

   operating   1024 or 2048

   magnetic tape store   40000

   perforated tape store   10000

Area occupied, square metres   not more than   50

Power requirement, kilowatts   7.5

For numbers and commands stored in the machine, there is a binary numeration scheme. The numbers are represented in the machine with the location of the decimal point in front of the high digit, and the scheme is command-address.

As already indicated above, machines with continuous action work on the principle of mathematical analogy, i.e. on the principle of the identity of the equations of the object and those of nature prior to the transformation of said analogy.

Continuous-action machines have found their most extensive application for solving systems of ordinary differential equations, since a major part of today's engineering problems reduces to the finding of solutions for equations of just this kind. However, there are also analogue computers for the solution of mathematical problems of another type, e.g. for solving differential equations in partial derivatives.

By considering the structure of a system of ordinary differential equations, it may be noted that it consists in repeating (in a definite sequence) the following mathematical operations upon known and sought quantities: *a*) integration, *b*) algebraic addition, *c*) taking of a nonlinear function, *d*) multiplication.

With a sufficient number of physical systems to perform these operations upon input quantities of any one physical kind, we can implement such an interconnection between these physical systems (blocks) as will correspond to the sequence of operations in the original system of differential equations.

If, in addition, we set up these physical systems (blocks) in such a way that the carrying out of the operations corresponds to the original system of differential equations, we shall obtain a physical system with the processes occurring in it being identical to those occurring in nature, in the sense of the identity of the differential equations prior to the transformation of the analogy, provided that the blocks carry out the operations *a*, *b*, *c*, *d* without errors.

In electronic computing machines the blocks for carrying out the mathematical operations are constructed on electronic principles. In such machines all quantities are represented in the form of direct-current potentials, corresponding (in some scale) to the sought and the original quantities, and all the mathematical operations are carried out on electric potentials, changing continuously in time, in correspondence to the set system of differential equations.

The variation of the sought quantities in dependence of the flow of "machine" time (duration of the process in the machine, counted from the start) may be observed with voltmeters or an oscilloscope screen.

The possibility of building an electronic machine in a moderate-size laboratory, simplicity of representation of the processes to be studied, and the comparative ease in mastering its operation have insured a wide adaptation of electronic analogue computers to engineering investigation procedures.

Into the complex of blocks for mathematical operations, in the general case, enter blocks designated to perform the following operations:

1) integration;

2) algebraic summation;

3) multiplication;

4) taking a nonlinear function of an "unknown" argument;

5) taking a nonlinear function of two "unknown" arguments;

6) change of sign;

7) multiplication by a constant coefficient less than unity;

8) taking a nonlinear function of the basic argument;

9) differentiation;

10) typical nonlinearities: "lag", "nonsensitive zone", "slack", "hysteresis", etc.

A commutation field serves for interconnecting the blocks in correspondence to the conditions of the problem and for convenience in measuring the intermediate quantities.

The control unit serves to accomplish the operations: "Start", "Stand by", and "Stop", which are usually carried out by means of electromechanical relays.

The input of the original data is accomplished by analysing the working cycle of the blocks of mathematical operations and its subsequent setting in conformity with the data of the analysis.

Recording units serve for receiving the output results. As recording units one makes use of voltmeters, oscilloscopes of various types, spark tracing instruments, cathode-ray tubes with recording film, automatic recording devices.

Since programming for a digital machine is much more complex than work with a commutation field, and the operation of information input is more complicated than the operation of setting up the blocks, therefore in general cases, work with electronic digital machines requires more specialized training than does work with analogue computers.

Analogue computers are most widely applied in the investigations of automatic control systems and for resolving problems in the dynamics of flight.

In many types of analogue computers there are arrangements for conjugating individual elements of the object under investigation with the actual apparatus. This allows one to study the apparatus without making use of the differential equations describing the functioning of that apparatus, and thus to carry out the testing of the apparatus in the absence of the object for which it is designed. In this case, the object upon which the apparatus should be acting is replaced by the computing machine.

The main deficiencies of analogue computers are the low accuracy of the calculations (3–15%) and the necessity for a sufficiently dependable and precise voltage stabilization. We shall note that of the total quantity of electric power consumed by the analogue computer, over 50% is expended for rectification and stabilization of the potential.

If one compares analogue computers with digital electronic computers with respect to the time required for the solution of a given problem (the time of programming; the total time of information input, including the punching and feeding the numbers into the machine; the time of processing the information and delivery of the result), then such a comparison, for problems not requiring high accuracy of the results, will speak in favour of analogue computers. A similar assertion holds for a comparison of the costs involved in the solution of a given problem.

Thus, as the appearance of electronic machines in no way excludes the use of office calculators, the slide rule, the arithmometer, etc., in the same way the utilization of electronic computing machines of a general purpose type which, in principle, can solve any problem, does not exclude the application of analogue computers to a certain class of problems.

Analogue computers produced in the U.S.S.R. possess operational and computational characteristics not inferior to the characteristics of corresponding American machines. Most widely used are the models MPT–9, IPT–4, MN–2, IPT–5, and MN–7.

Model MPT–9 is designed to solve systems of 16 linear ordinary differential equations of the first order. When equipped with KNB (a set of nonlinear blocks), the MPT–9 can also solve not too complex nonlinear problems.

Model IPT–4 is designed for solving systems of six ordinary linear differential equations of the first order.

Model MN–7 is designed to solve systems of six nonlinear ordinary differential equations of the first order with not too complex right-hand members. This model is small and requires very little electric power.

By means of the machine MN–2 one may investigate problems which reduce to the solution of systems of six (and less) nonlinear ordinary differential equations, in the right-hand members of which enter up to 10 products, 10 nonlinear relationships and 12 sums.

It is most expedient to utilize electronic computing machines for problems whose solutions depend on parameters, so that after the problem is set in the machine, the solution for any fixed values may be obtained almost instantaneously.

By scanning the solutions for various values of the parameters on an oscilloscope screen, the operator can choose the solutions possessing the required characteristics.

§ 30. Synthesis and analysis of automatic control systems from stability conditions

At the present time, the solution of the problem of stability of automatic control systems is based on the application of methods not meant for use in the latest computer technology. In §11 we have expounded an approach based on a new principle, which allows one to solve that question directly from the matrix of the system of coefficients with the aid of electronic digital computers.

Indeed, say it is required to choose a control system for a given object in such a way that the automatic control system obtained has some asymptotically stable trajectory. We shall assume that to the given object corresponds the system of differential equations

$$\frac{dx_s}{dt} = f_s(t, x_1, \ldots, x_n) \quad (s = 1, \ldots, n). \tag{30.1}$$

It is required to connect to it a control unit with k control organs. As a result of this, one obtains an automatic control system in which the transient processes are described by the system of equations

$$\left.\begin{aligned}
\frac{dx_s}{dt} &= g_s(t, x_1, \ldots, x_n, z_1, \ldots, z_k) \quad (s = 1, \ldots, n); \\
\frac{dz_j}{dt} &= h_j(t, x_1, \ldots, x_n, z_1, \ldots, z_k) \quad (j = 1, \ldots, k).
\end{aligned}\right\} \tag{30.2}$$

We shall assume that to the steady state corresponds the homogeneous solution of system (30.2)

$$x_1 = x_2 = \ldots = x_n = 0;$$

$$z_1 = z_2 = \ldots = z_k = 0.$$

In the right-hand members of system (30.2) we shall choose the linear terms in the variables $x_1, \ldots, x_n, z_1, \ldots, z_k$ and we shall obtain the system of equations

$$\left.\begin{aligned}
\frac{dx_s}{dt} &= \sum_{i=1}^{n} p_{si} x_i + \sum_{l=1}^{k} g_{sl} z_l + \check{f}_s; \\
\frac{dz_j}{dt} &= \sum_{i=1}^{n} q_{ji} x_i + \sum_{l=1}^{k} u_{jl} z_l + h_j,
\end{aligned}\right\} \tag{30.3}$$

$$(s = 1, \ldots, n; \; j = 1, \ldots, k).$$

The functions $\{\check{f}_s\}, \{h_j\}, (s = 1, \ldots, n; \; j = 1, \ldots, k)$ standing in the right-hand members of system (30.3), represent the set of nonlinear terms in $x_s \; (s = 1, \ldots, n)$ and $z_j \; (j = 1, \ldots, k)$.

The homogeneous solution of system (30.3) will be asymptotically stable for any choice of these functions (see § 14) if all the roots of the matrix P, constructed from the coefficients of the first approximation to system (30.3), lie in the left halfplane of the complex variable. The coefficients of the linear approximation to system (30.3) we shall consider as real. The coefficients p_{si} we shall consider to be given numbers, determined from the equation of the object (30.1). The remaining elements of the matrix P we shall consider as parameters of the automatic control system which have to be chosen so that the homogeneous solution of system (30.2) be asymptotically stable.

In this formulation of the problem of synthesizing an automatic control system, the design engineers are not concerned even with the preliminary analysis of diverse variants of control.

Below we shall give a programme for the solution of the problem formulated on a machine of the type "Strela". This programme is based on the principle expounded in § 11.

The considerations given above largely refer also to the case when the automatic control system includes elements with time lag, or elements with distributed parameters. For definiteness we shall assume that one wishes to investigate an automatic control system containing lagging elements, in the light of the choice of parameters from conditions for stability. We shall consider that this system is described by differential equations with lagging arguments

$$\frac{dx_s(t)}{dt} = \sum_{l=0}^{k} \sum_{i=1}^{n} p_{sil} x_i(t-h_l) + f_s \quad (s = 1, ..., n), \tag{30.4}$$

where the p_{sil} are real constants; $h_0 = 0$, and $h_1, ..., h_k$ are positive constants ordered according to size.

The functions f_s standing in the right-hand members of system (30.4) represent the set of nonlinear terms in the quantities

$$x_i(t-h_l) \quad (i = 1, ..., n; \ l = 0, ..., k).$$

Some of the coefficients of system (30.4) are given numbers, and the remaining are parameters of the automatic control system. These parameters have to be chosen so that the homogeneous solution of system (30.4) be, asymptotically stable.

This state of affairs will hold in almost all cases if and only if the homogeneous solution of the linear system

$$\frac{dx_s(t)}{dt} = \sum_{l=0}^{k} \sum_{i=1}^{n} p_{sil} x_i(t-h_l) \tag{30.5}$$

will also be asymptotically stable. We shall seek the solution of that system in the form

$$x_s = c_s e^{\lambda t} \quad (s = 1, \ldots, n). \tag{30.6}$$

Substituting functions (30.6) in (30.5) and simplifying by $e^{\lambda t}$, we shall obtain the homogeneous linear system of algebraic equations

$$\lambda c_s = \sum_{l=0}^{k} \sum_{i=1}^{n} p_{si\,l} c_i e^{-h_l \lambda} \quad (s = 1, \ldots, n). \tag{30.7}$$

It is known that for the existence of a nontrivial solution of that system, it is necessary and sufficient that its determinant become zero. We shall denote that determinant by $A(\lambda)$

$$A(\lambda) = \sum_{k=0}^{n} b_k \lambda^{n-k}, \tag{30.8}$$

where $b_0 = (-1)^n$, and the functions b_k represent polynomials in the quantities $e^{-h_l \lambda}$ with constant coefficients.

It has been demonstrated that the homogeneous solution of the system (30.5) will be asymptotically stable if and only if all the roots of the characteristic equation

$$A(\lambda) = 0 \tag{30.9}$$

lie in the left halfplane of the complex variable λ. For an approximate solution of that problem one may make use of the principle mentioned above. Its application may be realized in the following way. We shall replace the entire function $A(\lambda)$ by a polynomial $A_r(\lambda)$, obtained from $A(\lambda)$ by replacing the functions $e^{-h_l \lambda}$ entering in b_k by segments of their Maclaurin series, and we shall replace $e^{-h_l \lambda}$ by the sum

$$\sum_{j=0}^{r} \frac{(-h_l \lambda)^j}{j!}.$$

It is clear that the remainder now being discarded does not exceed in absolute value the function

$$\frac{|h_l \lambda|^{r+1}}{(r+1)!} e^{|h_l \lambda|}.$$

Correspondingly, the absolute value of the terms discarded in $A(\lambda)$ to obtain $A_r(\lambda)$ does not exceed the function

$$\phi(\lambda) = b \sum_{j=0}^{n-1} |\lambda|^j \frac{|h_k \lambda|^{r+1}}{(r+1)!} e^{|h_k \lambda|},$$

where b is some constant calculated in terms of the coefficients $p_{si\,l}$.

Thus, if in the right halfplane and on the imaginary axis

$$|A_r(\lambda)| > \phi(\lambda), \qquad (30.10)$$

then all the roots of equation (30.9) lie in the left halfplane.

Thus, the fulfillment of inequality (30.10) is a sufficient condition for asymptotic stability of the homogeneous solution of system (30.5). Condition (30.10) may be approximately replaced by the requirement that all the roots of the characteristic equation

$$A_r(\lambda) = 0 \qquad (30.11)$$

lie in the left halfplane.

It is clear that equation (30.11) represents the characteristic polynomial for the linear system of ordinary equations, obtained from system (30.5) by means of the following method: the functions $x_i(t - h_l)$ are expanded in Taylor series in powers of h_l, then in these series one retains only the terms dependent on the derivatives up to the r-th order inclusive.

Then we shall obtain

$$\frac{dx_s}{dt} = \sum_{i=1}^{n} \sum_{l=1}^{k} \sum_{j=0}^{l} p_{sil} \frac{d^{(j)} x_i(t)}{dt_j} \frac{(-h)_l}{j!}. \qquad (30.12)$$

This system may be rewritten so that it take a normal form, and then one may apply to it the method of analysis indicated above.

In §11 it was proposed that in applying this method of analysis, one distribute the set of values of the parameters over a network.

Let us consider a case of an automatic control system with 10 parameters. We shall consider that its functioning is described by 10 coordinates, so that the matrix P, undergoing the analysis, is of the tenth order. Let us divide the set of values of the parameters over a network in such a way that for every parameter 10 values are taken. Then one obtains 10^{10} nodes. In order to find the square of the matrix at one node of the network, one has to expend $2 \cdot 10^3$ operations. If it is necessary to compute the 32nd power of the matrix at a node, one has to expend 10^4 operations.

If such computations are carried out at every node of the network, one has to carry out 10^{14} operations. If we have in view a machine with a speed of 10 000 operations per second, then to carry out such a number of operations, it is necessary to have about 330 years of machine time. This elementary calculation shows that the utilization of the method of dividing the parameter space by means of a net for carrying out the calculations is not always efficient.

In this connection, it is recommended to reduce the process of calculation to the minimization of the function $L^{(k)} = \sum_{i,j=1}^{n} (b_{ij}^{(k)})^2$. For this one has to take a definite number k (for example, $k = 1024$; this degree of the matrix $B = E + 2(P-E)^{-1}$ is obtained in the tenth step). Broadly speaking, the method of calculation reduces to the following: we take some point in the parameter space of the system, i.e. we choose a numerically given matrix P. We compute the function $L^{(k)}$, and thereupon we change the initial point in the parameter space according to such a rule as to decrease the function $L^{(k)}$ on the following step. Here, the process is interrupted in two cases:

1) if the sum $\left| \sum_{i=1}^{n} b_{ii}^{(k)} \right| > n$;

2) if $L^{(k)} < 1$.

In the first case the point of the parameter space is of an unstable type and in the second, of a stable one (here $\lim_{n \to \infty} B_n = 0$).

For the realization of the minimization process of the function $L^{(k)}$, several methods may be proposed.

1) Say one is given a point $(\alpha_{10}, \ldots, \alpha_{m0})$ in the space of the parameters $\alpha_1, \ldots, \alpha_m$ entering in the matrix P. We shall compute $L^{(k)}$ and $\partial L^{(k)} / \partial \alpha_1$ at that point. The subsequent point in the parameter space we shall choose so that the quantities $\alpha_2, \ldots, \alpha_m$ be fixed, and α_1 vary by a step ε in the direction opposite to the sign of that derivative. We shall keep displacing it until we find a minimum value of the quantity $L^{(k)}$ with the condition $\alpha_2 = \alpha_{20}, \ldots, \alpha_m = \alpha_{m0}$. After this, the obtained number $\bar{\alpha}_1$ is again fixed, one fixes also the numbers $\alpha_3, \ldots, \alpha_m$ and the search for the minimum of $L^{(k)}$ with respect to α_2 is carried out. Carrying out such an operation with each of the parameters, we shall obtain the point $(\bar{\alpha}_1, \ldots, \bar{\alpha}_m)$. With this point we proceed just as with the initial one. The process of computation is continued as long as it is not interrupted on the basis of the conditions indicated above, or until the minimum of the quantity $L^{(k)}$ is found. The minimum point is investigated by computing the quantities $L^{(k)}$ and $\sum_{i=1}^{n} |b_{ii}^{(k)}|$. If they give no answer to the question of interest to us, then the next higher power of the matrix P is investigated.

2. At the point $(\alpha_{10}, \ldots, \alpha_{m0})$, arbitrarily chosen, one finds the quantity $L^{(k)}$ and its gradient. Then, in the direction opposite to that of the gradient, one takes a point situated in the parameter space, distant by ε from the initial one. At this point one computes the function $L^{(k)}$ and its gradient. This

process is continued until one crosses the bounds (indicated above) or arrives at the point of minimum.

3) At the initial point, chosen arbitrarily, one computes the quantity $L^{(k)}$ and its gradient. Then, in the direction opposite to that of the gradient, one seeks the point in parameter space at which the quantity $L^{(k)}$ takes its minimum value. This point is taken as the initial; at it one computes the quantity $L^{(k)}$ and its gradient, and then the process is repeated again.

It goes without saying, that at the basis of the programme one may put various methods of minimizing the quantity $L^{(k)}$; for example, in a series of cases it is expedient to combine the methods mentioned above.

In all three methods proposed above, it is necessary to know the partial derivatives of the quantity $L^{(k)}$ with respect to the system parameters

$$\frac{\partial L^{(k)}}{\partial \alpha_j} = 2 \sum_{i,s=1}^{n} b_{is}^{(k)} \frac{\partial b_{is}^{(k)}}{\partial \alpha_j}.$$

The quantities $\partial b_{is}^{(k)}/\partial \alpha_j$ are elements of the matrix $\partial B^k/\partial \alpha_j$.
It is easily verified that

$$2 \frac{\partial B}{\partial \alpha_j} = (B-E)\frac{\partial P}{\partial \alpha_j}(E-B).$$

Consequently, the gradient will be computed without special difficulties. In fact, the gradient represents a vector in the space of the parameters $\alpha_1, \ldots, \alpha_m$ whose components are the respective partial derivatives of the quantity $L^{(k)}$, i.e.

$$\operatorname{grad} L^{(k)} = \sum_{j=1}^{m} \vec{i}_j \frac{\partial L^{(k)}}{\partial \alpha_j},$$

where $\vec{i}_j$ is the j-th unit vector in the Cartesian coordinate system.

The expression $\partial P/\partial \alpha_j$ represents a quadratic matrix composed of the partial derivatives of the elements of the matrix P. Applying the concept of gradient already introduced, we shall give a fuller description of the second and third methods of minimalization of the quantity $L^{(k)}$. The direction cosines of the gradient will be the quantities

$$e_j = \frac{\dfrac{\partial L^{(k)}}{\partial \alpha_j}}{\sqrt{\displaystyle\sum_{i=1}^{m} \left(\frac{\partial L^{(k)}}{\partial \alpha_i}\right)^2}} \qquad (j=1,\ldots,n).$$

It is known that the gradient is a vector whose direction at a given point coincides with the direction of fastest rise of the function at that point. We shall take a positive number ε. Then the choice of the succeeding point according to method 2 is realized by means of the formulae

$$\alpha_{j1} = \alpha_{j0} - \varepsilon c_{j0} \quad (j = 1, \ldots, m);$$

the quantities c_{j0} denote the direction cosines calculated at the initial point.

The subsequent approximations are constructed according to the formula

$$a_{jl+1} = \alpha_{jl} - \varepsilon c_{jl} \quad (j = 1, \ldots, m).$$

The quantity ε, as a rule, is chosen from the conditions of the problem.

The realization of the third method is carried out in the following way. Starting with the initial point $\alpha_{10}, \ldots, \alpha_{m0}$, in the parameter space one constructs the straight line

$$\alpha_j = \alpha_{j0} - x c_{j0} \quad (j = 1, \ldots, m).$$

On the arc $x > 0$ one seeks the smallest value of the function $L^{(k)}$, for example, in the following way: we compute the quantities $L^{(k)}$ and $\partial L^{(k)}/\partial x$ at the point $\alpha_{j1} = \alpha_{j0} - \varepsilon c_{j0}$, where ε is some positive number (step) determined by the problem itself.

If it turns out that $\partial L^{(k)}/\partial x < 0$, we compute the quantities $L^{(k)}$ and $\partial L^{(k)}/\partial x$ at the point $\alpha_{j2} = \alpha_{j0} - 2\varepsilon c_{j0}$ etc., until the quantity $\partial L^{(k)}/\partial x$ changes sign or until the computational process leads us to the boundary of the admissible values of the parameters.

Thus, on the arc $x > 0$, having found the point $\bar{\alpha}_j$ at which the quantity $L^{(k)}$ reaches its smallest value, we shall construct a new straight line according to the formula $\alpha_j = \bar{\alpha}_j - x c_{j1}$, from which we proceed just as from the preceding one.

We shall note, that the nature of the parameters of an automatic control system may be different in the sense of their numerical characteristics, and therefore it is worthwhile to have in mind the following considerations when one sets up the programme for the electronic computing machine.

According to some characteristic indications, we shall divide all the parameters into groups. For definiteness, we shall consider that we have distinguished all the groups $(a_1, ..., a_r)$ and $(b_1, ..., b_s)$, $s + r = m$. Then, making use of the peculiarities of these groups of parameters, in each of the groups one may carry out the minimization of the quantity $L^{(k)}$ in its own way.

Let us choose arbitrarily the point $(a_{10}, ..., a_{r0}, b_{10}, ..., b_{s0})$. We shall fix the coordinates $b_1, ..., b_s$ at the point $(b_{10}, ..., b_{s0})$ and shall minimize the quantity $L^{(k)}$ with respect to the parameters $a_1, ..., a_r$ by any of the methods expounded, as a result of which we shall find the point $(\bar{a}_1, ..., \bar{a}_r)$. We shall fix the parameters $a_1, ..., a_r$ at the point $(\bar{a}_1, ..., \bar{a}_r)$ and minimize the quantity $L^{(k)}$ with respect to the parameters $b_1, ..., b_s$, starting from the initial point $(b_{10}, ..., b_{s0})$. As a result, we shall obtain the point $(\bar{b}_1, ..., \bar{b}_s)$. We proceed analogously with the further calculations, but as the initial point we take the point $(\bar{a}_1, ..., \bar{a}_r, \bar{b}_2, ..., \bar{b}_s)$.

In finding the regions of stability according to the method proposed here, it is expedient to have in view some characteristic traits of that method.

Note that many of the problems which arise in the analysis and synthesis of automatic control systems may in every case be reduced in the first approximation to some set of constraints upon the characteristic values of the matrix P. These constraints upon the characteristic values may be expressed in the form of the following requirement: let some region G be given in the plane of the complex variable λ. Denoting here and in what follows by H the region of variation of the controller parameters we choose a subregion $H_0 \subset H$, such that for it the characteristic values of the matrix P are located within G. The general approach to the solution of this problem, as follows from §11 consists in the following. We find the analytic mapping of the region G on the unit circle $\rho = f(\lambda)$ centred at the origin of coordinates. Then the matrix $B = f(P)$ will have the characteristic values located within the above mentioned circle if and only if all the characteristic values of the matrix P are located within G. To be more precise, in what follows we shall be considering only such mappings f. It is well known that when the boundary of G has a complicated configuration the function f has a form very complicated from the point of view of programming the problem on digital computers. However, below we shall propose a process doing away with these computational difficulties. This process is based on a more detailed consideration of fundamental problems encountered in the design of control systems. As the first of these problems we shall designate the problem of finding the controller parameters ensuring the given stability reserve. Thus, it is required to find $H_0 \subset H$ such that all the characteristic values of the matrix P satisfy the inequality $\mathrm{Re}\ \lambda > \alpha$. The region defined in the complex plane by these inequalities we shall denote as $g(\alpha)$.

Then the function

$$\rho = 1 + 2(\lambda - 1 - \alpha)^{-1} \tag{30.13}$$

maps $g(\alpha)$ onto the unit circle and therefore into H_0 enter those and only those parameters for which B^k tends to zero as $k \rightarrow + \infty$, where

$$B = E + 2[P - (\alpha + 1)E]^{-1} \tag{30.14}$$

In the design of control systems constraints are sometimes imposed on oscillations in the control loop. This constraint reduces to the requirement that all the characteristic values of the matrix P lie within the half-strip $g(\alpha.\beta)$ defined by the inequalities

$$\operatorname{Re}\lambda < \alpha, \quad |\operatorname{Im}\lambda| < \beta \tag{30.15}$$

It is therefore evident, that in order that all the characteristic values of the matrix P lie within $g(\alpha,\beta)$ it is necessary and sufficient that they lie concurrently in the three halfplanes

$$\operatorname{Im}\lambda < \beta, \quad \operatorname{Im}\lambda > -\beta.$$

We shall map each of these halfplanes on the unit circle by means of the formulas

$$\rho = 1 + 2(\lambda - \alpha - 1)^{-1},$$

$$\rho = 1 + 2(-i\lambda - \beta - 1)^{-1}, \tag{30.16}$$

$$\rho = 1 + 2(i\lambda - 1 - \beta)^{-1}. \tag{30.17}$$

It then turns out that for all the characteristic values of the matrix P to be located within $g(\alpha,\beta)$, it is necessary and sufficient that the relations

$$B^k \rightarrow 0, \; B_1^k \rightarrow 0, \; B_2^k \rightarrow 0 \quad \text{as} \quad k \rightarrow + \infty,$$

where

$$B_1 = E + 2[-iP - (\beta + 1)E]^{-1} \tag{30.18}$$

$$B_2 = E + 2[iP - (\beta + 1)E]^{-1}. \tag{30.19}$$

Let us note that if the matrix P has real elements then B_1 and B_2 are complex conjugates. Consequently, in the above criterion only two matrices B and B_1 or B and B_2 have to be considered.

The constraint upon oscillations frequently has a weaker form, and namely, it is considered that the matrix P may have characteristic values with large purey imaginary parts provided that the real parts of these numbers are also sufficiently great negative quantities.

This requirement is formulated analytically in the following fashion.

It is required to choose a set of parameters $H_0 \subset H$ such, that all the characteristic values of the matrices P corresponding to them be located within the region $g(\alpha,\beta,\phi)$ formed by the intersection of the halfplane $\text{Re}\,\lambda < \alpha$ with a sector whose vertex is the point β on the real axis and subtends an angle of 2ϕ, symmetrical about the real axis, and containing an infinite interval of the negative real halfplane. In order that all the characteristic values of the matrix P be located within the region $g(\alpha,\beta,\phi)$ it is necessary and sufficient that they be simultaneously located within the three halfplanes in the intersection of which the region $g(\alpha,\beta,\phi)$ is obtained. Hence follows the analytic criterion. We shall find the functions mapping the above halfplanes upon the unit circle

$$\rho = 1 + 2(\lambda - \alpha - 1)^{-1} \tag{30.20}$$

$$\rho = 1 + 2(ie^{-i\phi}\lambda - i\beta e^{-i\phi} - 1)^{-1} \tag{30.21}$$

$$\rho = 1 + 2(-ie^{i\phi}\lambda + i\beta e^{+i\phi} - 1)^{-1} \tag{30.22}$$

Then all the characteristic values of the matrix P will lie within $g(\alpha,\beta,\phi)$ if and only if simultaneously

$$B^k \to 0, \ B_3^k \to 0, \ B_4^k \to 0 \ \text{for} \ k \to +\infty,$$

where

$$B_3 = E + 2[ie^{-i\phi}P - (i\beta e^{-i\phi} + 1)E]^{-1}$$

$$B_4 = E + 2[-ie^{-i\phi}P + (i\beta e^{i\phi} - 1)E]^{-1}$$

If the matrix P is real, then the matrix B_4 is the complex conjugate of B_2. Therefore in that case it is necessary to consider the matrices B and B_3 or B and B_4. Note, that in all the criteria cited we encounter an operation connected with the inversion of some matrix. It is known that this fact leads to the loss of machine time. Consequently it prejudices the economic aspect of the proposed method.

Below we propose a method, in the general case free from the necessity of inverting a matrix in the solution of the problem of stability and oscillations in the control loop.

In the plane of the complex variable λ let us consider a circle of radius r centred at the point $a = \alpha - r$ Then, in order that all the characteristic values of the matrix P be located within the region $g(\alpha)$ it is necessary and sufficient that there exist a number $r > 0$ and that all the characteristic values of the matrix P be located within a circle of radius r centred at the point A. The function mapping that circle upon the unit circle $\rho = (\lambda - a)/r$ is extremely simple. It follows from these considerations that the characteristic values of the matrix P are located within the region $g(\alpha)$ if and only if the matrix $D^k \to 0$ as $k \to +\infty$, where

$$D = \frac{P - aE}{r} = E + \frac{P - \alpha E}{r}$$

Further, in the plane of the complex variable λ we construct three circles, each of which has the radius r and whose centres are located at the points

$$a = \alpha - r, \quad a_1 = \alpha + i(r - \beta), \quad a_2 = \alpha + i(\beta - r)$$

Obviously, all the characteristic numbers lie within the region $g(\alpha,\beta)$ if and only if there exists a number $r > 0$ such that all the characteristic values of the matrix P are located within these three circles, which, in turn, will hold if and only if the matrices D^k, D_1^k, D_2^k simultaneously tend to zero as $k \to +\infty$, where

$$D_1 = \frac{P - a_1 E}{r}, \qquad D_2 = \frac{P - a_2 E}{r}$$

Finally, let us construct in the plane of λ a new system of circles of radius r, centred at the points

$$a = \alpha - \tau, \quad a_3 = d - r \sin \phi + i[(\beta - \alpha)tg\phi - r \cos \phi], \quad a_4 = \bar{a}_3$$

It is obvious, that all the characteristic values of the matrix P are located within the region $g(\alpha, \beta, \phi)$ if and only if there exists an r such all the characteristic values of the matrix P are located simultaneously within circles centred at the points a, a_3, a_4 and with radius r. This is possible if and only if the matrices D^k, D_3^k, D_4^k tend to zero as $k \to + \infty$.

The approach just set forth has been tried out upon digital computers and has demonstrated its all-round convenience. We shall note that in that last approach, just as earlier, there has remained the process of raising a matrix to a power. It is known that the question of whether the power of some matrix A^k tends to zero as $k \to + \infty$ may be solved in the general case by the consideration of the traces of successive powers taken in a number corresponding to the order of the matrix. However, practical computations on the Russian digital computers BESM and "Strela" have shown in many sample problems that it is sufficient to consider only the trace of two or three powers, for example A^{32}, A^{64}, A^{128}. Moreover, a more detailed investigation of the results obtained also shows that if one aims to reduce the volume of computational labor still further it is possible to solve the problem of stability and oscillations in the control loop with a definite probability.

It is well known that the general solution of a linear system may be represented in the form $X = X_0 e^{Pt}$, where X is a vector with coordinates $x_1, \ldots, x_n$, and $X = X_0$ at $t = 0$.

We shall assume that the number α is the greatest real part of the roots of the matrix P. Then each of the coordinates of the vector may be written in the form

$$x_s = \sum_{i=1}^{n} y_{si}(t) x_i^0 \, e^{\alpha t} \qquad (s = 1, \ldots, n)$$

where $y_{si}(t)$ are elements of the matrix $\exp^{(P - \alpha E)t}$.

From these relations we find, that

$$|x_s| \leq \sqrt{\sum_{i=1}^{n} x_i^{02} A_s e^{\alpha t}} \quad (s = 1, \ldots, n)$$

where

$$A_s = \sup_{t \geqq 0} \sqrt{\sum_{i=1}^{n} y_{si}^2(t)} \qquad (s = 1, \dots, n)$$

We note, that the latter inequalities with such a choice of the quantities $A_1, \dots, A_n$ are strict.

The amplitudes $A_1, \dots, A_n$ characterize the quality of the control system. We shall set

$$A = \max\{A_1, \dots A_n\} \text{ and } q = \frac{\ln A}{|\alpha|}.$$

It is clear, that the quantity q will characterize the rate of damping of the transient processes in the automatic control system more completely than the quantity α. Therefore the quantity q may be taken as the quality index of the system, where the smaller q the better the quality.

We shall assume that the canonical structure of the matrix $\bar{P}$ is purely diagonal. Then $P = S^{-1}M_1 S$, where M_1 is a purely diagonal matrix. It is known, that

$$e^{\bar{P}t} = S^{-1} e^{M_1 t} S$$

By M_2 we shall denote the diagonal matrix obtained from M_1 by the transformation of the left halfplane of λ into the unit circle of the ρ plane. Then we shall obtain

$$\bar{B} = S^{-1} M_2 S,$$

hence

$$\bar{B}^n = S^{-1} M_2^n S = S^{-1} e^{nm_3} S,$$

where $M_3 = \ln M_2$.

From these relations follows that there exists a close connection between matrix $\bar{B}^N$ and the matrix $e^{\bar{P}t}$. Let us compute the number

$$\bar{A} = \sup_{i \, k=1 \, \cdots \, n} \sqrt{\sum_{j=1}^{n} b_{ij}^{(k)2}},$$

where $b_{ij}^{(k)}$ are the elements of the matrix $[\bar{B}]^{2k}$ $(k = 0, 1, 2, \dots, 7)$.

Let us set $\bar{q} = \dfrac{\bar{A}_1}{|\alpha|}$. The quantity $\bar{q}$ may be considered as a complete characteristic of the system quality.

After finding the regions of stability it is recommended to choose the subregions in which the quantity q does not exceed a given limit.

The following fact should be also noted here. The differential system

$$\frac{dx}{dt} = PX$$

may be replaced by a system in finite differences

$$X[(k+1)h] = X(kh) + hPX(kh) = (E + hP)X(kh)$$

whence we find

$$X[(k+1)h] = (E + hP)^{k+1}X^{(0)}$$

where $X^{(0)} = X(0)$. This solution of the system in finite differences is arbitrarily close to the solutions of the original system.

We further draw attention to the fact that the matrix $(E + hP)^k$ coincides with the matrix D^k for a zero stability depth $\alpha = 0$ and $h = .1/r$ Thus, by solving the problem of stability according to the proposed method it is also possible to construct all the transient processes within a broad range of variation of the independent variable.

It should be noted that considerable computational labor connected with the introduction of this method into engineering practice has been recently carried out by N.A. Sakharnikov and M. S. Mamsurov.

§ 31. Automatic optimization of automatic control systems

In the preceding section some considerations were expounded relating to the application of electronic digital computers to the analysis and synthesis of automatic control systems on the basis of determining the stability relative to the steady state. In this investigation, the class of automatic control systems is limited to such systems as are described by systems of differential equations whose right-hand members in the neighbourhood of the steady state have linear approximations with coefficients constant in time and dependent only on the system parameters.

In the present section we propose an approach to the solution of a more general problem of analysis and synthesis of automatic control systems. This approach is characterized by the fact that it can be realized by means of electronic computing machines both digital and combined.

As one of the general problems in the analysis and synthesis, one may propose the following.

Let us consider the system of differential equations

$$
\begin{aligned}
\frac{dx_s}{dt} &= f_s(t, x_1, \ldots, x_n, z_1, \ldots, z_k, \alpha_1, \ldots, \alpha_m) \quad (s = 1, \ldots, n) ; \\
\frac{dz_j}{dt} &= g_j(t, x_1, \ldots, x_n, z_1, \ldots, z_k, \alpha_1, \ldots, \alpha_m) \quad (j = 1, \ldots, k).
\end{aligned}
\right\} \tag{31.1}
$$

Say one is given the system of functionals

$$
V_i = V_i(x_1, \ldots, x_n, z_1, \ldots, z_k) \quad (i = 1, \ldots, l). \tag{31.2}
$$

In some problems one may consider that $x_1, \ldots, x_n$ are the coordinates of the regulated object, and $z_1, \ldots, z_k$ are the coordinates of the control organs.

Let us consider that the right-hand members of system (31.1) possess the properties characterizing a given class of automatic control systems, real and given for $t \in [0, T]$, and

$$
\{x_1, \ldots, x_n, z_1, \ldots, z_k\} \in \Omega, \tag{31.3}
$$

where Ω is some region of the $(n + k)$-dimensional space.

The functions g_j, f_s are dependent also on the parameters $\alpha_1, \ldots, \alpha_m$, which vary in the region F of the m-dimensional space.

We shall assume that to any point $\{x_{10}, \ldots, x_{n0}, z_{10}, \ldots, z_{n0}\} \in \Omega$ and to any point $\{\alpha_{10}, \ldots, \alpha_{m0}\} \in F$ for any given $t_0 \in [0, T]$ corresponds a system of continuous functions

$$
x_i = x_i(t, x_{10}, \ldots, x_{n0}, z_{10}, \ldots, z_{k0}, \alpha_{10}, \ldots, \alpha_{m0}, t_0) \quad (i = 1, \ldots, n) \tag{31.4}
$$

$$
z_j = z_j(t, x_{10}, \ldots, x_{n0}, z_{10}, \ldots, z_{k0}, \alpha_{10}, \ldots, \alpha_{m0}, t_0) \quad (j = 1, \ldots, k) \tag{31.5}
$$

satisfying system (31.1) for

$$\alpha_1 = \alpha_{10}, \ldots, \alpha_m = \alpha_{m0}.$$

Let us assume also that functions (31.5) are defined as long as the curves $x_1, \ldots, x_m, z_1, \ldots, z_k$, determined from (31.5), lie in the region Ω.

In what follows, we shall consider that functionals (31.2) are defined on all possible curves (31.5) and take real values on them.

If one manages to find functions (31.5) for all values of the parameters $\alpha_1, \ldots, \alpha_m$ and for all values of $\{x_{10}, \ldots, x_{n0}, z_{10}, \ldots, z_{k0}\} \in \Omega$, then functionals (31.2) define the functions

$$\phi_i = \phi_i(x_{10}, \ldots, x_{n0}, z_{10}, \ldots, z_{k0}, \alpha_1, \ldots, \alpha_m) \qquad (i = 1, \ldots, l). \qquad (31.6)$$

Let us find the largest values of these functions for

$$\{x_{10}, \ldots, x_{n0}\} \in \Omega_1, \quad \{z_{10}, \ldots, z_{k0}\} \in \Omega_2$$

for fixed $\alpha_1, \ldots, \alpha_m$, and we shall denote these greatest values by

$$\psi_i = \psi_i(\alpha_{10}, \ldots, \alpha_{m0}) \quad (i = 1, \ldots, l). \qquad (31.7)$$

Let us find the quantities $\bar{\alpha}_1, \ldots, \bar{\alpha}_m$, satisfying the two conditions:

1) $\{\bar{\alpha}_1, \ldots, \bar{\alpha}_m\} \in F$;

2) one of functions (31.7) found at that point takes the smallest value, and the remaining ones do not exceed the defined limits, independent of $\alpha_1, \ldots, \alpha_m$, or all functions (31.7) do not exceed the pre-specified limits.

It is understood that the last property will be possessed, in general, by points located in some neighbourhood of the point $\{\bar{\alpha}_1, \ldots, \bar{\alpha}_m\}$. The parameter $\{\bar{\alpha}_1, \ldots, \bar{\alpha}_m\}$, in what follows, we shall call *optimal*, and the automatic control system corresponding to these values of the parameters we shall refer to as an *optimal system*.

The sets Ω_1 and Ω_2 utilized above are determined as a rule by the technical conditions of the functions of the automatic control system.

The solution of the problem posed above may proceed by two paths. We shall dwell upon the first of them.

Let us differentiate system (31.1) through with respect to the parameters $\alpha_1, \ldots, \alpha_m$ and with respect to the initial conditions $x_{10}, \ldots, x_{m0}, z_{10}, \ldots, z_{k0}$, as a result of which we shall obtain the system of equations

$$\frac{dx_s}{dt} = f_s(t, x_1, \ldots, x_n, \ z_1, \ldots, z_k, \ \alpha_1, \ldots, \alpha_m)$$
$$(s = 1, \ldots, n);$$

$$\frac{dz_j}{dt} = g_j(t, x_1, \ldots, x_n, z_1, \ldots, z_k, \alpha_1, \ldots, \alpha_m)$$
$$(j = 1, \ldots, k);$$

$$\frac{dx_{si}}{dt} = \sum_{r=1}^{n} \frac{\partial f_s}{\partial x_r} x_{ri} + \sum_{r=1}^{k} \frac{\partial f_s}{\partial z_r} z_{ri}$$
$$(s = 1, \ldots, n; \ i = 1, \ldots, n);$$

$$\frac{dz_{ji}}{dt} = \sum_{r=1}^{n} \frac{\partial g_i}{\partial x_r} x_{ri} + \sum_{r=1}^{n} \frac{\partial g_i}{\partial z_r} z_{ri}$$
$$(j = 1, \ldots, k; \ i = 1, \ldots, n);$$

$$\frac{d\xi_{si}}{dt} = \sum_{r=1}^{n} \frac{\partial f_s}{\partial x_r} \xi_{si} + \sum_{r=1}^{k} \frac{\partial f_s}{\partial z_r} \zeta_{ri}$$
$$(s = 1, \ldots, n; \ i = 1, \ldots, k);$$

$$\frac{d\zeta_{ji}}{dt} = \sum_{r=1}^{n} \frac{\partial g_j}{\partial x_r} \xi_{ri} + \sum_{r=1}^{k} \frac{\partial g_i}{\partial z_s} \zeta_{ri}$$
$$(i, j = 1, \ldots, k);$$

$$\frac{d\eta_{si}}{dt} = \sum_{r=1}^{n} \frac{\partial f_s}{\partial x_r} \eta_{ri} + \sum_{r=1}^{k} \frac{\partial f_s}{\partial z_r} \theta_{ri} + \frac{\partial f_s}{\partial \alpha_i}$$
$$(s = 1, \ldots, n; \ i = 1, \ldots, m);$$

$$\frac{d\theta_j}{dt} = \sum_{r=1}^{n} \frac{\partial g_i}{\partial x_r} \eta_{ri} + \sum_{r=1}^{k} \frac{\partial g_i}{\partial z_r} \theta_{ri} + \frac{\partial g_i}{\partial \alpha_i}$$
$$(j = 1, \ldots, k; \ i = 1, \ldots, m),$$

(31.8)

where

$$x_{si} = \frac{\partial x_s}{\partial x_{i0}};$$

$$z_{ji} = \frac{dz_j}{\partial x_{i0}};$$

$$\xi_{si} = \frac{\partial x_s}{\partial z_{i0}}; \ \zeta_{ji} = \frac{\partial z_j}{\partial x_{i0}};$$

$$\eta_{si} = \frac{\partial x_s}{\partial \alpha_i}; \ \theta_{ji} = \frac{\partial z_j}{\partial \alpha_i}.$$

We shall note that the first six groups of equations of system (31.8) are in effect independent of the number i in their structure. On the number i are dependent only the seventh and the eighth groups of equations in which enter as components the partial derivatives of the functions f_s with respect to the system parameters.

Let us denote two positive numbers ε and δ whose values are determined by the conditions of the problem. We shall choose arbitrarily the initial point $x_{10}, \ldots, x_{n0}$ from Ω_1, $z_{10}, \ldots, z_{k0}$ from Ω_2, and $\alpha_{10}, \ldots, \alpha_{m0}$ from F.

We shall calculate the functional V_1 for this initial point.

Let us fix in system (31.1) the parameters at the point $\alpha_{10}, \ldots, \alpha_{m0}$ and compute the gradient of the quantity V_1.

We shall consider that the partial derivatives of the functional V_1 with respect to the initial conditions and with respect to the parameters of the system represent also functionals given on the integral curves of system (31.1), and also on the partial derivatives of the functions describing these integral curves with respect to the initial conditions and with respect to the parameters. Thus, the partial derivatives

$$\frac{\partial V_1}{\partial x_{s0}}, \quad \frac{\partial V_1}{\partial z_{j0}} \quad (s = 1, \ldots, n; \; j = 1, \ldots, k)$$

will be found, if one constructs the solutions of the first six groups of equations of system (31.8). Here, one should consider the initial conditions which define that solution

$$\left.\begin{array}{ll} x_i = x_{i0}, & x_{si} = \delta_{si}; \\ z_j = z_{j0}, & z_{ji} = 0 \quad (j = 1, \ldots, k; \; s = 1, \ldots, n); \\ \xi_{si} = 0, & \zeta_{ji} = \delta_{ji} \quad (i = 1, \ldots, k; \; s = 1, \ldots, n; \; j = 1, \ldots, k) \\ \text{for } t = 0. & \end{array}\right\} \quad (31.9)$$

Now we maximize the quantity V_1, for example, in the following way: let

$$\operatorname{grad} V_1 = \sum_{s=1}^{n} \vec{i}_s \frac{\partial V_1}{\partial x_{s0}} + \sum_{j=1}^{k} \vec{i}_{n+j} \frac{\partial V_1}{\partial z_{j0}},$$

where by $\vec{i}_s \; (s = 1, \ldots, n + k)$ are denoted the unit vectors of the $(n + k) -$ dimensional space.

We shall set

$$c_s = \cfrac{\cfrac{\partial V_1}{\partial x_{s0}}}{\sqrt{\sum\limits_{s=1}^{n}\left(\dfrac{\partial V_1}{\partial x_{s0}}\right)^2 + \sum\limits_{j=1}^{k}\left(\dfrac{\partial V_1}{\partial z_{j0}}\right)^2}} \quad (s = 1, \ldots, n);$$

$$c_{n+j} = \cfrac{\cfrac{\partial V_1}{\partial z_{j0}}}{\sqrt{\sum\limits_{s=1}^{n}\left(\dfrac{\partial V_1}{\partial x_{s0}}\right)^2 + \sum\limits_{j=1}^{k}\left(\dfrac{\partial V_1}{\partial z_{j0}}\right)^2}} \quad (j = 1, \ldots, k).$$

Let us choose a new initial point by means of the formula

$$x_{s1} = x_{s0} + \varepsilon c_s^{(0)} \quad (s = 1, \ldots, n; \quad j = 1, \ldots, k) \quad z_{j1} = z_{j0} + \varepsilon c_{n+j}^{(0)},$$

where by $c_s^{(0)}$ we denote the quantities c_s computed at the point x_{s0}, z_{j0}. With the point obtained we proceed just as with the initial one, i.e. we construct at it the gradient and carry out a displacement along it by a step ε. As a result of this process or of any other process of this kind, we shall find the point $(\bar{x}_1, \ldots, \bar{x}_n, \bar{z}_1, \ldots, \bar{z}_k)$ at which the greatest value of the functional V_1 is realized.

This highest value has been denoted above as

$$\dot{\psi}_1 = \psi_1(\alpha_1, \ldots, \alpha_m).$$

The idea of the further course of computation consists in finding the gradient of the functions ψ_1. With this aim we give an increment h to the coordinate α_{10}, and we apply the above method to compute the function $\psi_1(\alpha_{10} + h, \alpha_{20}, \ldots, \alpha_{m0})$, whereupon we set up the increment $\Delta\psi_1$, of the function ψ_1, which allows us to find approximately $\partial\psi_1/\partial\alpha_1$ at the point $(\alpha_{10}, \ldots, \alpha_{m0})$.

Analogously one may obtain all the partial derivatives of the function ψ_1, and consequently, also its gradient.

By D_i we shall denote the quantity

$$D = \cfrac{\cfrac{\partial\psi_1}{\partial\alpha_i}}{\sqrt{\sum\limits_{j=1}^{m}\left(\dfrac{\partial\psi_1}{\partial\alpha_j}\right)^2}}.$$

Let us choose a new point in the parameter space according to the formulae

$$\alpha_{i1} = \alpha_{i0} - \delta D_{i0} \quad (i = 1, \ldots, m), \tag{31.10}$$

where by D_{i0} we denote the quantities D_i computed at the points $a_{10}, \ldots, a_{m0}$.

The point defined by (31.10) in the parameter space and the point $(\bar{x}_1, \ldots, \bar{x}_n, \bar{z}_1, \ldots, \bar{z}_k)$ in the space of the initial conditions we shall take as the initial, and we shall proceed with it just as with the point $(x_{10}, \ldots, x_{n0}, z_{10}, \ldots, z_{k0}, \alpha_{10}, \ldots, \alpha_{m0})$. After a multiple repetition, this computational process will lead us to the optimal values of the system parameters.

In short, this concludes the method of solution of the problem of choosing an optimal automatic control system.

The second method differs from the preceding one in that the calculation of the gradient of the quantity V_1 is carried out directly by means of integrating system (31.1) at the initial point given and also at $n + k$ points distant by h from the initial one and situated upon straight lines parallel to the corresponding coordinate axes, i.e. the partial derivative $\partial x_s / \partial x_{i0}$ is replaced by the relation

$$\frac{1}{h} \left[x_s(t, x_{10}, \ldots, x_{i0} + h, \ldots, x_{n0}, z_{10}, \ldots, z_{k0}) - \right.$$
$$\left. - x_s(t, x_{10}, \ldots, x_{i0}, \ldots, x_{n0}, z_{10}, \ldots, z_{k0}) \right] .$$

As to the rest, the second method consists in carrying out the same computational operations as the ones indicated above.

The above methods of solution of the optimization problem in the case of one functional V_1 are expedient also for the solution of the problem in the general case. Indeed, say it is required to choose the parameters of the system in such a way that the function ψ_1 take the smallest value, with the condition that the functions ψ_i $(i = 1, \ldots, l)$ are included in the given bounds

$$|\psi_i| \leqq N_i, \tag{31.11}$$

where N_i are some constants.

To solve such a problem we shall first choose a set $F_1 \subseteq F$ in the parameter space of the system, in which inequalities (31.11) are satisfied. Then, in that set F_1 we seek a point such that at it the function ψ_1 takes its smallest value. The point thus found will be optimal. Of course, the solution of that problem is based on the finding of an algorithm allowing one to determine the set F_1.

As such an algorithm one may propose, for example, the following. We shall give in the space of initial conditions and in the space of the parameters an arbitrary point $(x_{10}, \ldots, x_{n0}, z_{10}, \ldots, z_{k0}, \alpha_{10}, \ldots, \alpha_{m0})$. Starting from it and applying the method indicated above, we shall construct sets F_i in which ψ_i satisfies the inequality $|\psi_i| \leqq N_i$. Thereupon, in the guise of F we take the intersection of the sets F_i. Here one should note the method which allows us to give a machine algorithm. Starting with the initial point, we construct the set F_2 at which the inequality $|\psi_2| \leqq N_2$ is satisfied, this being attained by a small modification of the above-described computational process. Then, in the set F_2 we choose an arbitrary point and, starting from it, we construct the set F_3 such that $F_3 \subseteq F_2$ and $|\psi_3| \leq N_3$, etc.

We shall note a series of important problems of the theory of automatic control which are contained in the general problem formulated at the beginning of this section.

1. In the theory of automatic control one encounters the problem of synthesizing a system where the state of the control object is previously described in some way or, more precisely, a system in which its state differs little from the given behaviour.

Say one is given the system of equations

$$\frac{dy_s}{dt} = h_s(t, y_1, \ldots, y_{n_1}) \quad (s = 1, \ldots, n_1). \tag{31.12}$$

From the class of automatic control systems described by system (31.3), it is required to choose one such that its states be in some sense close to the states described by system (31.12). To be more precise, the parameters of system (31.1) are to be chosen in such a way that the functional

$$V_1 = \sup_{t \geq 0} \sum_{i=1}^{p} (x_i - y_i)^2$$

have a minimum maximorum, where $x_1, \ldots, x_p$ are the coordinates of the solution of system (31.1), and $y_1, \ldots, y_p$ are the coordinates entering into the solution of system (31.12), it being the case that the initial data determining the solution of systems (31.1) and (31.12) coincide, i.e. $x_{i0} = y_{i0}$ $(i = 1, \ldots, n)$.

We shall show that such a problem enters into the general problem formulated at the beginning of §31. For this, in system (31.1) we shall perform the substitution for the sought functions according to the formulae

$$\xi_i = x_i - y_i \quad (i = 1, \ldots, n),$$

then for determining them we shall obtain the system of equations

$$\left.\begin{aligned}
\frac{dy_s}{dt} &= h_s(t, y_1, \ldots, y_{n_1}) \quad (s = 1, \ldots, n_1) \\
\frac{d\xi_s}{dt} &= f_s(t, \xi_1 + y_1, \ldots, \xi_n + y_n, z_1, \ldots, z_k, \alpha_1, \ldots, \alpha_m) - \\
&\quad - h_s(t, y_1, \ldots, y_n) \quad (s = 1, \ldots, n); \\
\frac{dz_j}{dt} &= g_j(t, \xi_1 + y_1, \ldots, \xi_n + y_n, z_1, \ldots, z_k, \alpha_1, \ldots, \alpha_m).
\end{aligned}\right\} \tag{31.13}$$

The functional V_1 is determined from the equality

$$V_1 = \sup_{t \geq 0} \sum_{i=1}^{p} \xi_i^2 \quad (p \leq n). \tag{31.14}$$

As Ω_1 of the region of variation of the initial conditions for the first two groups of equations one should take the set lying in the p-dimensional hyper-plane

$$\xi_i = 0 \quad (i = 1, ..., p) \tag{31.15}$$

of the $2n$-dimensional space $y_1, ..., y_n, \xi_1, ..., \xi_n$.

As Ω_2 we shall choose some set of variation of the quantities $z_{10}, ..., z_{k0}$ determined by the conditions of the problem.

It is required to choose the parameters $\alpha_1, ..., \alpha_m$ so that $\max_{\Omega_1 \Omega_2} V_1$ be minimal.

The modified form of Problem 1 shows that it is included in the general problem.

2. Let us assume that the automatic control system (31.1) has a steady motion $x_s - \bar{x}_s(t)$, $z_j = \bar{z}_j(t)$ $(s = 1, ..., n; j = 1, ..., k)$.

It is required to choose the system parameters so that the functional

$$V_1 = \sup_{t \geq 0} \left\{ \sum_{s=1}^{n} [x_s - \bar{x}_s(t)]^2 + \sum_{j=1}^{k} [z_j - \bar{z}_j(t)]^2 \right\}$$

possess the property $V_1 < L_1$ for

$$\left\{ \sum_{j=1}^{n} [x_{i0} - \bar{x}_i(0)]^2 + \sum_{j=1}^{k} [z_{j0} - \bar{z}_j(0)]^2 \right\} < L_2,$$

where L_1 and L_2 are given positive constants and $L_2 < L_1$.

By $\bar{\Omega}$ we shall denote a sphere of radius $\sqrt{L_2}$ in the space of the initial conditions of the system. Then this problem will reduce to that of choosing the parameters in system (31.1) so that the greatest value of V_1 on $\bar{\Omega}$ does not exceed L_2. This problem, as is easy to see, is included in the one described above.

3. Under the conditions of Problem 2 we shall define the functional V_1 in the following way

$$V_1 = \sup_{t \in [\tau, T]} \left\{ \sum_{s=1}^{P_1} (x_s - \bar{x}_s)^2 + \sum_{j=1}^{P_2} (z_j - \bar{z}_j)^2 \right\} \quad (P_1 \leq n, P_2 \leq k).$$

It is required to choose the parameters of system (31.1) so that the inequalities

$$V_1 < L_1 \quad (L_1 > 0) \tag{31.16}$$

be satisfied for

$$|x_{s0} - \bar{x}_s(0)| < k_s,$$ (31.17)

$$|z_{j0} - \bar{z}_j(0)| < M_j \quad (s = 1, ..., n; j = 1, ..., k).$$ (31.18)

It is easy to see that this problem is a very special case of the general problem.

We shall note that τ in this case may be considered as the time required to end the transient process (time of settling).

The method proposed is, apparently, laborious. In this connection a second method should be noted, as proposed in works [64], [65], which may be useful in a series of problems of this kind.

Whereas in § 30 we have been considering the choice of optimal parameters from the stability conditions, the present section contains recommendations as to the choice of optimal parameters from the conditions of the best quality of the system. Here the quality of the automatic control system is described by means of several functionals which are determined from the nature of the problem itself. It should be noted that in the literature there is a tendency to describe the quality of functioning of the system by only one quantity Q, which may be defined in such a way that in a sufficiently small neighbourhood of the boundary of the set $|V_i| \leq N_i$ $(i \geq 2)$, and also outside this set, the quantity Q have the values differing sharply from V_1, while within that set $Q \approx V_1$. After constructing such a quantity Q, one should proceed with it as with V_1, not taking into account the constraints imposed by the inequalities $|V_i| \leq N_i$.

4. Let us consider the linear system of automatic control, into whose input are given the random driving functions

$$\frac{dx_s}{dt} = \sum_{i=1}^{n} p_{si}(t) x_i + f_s(t) \quad (s = 1, ..., n),$$ (31.19)

where p_{si} are real continuous functions given for $t > 0$, dependent on real parameters $\alpha_1, ..., \alpha_k$, varying in the region Ω, and continuously differentiable with respect to these parameters.

We shall consider the functions $f_s(t)$ as random processes, defined for $t \geq 0$. Intending to consider further the problem of optimization of system (31.19) within the framework of the correlation theory of random processes, we shall assume that the random functions $f_s(t)$ $(s = 1, ..., n)$ are pairwise independent and also normally distributed. Considering the initial conditions $x_1^0, ..., x_n^0$ as random quantities, we shall make with respect to them the same assumptions as with respect to the functions $f_s(t)$ and, besides, we shall consider them as pairwise independent and independent of the $f_s(t)$.

The general solution of system (31.19) has the form [66]

$$x_s = \sum_{i=1}^{n} \left[y_{si}(t) x_i^0 + \int_0^t y_{si}(t, \tau) f_i(\tau) d\tau \right] \quad (s = 1, \dots, n), \qquad (31.20)$$

where $y_{si}(t)$ is the element of the matrix $Y(t)$ representing the matrix of the fundamental system of solutions for the system of equations

$$\frac{dx_s}{dt} = \sum_{i=1}^{n} p_{si}(t) x_i \quad (s = 1, \dots, n) \qquad (31.21)$$

defined by the condition $Y(0) = E$, where E is a unit matrix. The functions $y_{si}(t, \tau)$ are elements of the matrix $Z(t, \tau) = Y(t)Y^{-1}(\tau)$. The matrix Z is the matrix of the fundamental system of solutions for the system of equations

$$\frac{dz_s}{d\tau} = - \sum_{i=1}^{n} p_{si}(\tau) z_i \quad (s = 1, \dots, n) \qquad (31.22)$$

defined by the condition $Z = E$ for $\tau = t$.

By $M[f]$ we shall denote the mathematical expectation of the quantity f, and by $D[f]$ the dispersion of that quantity. We shall assume that the quantities

$$\begin{aligned} a_s(t) &= M[f_s(t)]; \\ b_s(\tau_1, \tau_2) &= M[\{f_s(\tau_1) - a_s(\tau_1)\} \{f_s(\tau_2) - a(\tau_2)\}] \quad (s = 1, \dots, n), \end{aligned} \right\} \qquad (31.23)$$

and

$$k_s = M[x_s^0] \text{ and } l_s = D[x_s^0] \quad (s = 1, \dots, n) \qquad (31.24)$$

are given.

From the form of the general solution it follows that every x_s coordinate is normally distributed. Here $M[x_s]$ and $D[x_s]$ are defined by the formulae

$$M[x_s] = \sum_{i=1}^{n} \left[y_{si}(t) k_i + \int_0^t y_{si}(t, \tau) a_i(\tau) d\tau \right] \quad (s = 1, \dots, n); \qquad (31.25)$$

$$D[x_s] = \sum_{i=1}^{n} \left[y_{si}^2(t) l_i + \int_0^t \int_0^t y_{si}(t, \tau_1) y_{si}(t, \tau_2) b_i(\tau_1, \tau_2) d\tau_1 d\tau_2 \right] \quad (s = 1, \dots, n).$$

$$(31.26)$$

We shall consider the point $\bar{\alpha}_1, \dots, \bar{\alpha}_k$, lying in the set Ω as optimal if it lies in the region $|M[x_n]| \leq L$ and for this $D[x_n]$ has the smallest value with fixed $t = T$.

Thus, denoting $M[x_n]$ by V_2 and $D[x_n]$ by V_1 for $t = T$, we shall obtain two functionals defined on the solutions of system (31.19), which will give the possibility of finding the optimal parameters $\bar{\alpha}_1, \dots, \bar{\alpha}_k$ if one proceeds accoirdng to the methods indicated above.

5. Under the conditions of the preceding Problem, we shall consider the parameters $\bar{\alpha}_1, \ldots, \bar{\alpha}_k$ lying in the region Ω as optimal in the case that the probability of realization of the inequality $|x_n| \leqq L$ at this point has the highest value for a fixed value of $t = T$.

It is clear that

$$P(|x_n| \leqq L) = \frac{1}{\sigma \sqrt{2\pi}} \int_{-L}^{L} e^{-\frac{(x-a)^2}{2\sigma^2}} dx = \frac{1}{\sqrt{2\pi}} \int_{-\frac{(L-a)}{\sigma}}^{\frac{(L-a)}{\sigma}} e^{-\frac{z^2}{2}} dz, \quad (31.27)$$

where

$$a = M[x_n(T)], \quad \sigma^2 = D[x_n(T)].$$

Thus, the problem of finding the optimal system in that case reduces to the finding of the largest value of the functional $V_1 = P(|x_n| \leqq L)$.

If the random processes $f_1, \ldots, f_n$ admit of the canonical expansion [53], then

$$f_s = \sum_{i=1}^{r} \phi_{si}\psi_{si} + a_s \quad (s = 1, \ldots, n), \tag{31.28}$$

where the ϕ_{si} are determinate continuous functions, given for $t \geqq 0$, and the ψ_{si} are random quantities pairwise independent and normally distributed.

Then

$$D[x_n] = \sum_{i=1}^{n} \left\{ y_{si}^2(t) l_i + \sum_{i=1}^{r} \left[\int_0^t y_{si}(t, \tau) \phi_{ij}(\tau) d\tau \right]^2 D[\psi_{ij}] \right\}. \tag{31.29}$$

If into an analogue computer one feeds a homogeneous system of equations (31.21), then an additional connection of summing blocks and multiplying blocks will allow us to work out $M[x_n]$ and $D[x_n]$ by means of a series of machine runs. If one finds the gradients of the quantities $M[x_n]$ and $D[x_n]$, then it is easy to convince oneself that they may be calculated in the case when the elements of the matrices $\partial Y/\partial \alpha_i$ and $\partial Z/\partial \alpha_i$ are known.

The elements of these matrices are determined by means of the following formulae

$$\frac{\partial Y}{\partial \alpha_i} = \int_0^t Z(t, \tau) \frac{\partial P}{\partial \alpha_i} Y(\tau) d\tau \quad (i = 1, \ldots, k), \tag{31.30}$$

where P is the matrix of the coefficients of system (31.21);

$$\frac{\partial Z}{\partial \alpha_i} = \frac{\partial Y(t)}{\partial \alpha_i} Y^{-1}(\tau) - Z(t, \tau) \frac{\partial Y(\tau)}{\partial \alpha_i} Y^{-1}(\tau) \quad (i = 1, \ldots, k), \tag{31.31}$$

where $Y^{-1}(\tau) = Z(0, \tau)$, which shows the possibility of designing a block for computing the gradients of the quantities $M[x_n]$ and $D[x_n]$, and consequently also of the quantity $V_1 = P(|x_n| \leq L)$.

However, even without the presence of such a block, by means of tentative steps, just as has been proposed above and in work [60], one may find the approximate gradients of the indicated quantities.

In relation to the above, one should have in view the following general remark.

In this and in the preceding sections, to realize the process of optimization, we have been making use of widely applied primitive methods which serve the purpose with particular efficiency in those cases when there is a strongly marked isolated extremum.

In practice, however, as a rule one encounters such cases when in the region Ω of the parameters $\alpha_1, \ldots, \alpha_k$ there are several extremal points from which one has to choose that at which the extremum is greatest.

For solving such a problem, the methods mentioned above are not very convenient. Nevertheless, by a generalization of these methods one may propose a method for solving such problems.

Let us expound one such method. We shall assume that in the region Ω of the n-dimensional space a real continuous function $f(X) \geq 0$ is given, where $X = (x_1, \ldots, x_n)$.

We are required to find the greatest value of that function, taking into account that this greatest value may lie within Ω. We shall arbitrarily take m points lying within Ω, $A_1, \ldots, A_m$.

Let us compute the values of the function $f(X)$ at these points and distinguish the smallest of these values [for example, $f(A_1)$].

We shall calculate the gradients of the function $f(X)$ at the points $A_1, \ldots, A_m$.

We shall find the point

$$B_1 = \frac{\sum_{i=1}^{m} A_i f(A_i)}{\sqrt{\sum_{i=1}^{n} f^2(A_i)}}$$

and the vector

$$\bar{C}_1 = \sum_{i=1}^{n} f(A_i) \operatorname{grad}_{A_i} f.$$

Moving in the region Ω along the line $X = B_1 + \tau \bar{C}_1$ in the direction $\tau < 0$, we shall find the point $A_1^{(1)}$ at which the function $f(X)$ has a maximum in this direction.

Having computed $f(A_1^{(1)})$, we shall find $\operatorname{grad}_{A_1^{(1)}} f$. The point $A_1^{(1)}$ we shall connect to the chosen points $A_1, ..., A_m$, having rejected A_1 from their number. With the newly obtained system of points, we proceed as with the initial one, etc. Sometimes it is useful to raise the function $f(X)$ preliminarily to some power l.

From geometrical considerations, it is obvious that for some classes of functions, such a process allows one to find the largest maximum.

The algorithms expounded in its section may be put at the basis of the design of specialized computing machines for the optimization of automatic control systems, particularly in response to the urgent need for such machines by KB [design bureaus] and NII [research institutes]. It goes without saying that some of the assumptions expounded in this section require more detailed treatment for their effective application to engineering practice. Nevertheless, on the basis of the mathematical methods proposed here one can create a scheme of an automatic computing machine meant especially for the optimization of automatic control systems.

METHODS OF APPROXIMATING FAMILIES OF SOLUTIONS OF DIFFERENTIAL EQUATIONS

As A RULE, in solving problems of analysis and synthesis of automatic control systems, one encounters systems of differential equations containing parameters which have to be chosen so that the automatic control system obtained as a result be, in some sense, of higher quality. The most widely used method of solution of this problem consists in the following: the set of values of the parameters is distributed over a net, and then at its nodes one studies the behaviour of the solutions of the above-mentioned system of differential equations by integrating it directly (for example, on digital or analogue computers). This method is very cumbersome and inconvenient. Therefore one also uses another method, consisting in finding functions depending on the same number of parameters as the system of differential equations which are the approximate solutions of that system. By means of these functions one can compute other functions, which characterize the quality of the automatic control system, and thereupon find the extremals of these latter. The most difficult part of this second method undoubtedly consists in the finding of a family of approximate solutions of the system of differential equations. Nevertheless, one may propose several methods of finding functions of this type.

§ 1. Interpolation of solutions

Say one is given a system of differential equations

$$\frac{dy_s}{dt} = F_s(t, y_1, \ldots, y_n, a_1, \ldots, a_m) \qquad (s = 1, \ldots, n), \tag{1.1}$$

where F_s are real continuous functions given for $t \in [0, T]$ and $-\infty < y_i < +\infty$ $(i = 1, \ldots, n)$, $(a_1, \ldots, a_m) \in \Omega$. The quantities $a_1, \ldots, a_m$ represent parameters taking real values from the set Ω of the m-dimensional space. We shall note that if necessary, one may introduce the initial conditions $y_1^0, \ldots, y_n^0$ into the set of parameters of system (1.1) by way, for example, of replacing the sought functions y_s with new functions η_s according to the formulae $\eta_s = y_s - y_s^0$. Thus, we shall consider only such solutions as are defined by the conditions $y_s = 0$ at $t = 0$. These conditions define continuous differentiable functions

$$y_s = y_s(t, a_1, ..., a_m), \tag{1.2}$$

satisfying system (1.1) and depending on m parameters. As a rule, the exact construction of such functions is very difficult in practice, however for some fixed values of the parameters they may be found with the aid of analogue or digital computers. This fact plays a special role in what follows.

Say in the parameter-space one is given a system of points

$$a_1^k, ..., a_m^k \quad (k = 1, ..., p).$$

We shall consider that functions (1.2) are computed at these points. We shall denote them as

$$y_s^{(k)}(t) = y_s(t, a_1^k, ..., a_m^k).$$

Starting with these data, we may indicate any interpolation process as a result of which we shall obtain functions approximating (1.2). We shall dwell on the construction of the Lagrange interpolation polynomial. For this, we shall first construct the polynomials P_k, which become zero at the points $a_1^j, ..., a_m^j$ $(j \neq k)$ and at the points $a_1^k, ..., a_m^k$ are equal to unity. It is not hard to convince oneself that this property is possessed by the polynomial $P_n = \prod\limits_{i=1}^{n} P_i$, where

$$P_i = \frac{\prod\limits_{j \neq k} (a_i - a_i^j)}{\prod\limits_{j \neq k} (a_i^k - a_i^j)}.$$

We shall set

$$y_s^{(p)} = \sum_{k=1}^{p} y_s^{(k)} P_k. \tag{1.3}$$

Functions (1.3) are multinomials in the parameters of system (1.1) and, at the same time, coincide at the chosen points with the values of functions (1.2). Thus, they represent the interpolation polynomials for function (1.2) [54].

Let us consider the system of operators

$$z_s = \frac{dy_s}{dt} - F_s(t, y_1, ..., y_n, a_1, ..., a_m), \tag{1.4}$$

taking values from the set of continuous functions, given on $[0, T]$, for any choice of continuously differentiable functions $y_1, ..., y_n$ given on the same interval. We shall compute the value of these operators on the functions $y_s^{(p)}$ and denote them by $z_s^{(p)}$. The functions thus obtained may be considered as errors resulting from the substitutions of function (1.3) in system (1.1).

By Ω_1 we shall denote a set of points $a_1, ..., a_m$ where, in the interval $[O, T_1]$, the functions $z_s^{(p)}$ are small compared to $y_s^{(p)}$. If this smallness is such that within the limits of accuracy adopted in the construction of system (1.1) the functions $z_s^{(p)}$ may be considered as zero, then the polynomials $y_s^{(p)}$ for $t \in [0, T_1]$ on the set Ω_1 may be considered as the family of solutions of system (1.1).

This approach to the construction of families of approximate solutions dependent on the parameters of system (1.1), may be generalized if, instead of the functions $y_s^{(p)}$, one takes the functions

$$\bar{y}_s^{(p)} = \phi_s(t, a_1, ..., a_m) + \sum_{k=1}^{p} \frac{P_k y_s^{(k)} \phi_s^{(k)}(t, a_1, ..., a_m)}{\phi_s^{(k)}(t, a_1^k, ..., a_m^k)}, \tag{1.5}$$

where ϕ_s and $\phi_s^{(k)}$ are some continuously differentiable functions given for $t \in [0, T]$ and possessing the properties $\phi_s \equiv 0$ at all the nodes of the interpolation, $\phi_s^{(k)} \neq 0$ for all t at every node of interpolation. We shall substitute functions (1.5) in (1.4) and denote the result of the substitution by $\bar{z}_s^{(p)}$. The role of the functions ϕ_s and $\phi_s^{(k)}$ consists in that the set Ω_1 is extended by their choice.

§ 2. Expansion into series in the parameters

Another method of construction of families of approximate solutions for a system of differential equations is based on the application of an idea of Poincaré – Lyapunov on the expansion of solutions into series in the parameters.

We shall give a short exposition of this method.

We shall assume that the right-hand members of system (1.1) may be expanded in series in powers of the quantities $y_1, ..., y_n, a_1, ..., a_m$, whose coefficients are continuous functions of time for $t \in [0, T]$. We shall consider that these series converge for all possible real values of $y_1, ..., y_n, a_1, ..., a_m$ uniformly with respect to t. System (1.1), possessing the properties just indicated, shall be denoted by (2.1). Those values which are taken by the right-hand members of system (2.1) for $a_1 = a_1^0, \ldots, a_m = a_m^0$, we shall denote as $F_s^0(y_1, \ldots, y_n, t)$. By

$$y_s = y_s(t, c_1, \ldots, c_n) \tag{2.2}$$

we shall denote the general solution of the system

$$\dot{y}_s = F_s^0(y_1, \ldots, y_n, t). \tag{2.3}$$

We shall seek the solution of system (2.1) defined by the conditions $y_s = 0$ for $t = 0$ in the form of series

$$y_s = \sum_{k=0}^{+\infty} y_s^{(k)}, \tag{2.4}$$

where $y_s^{(k)}$ are functions representing homogeneous forms of degree k in the quantities $a_1 - a_1^0, \ldots, a_m - a_m^0$ with coefficients to be determined.

We shall substitute series (2.4) in the system (2.1), the functions obtained as a result of this substitution in the right-hand members we shall expand in increasing powers of the quantities $a_1 - a_1^0, \ldots, a_m - a_m^0$. Thereupon we shall equate on the right and left the forms of the same degree in these quantities. Then, for the determination of the functions $y_s^{(k)}$ we shall obtain the sequence of systems of equations

$$\dot{y}_s^{(k)} = \sum_{i=1}^{n} P_{si}(t) y_i^{(k)} + R_s^{(k)} \quad (s = 1, \ldots, n; \; k = 1, \ldots, +\infty). \tag{2.5}$$

In system (2.5), we shall denote by $P_{si}(t)$ the functions $\partial F_s(y_1^{(0)}, \ldots, y_n^{(0)})/\partial y_i$, and by $R_s^{(k)}$ the functions which are polynomials in $y_s^{(l)}$, $l < k$, with known coefficients.

The initial conditions for the determination of the functions $y_s^{(k)}$ are defined by the formulae $y_s^{(k)} = 0$ for $t = 0$ $(s = 1, \ldots, n; k = 0, \ldots, n, \ldots)$.

As follows from (2.1), the functions $y_s^{(0)}$ will satisfy equations (2.3). Consequently, they may be obtained from functions (2.2) by some choice of the quantities $c_1 = c_1^0, \ldots, c_n = c_n^0$.

We shall substitute functions (2.2) in system (2.3) and differentiate both members through with respect to the variable c_j.

Then we shall obtain

$$\frac{d}{dt}\left(\frac{\partial y_s}{\partial c}\right) = \sum_{i=1}^{n} \frac{\partial F_s}{\partial y_i}(t, y_1^{(0)}, \ldots, y_n^{(0)}) \frac{\partial y_i}{\partial c}. \tag{2.6}$$

If in system (2.6) we set $c_1 = c_1^0, ..., c_n = c_n^0$, we shall obtain that the functions

$$\frac{\partial y_s}{\partial c_j}, \tag{2.7}$$

calculated for $c_1 = c_1^0, ..., c_n = c_n^0$, are the solution of the linear system

$$\frac{dy_s}{dt} = \sum_{i=1}^{n} P_{si}(t)\, y_i. \tag{2.8}$$

As functions (2.2) are the general solution of system (2.3), then giving to j different values from unity to n, from functions (2.7) we shall obtain the fundamental system of solutions of system (2.8). For convenience, we shall denote as y_{sj} functions (2.7) entering into the fundamental system of solutions of system (2.8). The fact indicated above allows us to find from system (2.5) all the functions $y_s^{(k)}$ according to the formula

$$y_s^{(k)} = \int_0^t \sum_{j=1}^{n} y_{sj}(t, \tau)\, R_j^{(k)}\, d\tau. \tag{2.9}$$

These formulae allow us to find successively all the functions $y_s^{(k)}$, and therefore series (2.4) may be considered as constructed.

It is obvious that for actual calculations, the use of series (2.4) is very difficult. Therefore, into the argument we shall introduce the functions

$$y_s(q) = \sum_{k=0}^{q} y_s^{(k)}. \tag{2.10}$$

Let us substitute functions (2.10) in (1.4) and denote the result of the substitution by $z_s(q)$.

By Ω_1 we shall denote the set of those values of the parameters $a_1, ..., a_m$ for which in the interval $[0, T_1]$ the functions $z_s(q)$ are small in comparison with the functions $y_s(q)$. In that set, the functions $y_s(q)$ may be considered as the solution of system (2.1).

Let us make a series of remarks relating to the method presented for constructing the family of approximate solutions.

1. The construction of solutions with zero initial conditions does not decrease the generality, as the initial conditions may be introduced among the parameters of the system, as has been shown in §1.

2. The construction of the general solution (2.2) of system (2.3) is very difficult, and therefore it is expedient to apply the following modification of the method given above.

We shall find the solution of system (2.3), $y_s^{(0)}$ $(s = 1, \ldots, n)$. By means of it we shall compute the functions $P_{si}(t)$, and then we shall find the fundamental system of solutions for system (2.8) (all of these operations can be carried out on analogue or digital computers).

3. One encounters cases when it is inexpedient to carry out the construction of the approximate solutions by means of expansion in series in powers of the parameters $b_1, \ldots, b_r$, as a result of which one obtains the system of equations

$$\dot{y}_s = F_s(t, y_1, \ldots, y_m, a_1, \ldots, a_m, b_1, \ldots, b_r). \tag{2.11}$$

The introduction of the parameters is carried out in such a way that system (2.11) possess the same properties as system (2.1) in the sense of "analyticity" of the right-hand members. Besides, it is required that for some values of the quantities $b_1 = \bar{b}_1, \ldots, b_r = \bar{b}_r$, system (2.11) be transformed into system (2.1).

The solution of system (2.11) is constructed in the form of series in powers of the quantities $b_1, \ldots, b_r$, one computes the functions $y_s^{(q)}$ and $z_s^{(q)}$ in which one then sets $b_1 = \bar{b}_1, \ldots, b_r = \bar{b}_r$.

This remark extends considerably the possibilities of the method indicated and makes it more flexible.

As an example we shall consider the equation

$$\dot{y} = \left(-1 + \frac{1}{10 + t} \right) y,$$

and also the equations

$$\dot{y} = \left(-b + \frac{1}{10 + t} \right) y \quad \text{and} \quad \dot{y} = \left(-1 + \frac{b}{10 + t} \right) y$$

which for $b = 1$ turn into the original one. We shall seek the solution of the last two equations $y(t)$ with the conditions $y = y_0$ for $t = 0$ in the form of series in powers of the parameter b.

For the first equation the zero-th approximation has the form $y = 0.1\, y_0(t + 10)$ and the error $z = -0.1\, y_0 b(t + 10)$.

For the second equation the zero-th approximation has the form $y = y_0 e^{-t}$ and the error $z_0 = b y_0 e^{-t}/(10 + t)$

In the second case, for $b = 1$ the error constitutes no more than 10% of the value of the zero-th approximation, and this may be considered as the exact solution of the original equation if it corresponds to the adopted criterion of accuracy.

In the first case the error constitutes 100% of the zero-th approximation, and therefore the latter may not be considered as a solution to the original equation.

This example shows that various methods of introducing the parameters may influence considerably the volume of computation required to find the families of approximate solutions.

§ 3.   Series expansion in the neighbourhood of a singular point

For constructing families of approximate solutions of a system of differential equations, one may propose a method based on the subtle properties of one or another system of equations. These properties are established by a preliminary analysis and are contained in the analytic nature of the functions satisfying the system of equations.

In chapter IV and §10 of chapter II we give the construction of solutions of a system of differential equations with a regular singularity in the form of series of a special type. These series may be applied to the construction of a family of approximate solutions, for which it is sufficient to truncate them after a definite term and compute the errors z_s. Thereupon one can establish the relative value of the error z_s in relation to the approximations for these or other values of the system parameters. Also, where that relative value satisfies the adopted accuracy criterion, the approximation taken may be considered as an exact solution of the system. This method gives a considerable advantage over the remaining ones in the construction of the solutions in a sufficiently small neighbourhood of a singularity.

THE THEORY OF LINEAR STATIONARY SYSTEMS WITH A LAGGING ARGUMENT

IN THIS appendix we consider the problem of representing the solutions of linear equations with a lagging argument, and also carry out an investigation of the solutions from the point of view of their asymptotic stability and boundedness.

§ 1. Formulation of the problem

According to the convention adopted in the literature, the system of equations

$$\frac{dx_s}{dt} = \sum_{l=1; j=0}^{n, v} a_{sl, j} x_l (t - h_j) \qquad (s = 1, ..., n), \tag{1.1}$$

where $a_{sl, j}$ are real constants, $h_0 = 0$, and $0 < h_1 < h_2 < ... < h_v$, is called a system of linear stationary homogeneous equations with v lags.

By $g_{sl}(\theta)$ $(s, l = 1, ..., n)$ we shall denote the totality of functions of bounded variation given on $[-h, 0]$. We shall consider the system

$$\frac{dx_s}{dt} = \sum_{l=1}^{n} \int_{-h}^{0} x_l (t + \theta) \, dg_{sl}(\theta) \qquad (s = 1, ..., n). \tag{1.2}$$

It is easy to see that system (1.2) includes system (1.1) as a special case.

We shall further set $G(\theta) = \| g_{sl}(\theta) \|$. Then system (1.2) may be written in the matrix form

$$\frac{dX}{dt} = \int_{-h}^{0} dG(\theta) X(t + \theta), \tag{1.3}$$

where X is a vector function, and $dG(\theta) = \| dg_{sl}(\theta) \|$. In (1.3) the differential refers only to the elements of the matrix G.

The problem considered here consists in proposing ways of representing the solutions of system (1.3) with the condition that $X(t) = \phi(t)$; $t \in [-h, 0]$ (where ϕ is some vector function which will be dealt with below), and in investigating the behaviour of that solution as $t \to +\infty$.

We shall note that similar problems for systems of form (1.1) or, to be more precise, for special cases of such systems, have been considered also in works [55], [56], [57].

In what follows, we shall everywhere make use of the fact that the solution of system (1.3) exists for any continuous vector function $\phi(t)$ given in $[-h, 0]$, and in the entire interval $[-h, +\infty]$ the estimate $|X(t)| \leq Me^{ct}$ holds.

Within the last few years the major role played by systems with a lagging argument in various problems of physics, technology, and mathematics was clarified. However, up to the present time there exist no publications containing a more or less complete theory of such equations. Therefore this appendix may be considered as a first attempt to publish the complete theory of the most important class of systems of differential equations with lagging arguments—linear systems with constant coefficients and constant lags.

§ 2.   Representation of the solutions of system (1.3)

By $A(\lambda)$ we shall denote a matrix of the form $\int\limits_{-h}^{0} e^{\lambda\theta}\, dG(\theta) - \lambda E$.

In work [34] it has been shown that all roots of the equation $\Delta A(\lambda) = 0$ lie in the halfplane

$$\operatorname{Re}\lambda \leq c. \tag{2.1}$$

By $\lambda_1, \ldots, \lambda_n, \ldots$ we shall denote all the points of the complex plane at which the entire function $\Delta A(\lambda)$ becomes zero. Here these points are numbered in such a way that $\operatorname{Re}\lambda_1 \geq \operatorname{Re}\lambda_2 \geq \ldots$.

Let s_j be the multiplicity of the root λ_j of equation (2.1). Let us distribute the points $\lambda_j \ (j = 1, 2, \ldots)$ into groups, referring to one group those which have the same real parts. Thus, each of the groups will be characterized by one of the numbers $\sigma_1 > \sigma_2 > \ldots$, where σ_j is the real part of the roots entering the j-th group. We shall now show that every such group is finite.

LEMMA 1. The number of roots of equation (2.1) distributed in a vertical strip is finite,

$$a \leq \operatorname{Re}\lambda \leq b, \qquad a > -\infty. \tag{2.2}$$

The elements of the matrix $\int\limits_{-h}^{0} e^{\lambda\theta}\, dG(\theta)$ are entire functions, $\psi_{sl}(\lambda) = \int\limits_{-h}^{0} e^{\lambda\theta}\, dg_{sl}(\theta)$.

It is easy to see that these functions are bounded in strip (2.2). Therefore the functions b_k in the relation $\Delta A(\lambda) = (-1)^n \lambda^n + \sum\limits_{k=1}^{n} b_k \lambda^{n-k}$ will also be bounded in the indicated strip, as they are finite polynomials in the functions $\psi_{sl}(\lambda)$.

Hence it follows that if λ belongs to strip (2.2) and $|\lambda| > B > 0$, where B is a sufficiently large number, then $|\Delta A(\lambda)| > 0$. Thus, the roots of the equation (2.1) lying in strip (2.2) are located completely within the region $a \leq \operatorname{Re} \lambda \leq b$, $|\lambda| \leq B$, and then there can exist only a finite number of roots.

THEOREM 1. To every root λ_j of equation (2.1) corresponds a solution of equation (1.3), $x_j(t)$, represented in the form

$$\frac{1}{2\pi i} \int_{c_j^+} e^{\lambda t} A^{-1}(\lambda) F(\lambda) \, d\lambda, \tag{2.3}$$

where c_j^+ is a circumference with radius r_j centred at λ_j such that in the circle $|\lambda - \lambda_j| \leq r_j$ there are no other roots of equation (2.1), and $F(\lambda)$ is an arbitrary single-valued analytic function in that closed circle. The integration in formula (2.3) is carried out counterclockwise.

PROOF: The function x_j, defined by equality (2.3), is defined for $t \in (-\infty, +\infty)$, is continuously differentiable and, moreover, is an entire function in t. We shall substitute function (2.3) in system (1.3). Then we shall obtain

$$\frac{d}{dt} \int_{c_j^+} e^{\lambda t} A^{-1}(\lambda) F(\lambda) \, d\lambda - \int_{-R}^{0} dG \int_{c_j^+} e^{\lambda(t+\theta)} A^{-1}(\lambda) F(\lambda) \, d\lambda =$$

$$= \int_{c_j^+} e^{\lambda t} \left(\lambda - \int_{-h}^{0} e^{\lambda \theta} \, dG \right) A^{-1}(\lambda) F(\lambda) \, d\lambda = - \int_{c_j^+} e^{\lambda t} F(\lambda) \, d\lambda.$$

The last integral standing in this string of equalities, according to the Cauchy theorem, is equal to zero. Thus, the functions x_j satisfy system (1.3).

COROLLARY 1. To every root λ_j of equation (2.1) there corresponds an entire function $P_j(t) e^{\lambda_j t}$ which is a solution of system (1.3), where $P_j(t)$ represents a polynomial in t of degree no higher than $s_j - 1$, and with constant vector coefficients.

Indeed, function (2.3) according to the Theorem on residues may be represented in the following form:

$$x_j(t) = \operatorname*{Re}_{\lambda = \lambda_j} se^{\lambda t} A^{-1}(\lambda) F(\lambda).$$

We shall set

$$A^{-1}(\lambda) = \frac{\bar{A}(\lambda)}{\Delta A(\lambda)},$$

where $\bar{A}(\lambda)$ is the matrix of algebraic complements for the elements of $A(\lambda)$. Then x_j may be represented in the form

$$x_j(t) = \frac{1}{(s_j - 1)!} \frac{d^{s_j-1}}{d\lambda^{s_j-1}} \left[\frac{e^{\lambda t} \bar{A}(\lambda) F(\lambda) (\lambda - \lambda_j)^{s_j}}{\Delta A(\lambda)} \right]\Bigg|_{\lambda=\lambda_j} = e^{\lambda_j t} \sum_{l=1}^{s_j-1} t^l c .$$

Here in view of the arbitrariness of the single-valued analytic function F the constant vectors c_l are expressed in terms of s_j arbitrary vectors

$$\frac{d^l F}{d\lambda^l}\Bigg|_{\lambda=\lambda_j} \qquad (l = 0, ..., s_j)$$

by means of linear combinations with coefficients dependent only on the matrix $A(\lambda)$.

COROLLARY 2. If equation (2.1) has pure imaginary roots, then system (1.3) has periodic solutions. Because of linearity of system (1.3) any combination of functions x_j taken in finite number will also be a solution of system (1.3). Consequently, if there are several rationally independent pure imaginary roots, then system (1.3) has also almost-periodic solutions (we have in view the presence of pairwise incommensurate roots).

Into the argument we shall introduce the space of vector functions $\phi(t)$, given and continuous in the segment $[-h_1, 0]$, $h_1 > h$, $\phi(-h_1) = 0$, and satisfying in $[-h_1, 0]$ the Dirichlet conditions. The totality of these functions we shall denote C_0.

Into the argument we shall introduce the vector function

$$B(\lambda, \phi) = \int_{-h_1}^{0} e^{\lambda\theta} dG \int_{-h_1}^{\theta} e^{-\lambda\tau} \phi(\tau) d\tau - \lambda \int_{-h_1}^{0} e^{-\lambda\tau} \phi(\tau) d\tau - \phi(0). \qquad (2.4)$$

Here $G(\theta) = G(-h)$ for $\theta \in [-h_1, h]$.

The function $B(\lambda, \phi)$, defined by equality (2.4), is an entire function of the parameter λ for any $\phi \in C_0$, and with fixed λ is a linear bounded operator of C_0 in E'_n, where E'_n is the n-dimensional complex space.

THEOREM 2. The function

$$X(t) = \frac{V.P.}{2\pi i} \int_{\sigma-i\infty}^{\sigma+i\infty} e^{\lambda t} A^{-1}(\lambda) B(\lambda, \phi) d\lambda \qquad (2.5)$$

where $\sigma > C$ is a continuous solution of system (1.3) satisfying the condition

$$X(t) = \phi(t), \ t \in [-h, 0], \ \phi \in C_0,$$

i.e. any solution of system (1.3) satisfying the condition

$$X(t) = \phi(t), \quad t \in [-h_1, 0] \tag{2.6}$$

for any $\phi(t) \in C_0$ is representable by formula (2.5).

PROOF: Vector function (2.5) is obtained by means of the Laplace transform from system (1.3) and is therefore defined and continuous for $t \geq -h_1$.

Let us show first that function (2.5) satisfies condition (2.6). For this we shall consider the function $\bar{\phi}(t) = \phi(t)$ for $t \in [-h_1, 0]$ and $\bar{\phi}(t) = \phi(0)$ for $t \geq 0$.

It is easy to see that this function may be represented in the form

$$\bar{\phi}(t) = \frac{V.P.}{2\pi i} \int\limits_{\sigma - i\infty}^{\sigma + i\infty} e^{\lambda t} \left(\int\limits_{-h_1}^{0} e^{-\lambda \tau} \phi(\tau) d\tau + \frac{\phi(0)}{\lambda} \right) d\lambda. \tag{2.7}$$

Subtracting equality (2.7) term by term from equality (2.5), we shall obtain

$$X(t) - \bar{\phi}(t) = \frac{V.P.}{2\pi i} \int\limits_{\sigma - i\infty}^{\sigma + i\infty} e^{\lambda t} R(\lambda) d\lambda, \tag{2.8}$$

where

$$R(\lambda) = -A^{-1}(\lambda) \int\limits_{-h_1}^{0} dG \left(\int\limits_{\theta}^{0} e^{\lambda(\theta - \tau)} \phi(\tau) d\tau + \frac{\phi(0)}{\lambda} e^{\lambda \theta} \right).$$

We shall evaluate the integral standing in the right-hand member of equality (2.8), for which we shall consider the system of circumferences c_r centred at zero, with radius $r > 0$, $r \to +\infty$. We shall consider the closed contour L_r formed by arcs of these circumferences c_r' lying in the half plane $\operatorname{Re} \lambda \geq \sigma$, and the segment of the straight line $\operatorname{Re} \lambda = \sigma$ lying within c_r.

For any $t \geq -h_1$ we shall have

$$\frac{1}{2\pi i} \int\limits_{L_2} e^{\lambda t} R(\lambda) d\lambda = 0,$$

since in the interior and on the boundary of the contour L_r the function under the integral sign is single-valued and analytic. Hence, it follows that the evaluation of integral (2.8) reduces to finding the limit

$$J = \lim_{r \to +\infty} \int\limits_{c_r'} e^{\lambda t} R(\lambda) d\lambda. \tag{2.9}$$

It is easy to see that $|R(\lambda)| \to 0$ for $\lambda \in C'_r$ and $r \to +\infty$. Therefore according to Jordan's lemma we shall have $J \equiv 0$ for $t < 0$. Hence we have that $X(t) - \bar{\phi}(t) = 0$ for $t \in [-h_1, 0]$. From the continuity of the functions $X(t)$ and $\bar{\phi}(t)$ it follows that $X(t) = \bar{\phi}(t)$ on $t \in [-h_1, 0]$.

Let us now show that the function $X(t, \phi)$ satisfies system (1.3) for $t \geq 0$. For this we shall introduce into the argument the auxiliary function

$$Y = e^{-2ct} X(t, \phi). \tag{2.10}$$

Then the vector function (2.10) will satisfy the system of equations

$$\frac{dy}{dt} = \int_{-h_1}^{0} dG_c(\theta) Y(t + \theta), \tag{2.11}$$

where

$$dG_c(\theta) = e^{2c\theta} dG(\theta) - 2c \, dG_0(\theta),$$

if only the function $X(t, \phi)$ satisfies system (1.3) and the condition $Y = \phi e^{-2ct}$ for $t \in [-h_1, 0]$. Here by G_0 we denote a matrix function of bounded variation such that the relation

$$\int_{-R_1}^{0} dG_0(\theta) Y(t + \theta) = Y(t)$$

holds.

From [34] it follows that the function Y introduced by us satisfies the inequality $|Y(t)| < \mu e^{-ct}$ for $t \geq 0$. We shall set $\phi_1(t) = \phi e^{-2ct}$, $\phi \in C_0$. We shall show that the function

$$Y = \frac{V.P.}{2\pi i} \int_{\sigma - i\infty}^{\sigma + i\infty} e^{\lambda t} A_c^{-1}(\lambda) B_c(\lambda, \phi_1) \, d\lambda \tag{2.12}$$

satisfies system (2.11) for $t \geq 0$. Here $-c < \sigma < 0$, and the matrix functions A_c and B_c are defined just as above, but in terms of G_c.

Let us consider the function

$$Y_1 = \frac{V.P.}{2\pi i} \int_{\sigma - i\infty}^{\sigma + i\infty} \frac{e^{\lambda t} A_c^{-1}(\lambda) B_c(\lambda, \phi_1) \, d\lambda}{\lambda}.$$

This function will be continuously differentiable, its derivative coinciding with the vector function y. We shall substitute the vector function Y_1 in system (2.11), then we shall obtain

$$\frac{V.P.}{2\pi i} \int_{\sigma - i\infty}^{\sigma + i\infty} \left[e^{\lambda t} A_c^{-1}(\lambda) B_c(\lambda, \phi_1) - \int_{-h_1}^{0} \frac{dG e^{\lambda(t + \theta)} A_c^{-1} B_c}{\lambda} \right] d\lambda =$$

$$= \frac{V.P.}{2\pi i} \int_{\sigma - i\infty}^{\sigma + i\infty} \left[-\frac{e^{\lambda t} B_c(\lambda, \phi_1)}{\lambda} \right] d\lambda.$$

We shall show that the integral standing in the right-hand member of the last equality for $t > 0$ zero

$$\frac{V.P.}{2\pi i} \int_{\sigma-i\infty}^{\sigma+i\infty} \left[-\frac{e^{\lambda t} B_c(\lambda, \phi_1)}{\lambda} \right] d\lambda = \frac{V.P.}{\pi 2i} \int_{\sigma-i\infty}^{\sigma+i\infty} \left(-\frac{e^{\lambda t}}{\lambda} \right) \left[\int_{-h_1}^{0} e^{\lambda \theta} dG_c \times \right.$$

$$\left. \times \int_{-h_1}^{\theta} e^{-\lambda \theta} \phi_1(\tau) d\tau - \phi_1(0) \right] d\lambda + \frac{V.P.}{2\pi i} \int_{\sigma-i\infty}^{\sigma+i\infty} e^{\lambda t} \int_{-h_1}^{0} e^{-\lambda \tau} \phi_1(\tau) d\tau\, d\lambda = J_1 + J_2.$$

The integral J_1 may be evaluated by means of the Jordan lemma and becomes zero for $t > 0$. The integral J_2 is a transformation of the Laplace transform over the function $f(t)$, where

$$f(t) = \begin{cases} \phi_1(t) & \text{for } t \in [-h_1, 0], \\ \tfrac{1}{2}\phi_1 & \text{for } t = 0, \\ 0 & \text{for } t > 0, \end{cases}$$

therefore it also becomes zero jor $t > 0$. Consequently, the function Y_1 for $t > 0$ satisfies system (2.11). Because of continuity of that function and of its derivative, it will also satisfy that system for $t \geq 0$. Thus, we have the identity

$$\frac{dY_1}{dt} = \int_{-h_1}^{0} dG_c Y_1(t + \theta)$$

for $t \geq 0$ (for $t = 0$ the derivative is taken from the right). Differentiating both members of that equality with respect to t, we shall obtain that function (2.12) also for $t \geq 0$ satisfies system (2.11). Hence it follows that function (2.12) multiplied by e^{2ct} will satisfy system (1.3) and the condition $Ye^{2ct} = \phi$; $t \in [-h_1, 0]$.

We shall show that Ye^{2ct} coincides with function (2.5).

Indeed

$$Ye^{2ct} = \frac{V.P.}{2\pi i} \int_{\sigma-i\infty}^{\sigma+i\infty} e^{(\lambda + 2c)t} A_c^{-1}(\lambda) B_c(\lambda, \phi_1)\, d\lambda.$$

In the last integral we shall perform the identical transformations, setting

$$\lambda + 2c = \mu; \quad \phi_1 = e^{-2ct}\phi; \quad dG_c = e^{2c\theta} dG(\theta) - 2c\,dG_0(\theta).$$

Then we shall obtain

$$A_c(\lambda) = \int_{-h_1}^{0} e^{\lambda \theta} dG_c - \lambda E = \int_{-h_1}^{0} e^{(\lambda + 2c)\theta} dG(\theta) - E(\lambda + 2c) = A(\lambda + 2c) = A(\mu).$$

Thus, we have

$$B_c(\lambda, \phi_1) = \int_{-h_1}^{0} e^{\lambda\theta} dG_c \int_{-h_1}^{\theta} e^{-\lambda\tau}\phi_1(\tau)\,d\tau - \lambda \int_{-h_1}^{0} e^{-\lambda\tau}\phi_1(\tau)\,d\tau - \phi_1(0) =$$

$$= \int_{-h_1}^{0} e^{(\lambda+2c)\theta} dG(\theta) \int_{-h_1}^{\theta} e^{-\tau(\lambda+2c)}\phi(\tau)\,d\tau - (\lambda+2c)\int_{-h_1}^{0} e^{-\tau(\lambda+2c)}\phi(\tau)\,d\tau - \phi(0) =$$

$$= B(\mu, \phi).$$

Finally, we shall obtain

$$Ye^{2ct} = \frac{V.P.}{2\pi i} \int_{\sigma+2c-i\infty}^{\sigma+2c+i\infty} e^{\mu t} A^{-1}(\mu) B(\mu, \phi)\,d\mu,$$

where $\sigma = 2c > c$.

Thus we have obtained that $Ye^{2ct} = X(t, \phi)$, where $X(t, \phi)$ is defined by formula (2.5). It has thus been shown that formula (2.5) supplies the solution of system (1.3), satisfying the condition $X(t, \phi) = \phi$, $t \in [-h, 0]$, and system (1.3) for $t \geq 0$.

In Theorem 1 we gave a representation of the particular solutions of system (1.3) by means of formula (2.3). If we take linear combinations of the functions $x_j(t)$ in an infinite number, then we shall obtain a series which, in general, satisfies formally system (1.3). The question arises: which solution of system (1.3) may be represented by such series, and in which sense? To clarify this question we shall introduce the following definitions.

We shall consider a denumerable set of points r_j of the complex plane λ possessing the properties: 1) Re $r_j < c$; 2) $|r_j| \to \infty$; 3) in any strip $a \leq$ Re $\lambda \leq b$; $a \to -\infty$ there exists only a finite number of numbers r_j; 4) Re $r_1 \geq$ Re $r_2 \geq$ Re $r_3 \geq \ldots$.

To the point r_j we shall ascribe a finite multiplicity m_j and we shall divide these points into groups, referring to one and the same group those points r_j which have the same real parts, and denoting them by $n_1, n_2, \ldots$, where n_j denotes the number of elements of the j-th group. Into the argument we shall introduce the functions $F_j(t) = P_j(t)e^{n_j t}$, where $P_j(t)$ is a polynomial of degree $m_j - 1$ whose coefficients represent scalar n-dimensional vectors.

DEFINITION 1. The series $\sum_{j=1}^{\infty} F_j$ we shall call an asymptotic expansion of the first kind of the function $\mu(t)$, given for $t \geq 0$, if the following two conditions are satisfied:

$$1) \quad n_1 = n_2 = \ldots = 1;$$

$$2) \quad \left| \mu(t) - \sum_{j=1}^{k} F_j \right| e^{-\text{Re } r_k t} \to 0,$$

as $t \to \infty$ for all k. To be more precise,

$$\left| \mu(t) - \sum_{j=1}^{k} F_j \right| e^{-\operatorname{Re} r_k t} \leqq c_k(\varepsilon) e^{-[\operatorname{Re}(r_k - r_{k+1}) - \varepsilon]t} \qquad (2.13)$$

for every $\varepsilon > 0$, $c_k(\varepsilon)$ being some continuous functions given for $\varepsilon \in [0, 1]$.

DEFINITION 2. The series $\sum_{j=1}^{k} F_j$ is called an asymptotic expansion of the function $\mu(t)$ of the second kind, given for $t \geqq 0$, if for any number k, represented in the form $k = \sum_{j=1}^{l} n_j$, relation (2.13) is satisfied.

By $y_j(t, \phi)$ we shall denote those vector functions which are obtained from the functions $x_j(t)$, if in formula (2.3) the function $F(\lambda)$ is replaced by an entire function $B(\lambda, \phi)$.

THEOREM 3. If in the group σ_j there enter only one each of the roots λ_j of equation (2.1) $(j = 1, ..., \infty)$, then solution (1.3) of $X(t, \phi)$ may be expanded in an asymptotic series of the first kind $\sum_{j=1}^{\infty} Y_j(t, \phi)$.

PROOF: We shall consider the function $\phi^+(t)$

$$\phi^+(t) = \begin{cases} \phi(t), & t \in [-h_1, 0] \\ \tfrac{1}{2}\phi(0), & t = 0 \\ 0, & t > 0. \end{cases}$$

This function may be represented in the following form:

$$\phi^+(t) = \frac{V.P.}{2\pi i} \int_{\sigma - i\infty}^{\sigma + i\infty} e^{\lambda t} \int_{-h_1}^{0} \phi(\tau) e^{-\lambda \tau} d\tau \, d\lambda.$$

By $X^+(t)$ we shall denote the function obtained from $X(t, \phi)$ by the formula

$$X^+(t) = X - \phi^+ = \frac{V.P.}{2\pi i} \int_{\sigma - i\infty}^{\sigma + i\infty} e^{\lambda t} A^{-1}(\lambda) \times \left[B(\lambda, \phi) - A(\lambda) \int_{-h_1}^{0} \phi(\tau) e^{-\lambda \tau} d\tau \right] d\lambda. \qquad (2.14)$$

From formula (2.14) it can be seen that the vector function X^+ for $t > 0$ coincides with the function $X(t, \phi)$, and therefore to prove the Theorem it is sufficient to show that the function X^+ can be expanded in an asymptotic series of the first kind, $X^+ = \sum_{j=1}^{\infty} y_j(t, \phi)$. Carrying out the transformation in formula (2.14), we shall obtain

$$X^+ = \frac{V.P.}{2\pi i} \int_{\sigma - i\infty}^{\sigma + i\infty} e^{\lambda t} A^{-1}(\lambda) \left[-\int_{-h_1}^{0} e^{\lambda \theta} dG \int_{\theta}^{0} \phi(\tau) e^{-\lambda \tau} d\tau - \phi(0) \right] d\lambda. \qquad (2.15)$$

In the interval (σ_{k+1}, σ_k) we shall choose the point $\bar{\sigma}$ and consider the sequence of closed rectangular contours formed by the segments

$$l_N = [\sigma - i\mu_N; \ \sigma + i\mu_N]; \ \bar{e}_N = [\bar{\sigma} + i\mu_N; \ \bar{\sigma} - i\mu_N];$$

$$P_N = [\sigma + i\mu_N; \ \bar{\sigma} + i\mu_N]; \ q_N = [\bar{\sigma} - i\mu_N; \ \sigma + i\mu_N].$$

As $N \to \infty$, $\mu_n \to +\infty$. The closed contour formed by these segments we shall, in what follows, denote by S_N. The number N may be chosen so large that all the roots of equation (2.1) lying in the halfplane $\text{Re } \lambda > \bar{\sigma}$ will fall in a rectangle bounded by the contour S_N. Therefore the following relation will hold:

$$\frac{1}{2\pi i} \int_{S_N} e^{\lambda t} A^{-1}(\lambda) \left[-\int_{-h_1}^{0} e^{\lambda\theta} dG \int_{\theta}^{0} \phi(\tau) e^{-\lambda\tau} d\tau - \phi(0) \right] d\lambda = \sum_{j=1}^{k} y_j(t, \phi) =$$

$$= \frac{1}{2\pi i} \int_{l_N} e^{\lambda t} A^{-1}(\lambda) \left[-\int_{-h_1}^{0} e^{\lambda\theta} dG \int_{\theta}^{0} \phi(\tau) e^{-\lambda\tau} d\tau - \phi(0) \right] d\lambda +$$

$$+ \frac{1}{2\pi i} \int_{P_N + q_N + \bar{l}_N} e^{\lambda t} A^{-1}(\lambda) \left[-\int_{-h_1}^{0} e^{\lambda\theta} dG \int_{\theta}^{0} \phi(\tau) e^{-\lambda\tau} d\tau - \phi(0) \right] d\lambda. \quad (2.16)$$

We shall transform the second integral standing in the right-hand member of the last equality, for which we shall add and subtract the expression

$$\frac{1}{2\pi i} \int_{P_N + q_N + \bar{l}_N} e^{\lambda t} \left[-\int_{-h_1}^{0} e^{\lambda\theta} dG \int_{\theta}^{0} e^{-\lambda\tau} \phi(\tau) d\tau - \phi(0) \right] \frac{d\lambda}{\lambda}$$

Then we shall obtain

$$\frac{1}{2\pi i} \int_{P_N + q_N + \bar{l}_N} e^{\lambda t} A^{-1}(\lambda) \left[-\int_{-h_1}^{0} e^{\lambda\theta} dG \int_{\theta}^{0} \phi(\tau) e^{-\lambda\tau} d\tau - \phi(0) \right] d\lambda =$$

$$= \frac{1}{2\pi i} \int_{P_N + q_N + \bar{l}_N} \left\{ e^{\lambda t} A^{-1}(\lambda) \left[-\int_{-h_1}^{0} e^{\lambda\theta} dG \int_{\theta}^{0} \phi(\tau) e^{-\lambda\tau} d\tau - \phi(0) \right] + \right.$$

$$\left. + \frac{1}{\lambda} \left[e^{\lambda t} \int_{-h_1}^{0} e^{\lambda\theta} dG \int_{\theta}^{0} e^{-\lambda\tau} \phi(\tau) d\tau - \phi(0) \right] \right\} d\lambda +$$

$$+ \frac{1}{2\pi i} \int_{P_N + q_N + \bar{l}_N} \left[e^{\lambda t} - \int_{-h_1}^{0} e^{\lambda\theta} dG \int_{\theta}^{0} e^{-\lambda\tau} \phi(\tau) d\tau + \phi(0) \right] \frac{d\lambda}{\lambda} = J_1(t) + J_2(t).$$

In the integral J_2 the contour of integration may be replaced by an arc of the circumference centred at the point $\lambda = 0$ with ends at the points $\sigma - \mu_N i$; $\sigma + \mu_N i$, lying in the halfplane $\operatorname{Re} \lambda \leq \sigma$. If $N \to +\infty$, then according to Jordan's lemma, $J_2 \to 0$ for $t > h$. Passing to the limit as $N \to \infty$ in the integral

$$- \int_{P_N + q_N} e^{\lambda t} \left\{ A^{-1}(\lambda) \int_{-h_1}^{0} e^{\lambda \theta} dG \int_{\theta}^{0} \phi(\tau) e^{-\lambda \tau} d\tau + A^{-1}(\lambda) \phi(0) + \right.$$

$$\left. + \frac{1}{\lambda} \left[\int_{-h_1}^{0} e^{\lambda \theta} dG \int_{\theta}^{0} e^{-\lambda \tau} \phi(\tau) d\tau + \phi(0) \right] \right\} d\lambda$$

we obtain that its limit is equal to zero, as the modulus of the function under the integral sign may be estimated by an expression of the form $c|\lambda|^{-2} \exp(\operatorname{Re} \lambda t)$. For the same reason there exists a limit for the integral

$$\lim_{N \to \infty} \frac{1}{2\pi i} \int_{l_N} e^{\lambda t} [\dots] d\lambda,$$

which does not exceed the quantity $c(\bar{\sigma})e^{t\bar{\sigma}}$ in modulus. Thus, from formula (2.16) we have $\left| X(t) - \sum_{j=1}^{k} y_j(t, \phi) \right| \leq c(\bar{\sigma})e^{t\bar{\sigma}}$, where $\bar{\sigma}$ is any number from the interval (σ_{k+1}, σ_k).

Multiplying both members of the last inequality by $e^{-\sigma_k t}$ and setting $\bar{\sigma} = \sigma_{k+1} + \varepsilon$, we shall find that

$$\left| X(t) - \sum_{j=1}^{k} y_j(t, \phi) \right| e^{-\sigma_k t} \leq c_k(\varepsilon) e^{-(\sigma_k - \sigma_{k+1} - \varepsilon)t}$$

for $t > h_1$.

Thus, it has been shown that the solution of system (1.3), $X(t, \phi)$, may be expanded in an asymptotic series of the first kind. This completes the proof of the Theorem.

THEOREM 4.   If at least one of the groups σ_j consists of more than one point λ_j, then the function $X(t, \phi)$, which is the solution of system (1.3), may be expanded in an asymptotic series of the second kind $\sum_{j=1}^{\infty} Y_j$.

PROOF: The assertion of Theorem 4 will be established if it is shown that

$$\left| X(t, \phi) - \sum_{j=1}^{k} y_j(t, \phi) \right| e^{-\sigma_k t} \leq c_k(\varepsilon) e^{-(\sigma_k - \sigma_{k+1} - \varepsilon)t}$$

as $t \to +\infty$, where k is a number represented in the form $k = \sum_{j=1}^{l} n_j$, where n_j

is the number of roots entering in the group defined by the real number σ_j. This fact is established in exactly the same way as in Theorem 3, with only the difference that each time $k = \sum\limits_{j=1}^{l} n_j$.

Remark 1. By c we shall denote the space of continuous vector functions given on $[-h, 0]$. Then for any function $\phi(t) \in c$ there exists a solution of system (1.3) $\bar{X}(t, \phi)$

$$\bar{X}(t,\phi) = \phi; \; t \in [-h, 0],$$

which may be represented in the following form

$$\frac{V.P.}{2\pi i} \int\limits_{\sigma-i\infty}^{\sigma+i\infty} e^{\lambda t} A^{-1}(\lambda) Q(\lambda, \phi) \, d\lambda,$$

where

$$Q(\lambda, \phi) = - \left[\int\limits_{h}^{0} e^{\lambda v} \, dG(v) \int\limits_{v}^{0} e^{-\lambda \tau} \phi(\tau) \, d\tau + \phi(0) \right] \qquad (2.17)$$

for $t > 0$.

Literally, as has been done in Theorem 2, one may show that the function $\bar{X}(t,\phi)$ satisfies for $t > 0$ system (1.3). If $\phi \in c$, then $\bar{X}(t,\phi)$ may also be expanded in an asymptotic series $\sum\limits_{j=1}^{\infty} \bar{Y}_j(t, \phi)$ of the first or the second kind, where $\bar{Y}_j(t, \phi)$ are obtained from the functions x_j by replacing $F(\lambda)$ with entire functions $Q(\lambda)$. Besides, it can be seen that $\bar{Y}_j(t,\phi) = Y_j(t, \phi)$.

Remark 2. If one considers the space $\bar{c}$ of vector functions $\phi(t)$ piecewise-continuous in the interval $[-h, 0]$, then one may assert that the solution of system (1.3) exists, may be represented in form (2.17), and may be expanded in an asymptotic series $\sum\limits_{j=1}^{\infty} Y_j$ of the first or second kind.

THEOREM 5. Every solution of system (1.3), $X(t, \phi); \; \phi \in c$ may be expanded in a class of functions F_j for $r_j = \lambda_j \; (j = 1, 2, \dots)$ in an asymptotic series of the first or the second kind in a unique manner.

PROOF: Let us carry out the proof of Theorem 5 for an asymptotic expansion of the second kind. Let $X(t, \phi)$ be expanded in an asymptotic series $\sum\limits_{j=1}^{\infty} F_j$ of the second kind. We shall then show that necessarily $Y_j(t, \phi) = F_j(t)$

for $j = 1, 2, \ldots, \infty$. In fact, we shall at first assume that $F_j = Y_j$ for $j \leq \sum\limits_{1 \leq l \leq m} n_l$. We shall show that with this assumption, $Y_j = F_j$ with $j \leq \sum\limits_{l=1}^{m+1} n_l$.

By virtue of the fact that the series $\sum\limits_{j=1}^{\infty} F_j$ is an asymptotic expansion of the function $X(t, \phi)$ of the second kind, we shall have

$$\left| X(t, \phi) - \sum_{j=1}^{n_1 + \ldots + n_{m+1}} F_j \right| e^{-t\sigma_{m+1}} \leq c'_{m+1}(\varepsilon) e^{-t(\sigma_{m+1} - \sigma_{m+2} - \varepsilon)} , \quad \varepsilon \geq 0. \quad (2.18)$$

Replacing the left-hand member of inequality (2.18) by the difference of the moduli, we shall obtain

$$\left| \sum_{j=n_1 + \ldots + n_m}^{n_1 + \ldots + n_{m+1}} F_j - Y_j \right| e^{-t\sigma_{m+1}} \leq$$

$$\leq c'_{m+1} e^{-t(\sigma_{m+1} - \sigma_{m+2} - \varepsilon)} + \left| X(t, \phi) - \sum_{j=1}^{n_1 + \ldots + n_{m+1}} Y_j \right| e^{-t\sigma_{m+1}}. \quad (2.19)$$

The right-hand member of inequality (2.19) tends to zero as $t \to \infty$, whereas in the left-hand member stands the modulus of the polynomial whose coefficients are, in general, linear combinations of $\sin \varepsilon_j t$ and $\cos \varepsilon_j t$, where ε_j are the imaginary parts of the roots entering in the n_{m+1}-th group. Hence it follows that $\left| \sum Y_j - F_j \right| \equiv 0$, i.e. $Y_j = F_j$ for $j \leq \sum\limits_{i=1}^{m+1} n_i$.

To complete the proof of the Theorem, it remains to be shown that the relation $Y_j = F_j; j \leq n_1$ holds. These equalities will follow also from (2.19), if in them one sets $m = 0$. Then we shall obtain

$$\left| \sum_{j=1}^{n_1} F_j - Y_j \right| e^{-t\sigma_1} \leq c'_1 e^{-t(\sigma_1 - \sigma_2 - \varepsilon)} + \left| X(t, \phi) - \sum_{j=1}^{n_1} Y_j \right| e^{-\sigma_2 t}. \quad (2.20)$$

The right-hand member of inequality (2.20) tends to zero as $t \to \infty$, therefore, as above, we conclude that $Y_j = F_j$ for $j \leq n_1$. This completes the proof of the Theorem.

§ 3.   Behaviour of solutions of the system (1.3) as time increases without bound

Into the argument we shall introduce the space c^* of matrices $G(v)$ of the n-th order, whose elements are real functions of bounded variation, given on $[-h, 0]$. We shall divide the space c^* into non-intersecting sets c^*_{km}, to each of them referring those and only those matrices $G(v)$ for which m roots of equation (2.1) have a positive real part and k roots have a real part equal to zero. It is clear that the sets c^*_{km} do not intersect and cover c^*.

Let $G \in c_{km}^*$; let $\lambda_1, \ldots, \lambda_{l_1}$ be the roots of equation (2.1) with positive real parts of multiplicity $\rho_1, \ldots, \rho_{l_1}$, and let $\lambda_{l_1+1}, \ldots, \lambda_{l_1+l_2}$ be the roots of equation (2.1) with zero real parts of multiplicity $\rho_{l_1+1}, \ldots, \rho_{l_1+l_2}$. By L_{jr} we shall denote the vector which is the coefficient in the polynomial $e^{-\lambda_j t} y_j(t, \phi)$ standing next to t^r, $r \leq \rho_j - 1$. Each of the quantities L_{jr} is a linear bounded operator acting from c in E_n. By O_{jr} we shall denote the set of the vector functions $\phi \in c$ for which $L_{jr} \phi = 0$.

It is clear that the set O_{jr} is a closed linear subspace of the space c. By c_{km} we shall denote the subspace formed by the intersection of all the subspaces O_{jr}, $j \leq l_1 + l_2$, $r \leq s_j - 1$, with the intersection of the space O_{jr}, $j \geq l_1 + 1$, $j \leq l_1 + l_2$, $r \leq s_j - 1$; $r \neq 0$.

It is clear that c_{km} and Γ_{km} are closed linear subspaces of the space c. Here $c_{km} \subseteq \Gamma_{km}$.

THEOREM 6. If the matrix $G \in c_{00}^*$, then the homogeneous solution of system (1.3) is asymptotically stable. Here there exist numbers $\gamma > 0$; $c > 0$ such that

$$|\bar{X}(t, \phi)| \leq ce^{-\gamma t} . \tag{3.1}$$

In other words, if all the roots of equations (2.1) lie in the left halfplane, then the homogeneous solution of system (1.3) is asymptotically stable and estimate (3.1) holds.

PROOF: Let $\sigma_1 < 0$ be the greatest real part of the roots of equation (2.1) In Theorems 4 and 5 it has been shown that any solution of equations (1.3) may be represented in the form of asymptotic series of the form $\sum_{j=1}^{\infty} Y_j(t, \phi)$.

In particular, it has been shown that

$$\left| X(t, \phi) - \sum_{j=1}^{k} Y_j(t, \phi) \right| e^{-t\sigma_k} \leq c_k(\varepsilon) e^{-t(\sigma_k - \sigma_{k+1} - \varepsilon)} ,$$

whence we have that

$$|X(t, \phi)| \leq c_0(\varepsilon) e^{-t(+\sigma_1 + \varepsilon)} < \bar{c} e^{-\gamma t}; \quad \gamma = \tfrac{1}{2}|\sigma_1|.$$

From the proof of Theorem 4 it is easy to see that the constant $\bar{c}$ is arbitrarily small if $|\phi|$ is sufficiently small, as follows from the linearity and boundedness of the operator $Q(\lambda, \phi)$ from c in E_n. This proves the Theorem.

THEOREM 7. If $G \in c_{km}^*$, then the homogeneous solution of system (1.3) is conditionally asymptotically stable, namely

$$X(t, \phi) \to 0 \text{ for } \phi \in c_{km} \text{ and } t \to \infty .$$

PROOF: According to Theorems 3 and 4, the solution of equation (1.3) $X(t, \phi)$ may be expanded in an asymptotic series $X(t, \phi) \sim \sum Y_j(t, \phi)$ of the first or the second kind. Here holds the estimate

$$\left| X(t, \phi) - \sum_{j=1}^{l_1+l_2} Y_j(t, \phi) \right| < c_{l_1+l_2}(\varepsilon) e^{t(\sigma_{l_1+l_2+1}+\varepsilon)}.$$

Let us choose $\varepsilon = -\frac{1}{2}(\sigma_{l_1+l_2+1})$. Then $c_{l_1+l_2}$ will be arbitrarily small if ϕ is sufficiently small. For $\phi \in c_{km}$ we have $Y_j(t, \phi) \equiv 0$ for $j \leq l_1 + l_2$, therefore in the subspace c_{km} there will hold the inequality $|X(t, \phi)| \leq c e^{-\gamma t}$, i.e. the homogeneous solution of system (1.3) is conditionally asymptotically stable.

THEOREM 8. If $G \in c_{km}^*$; $k \neq 0$, then the homogeneous solution of system (1.3) is conditionally stable for $\phi \in \Gamma_{km}$. Here system (1.3) has a family of periodic and almost-periodic solutions if among the pure imaginary roots there are rationally independent ones each of which is conditionally asymptotically stable.

PROOF: In the case under consideration, as has been shown in § 2, system (1.3) has periodic and also almost-periodic solutions if the pure imaginary roots are rationally independent. From Theorems 3 and 5 we have

$$\left| X(t, \phi) - \sum_{j=1}^{l_1+l_2} Y_j(t, \phi) \right| \leq c_{l_1+l_2}(\varepsilon) e^{t(\sigma_{l_1+l_2}+\varepsilon)},$$

$$\varepsilon = -\frac{1}{2}\sigma_{l_1+l_2+1}.$$

For $\phi \in \Gamma_{km}$ and $\phi \in c_{km}$ the function $\sum_{j=l_1+1}^{l_1+l_2} Y_j(t, \phi)$ is periodic or almost periodic, and the constant $c_{l_1+l_2}$ is arbitrarily small if $|\phi|$ is sufficiently small. Hence it follows that the homogeneous solution of system (1.3) is conditionally stable for $\phi \in \Gamma_{km}$.

In the formulation and the proof of the last two Theorems we have made use of the following definition.

DEFINITION. A homogeneous solution of system (1.3) is called conditionally stable in the subspace $c_1 \subset c$, if for every $\varepsilon > 0$ there exists a number $\delta > 0$ such that if $|\phi| < \delta$ then $|X(t, \phi)| < \varepsilon$ for all $t > 0$ and $\phi \in c_1$. If here $|X(t, \phi)| \to 0$ as $t \to +\infty$, then the homogeneous solution of system (1.3) is called conditionally asymptotically stable in c_1.

Remark. Following work [55], it may be shown that when the conditions of Theorem 6 are satisfied, the homogeneous solution of the system

$$\frac{dx}{dt} = \int_{-h}^{0} dG(\theta)\{X(t + \theta) + F[t, X(t + \theta)]\} \tag{3.2}$$

(where $F[t, X(t + \theta)]$ is a vector each of whose components is a nonlinear functional) will also be asymptotically stable with the proper satisfaction of certain conditions imposed on F.

§ 4. Degenerate case

So far we have been considering the case when equation (2.1) has an infinite number of roots. Cases when there is only a finite number of such roots (the degenerate case) however, are also possible. The present section is devoted to the analysis of this case.

LEMMA 2. The function $\Delta A(\lambda)$ has a finite order $\rho \leq 1$.

Let us estimate the function $\Delta A(\lambda)$ in the right halfplane $\operatorname{Re} \lambda > 0$

$$\Delta A(\lambda) = (-1)^n \lambda^n + \sum_{k=1}^{n} b_k \lambda^{n-k},$$

where the functions $b_k(\lambda)$ represent homogeneous multinomials of degree k in the quantities

$$\psi_{sl}(\lambda) = \int_{-R}^{0} e^{\lambda \theta} dg_{sl}(\theta).$$

Therefore $|b_k| \leq q_k$, where q_k is the same multinomial of degree k as b_k, whose coefficients are replaced by their absolute values, and the functions $\psi_{sl}(\lambda)$ by the total variations V_{sl} of the functions $g_{sl}(\lambda)$. Thus, in the right halfplane there holds the inequality

$$|\Delta A(\lambda)| \leq |\lambda|^n + \sum_{k=1}^{n} q_k |\lambda|^{n-k}. \tag{4.1}$$

We shall now estimate the function $\Delta A(\lambda)$ in the left halfplane $\operatorname{Re} \lambda \leq 0$. In that case we shall have $|\psi_{sl}(\lambda)| \leq e^{-h\operatorname{Re}\lambda} V_{sl}$, whence

$$|\Delta A(\lambda)| \leq |\lambda|^n + \sum_{k=1}^{n} q_k |\lambda|^{n-k} e^{-kh\operatorname{Re}\lambda}. \tag{4.2}$$

From (4.1) and (4.2) it follows that the function $\Delta A(\lambda)$ is of a finite order $\rho \leq 1$.

THEOREM 9. If equation (2.1) has a finite number of roots, then the function $\Delta A(\lambda)$ is a polynomial of the same degree n, where n is the number of equations (1.3).

PROOF: Let the number of roots of the function $\Delta A(\lambda)$ be finite and equal to ρ, and let $\rho \neq n$. Then $\Delta A(\lambda) = P_s(\lambda)\, e^{q(\lambda)}$, where on the basis of Lemma 2 $q(\lambda)$ has the form $q(\lambda) = \alpha\lambda$. It has to be shown that $s = n$ and $\alpha = 0$.

Let $s > n$, then $e^{\mathrm{Re}\alpha\lambda} = \dfrac{|\Delta A(\lambda)|}{|P_s(\lambda)|}$ for $\mathrm{Re}\lambda \geqq 0$, i.e.

$$e^{\mathrm{Re}\alpha\lambda} = \frac{|\Delta A(\lambda)|}{|P_s(\lambda)|} \leqq \frac{|\lambda|^n + \sum\limits_{k=1}^{n} q_k |\lambda|^{n-k}}{|P_s(\lambda)|}. \tag{4.3}$$

For $\mathrm{Re}\,\alpha\lambda = 0$ and $|\lambda| \to +\infty$ we have

$$1 \leqq \frac{|\lambda|^n + \sum\limits_{k=1}^{n} q_k |\lambda|^{n-k}}{|P_s(\lambda)|},$$

which is impossible with $s > n$. Consequently, $s \leqq n$, because on the imaginary axis $\Delta A(\lambda)$ increases as $|\lambda|^n$, therefore $s = n$.

We shall now show that $\alpha = 0$. For this we shall first establish that α is a real nonpositive number. In fact, if α were a complex number, then on the axis $\mathrm{Re}\lambda = 0$ the left-hand member of inequality (4.3) would be a function of an exponential type, and the right-hand member would be bounded. Consequently, α is real.

Thus, we conclude that

$$\alpha \leqq 0. \tag{4.4}$$

In the left halfplane there holds the inequality

$$|P_s(\lambda)| e^{\mathrm{Re}\alpha\lambda} \leqq |\lambda|^n + \sum_{k=1}^{n} |\lambda|^{n-k} q_k e^{-kh\mathrm{Re}\lambda}.$$

We shall consider the vertical straight line $\mathrm{Re}\lambda = \alpha^{-1}\ln 10$. On that straight line we shall have

$$10 \leqq \frac{|\lambda|^n + \sum\limits_{k=1}^{n} q_k |\lambda|^{n-k} e^{-kh\alpha^{-1}\ln 10}}{|P(s)|}. \tag{4.5}$$

It is clear that for $|\lambda| \to \infty$ the right-hand member of (4.5) $\to 1$, but this is impossible. Consequently,

$$\alpha \geqq 0. \tag{4.6}$$

From (4.4) and (4.6) it follows that $\alpha = 0$. Thus,

$$\Delta A(\lambda) = P_n(\lambda).$$

COROLLARY 1. If $\Delta A(\lambda) = P_n(\lambda)$ has a finite number of roots, then every solution of system (1.3) may be represented in the form of a finite sum

$$X(t, \phi) = \sum_{k=1}^{n} Y_j(t, \phi); \quad \phi \in c,$$

where k is the number of different roots of the function $\Delta A(\lambda)$ to which correspond the characteristic groups of solutions.

COROLLARY 2. All the Theorems of § 3 may be carried over to the degenerate case without any modification.

Remark. From Theorem 1 it follows that the homogeneous solution of system (1.3) will be stable, but not asymptotically so, if among the roots of $\Delta A(\lambda)$ there are pure imaginary roots with simple elementary divisors. The homogeneous solution will be unstable if there are pure imaginary roots with nonsimple elementary divisors, or if at least one root has a positive real part. The remark formulated also applies to the case dealt with in § 3.

THE CORRELATION FUNCTIONS OF STOCHASTIC SOLUTIONS

FOR CLARITY of exposition we shall dwell on the fundamental definitions from the theory of probability.

A random quantity X is a quantity which may take various numerical values under different outcomes of experimentation, i.e., in other words, a random quantity is a function given on Ω, where Ω is the set of elementary events. The random quantity is considered as given, if on the set Ω is given a probabilistic measure and if for every real number λ the inequality $X(\omega) \leq \lambda$ defines the set of points ω, whose probability we shall denote as $F(\lambda)$, i.e.

$$F(\lambda) = P[X(\omega) \leq \lambda]. \tag{1}$$

The function $F(\lambda)$, defined by equality (1), is called the distribution function of the random quantity X. This function is nondecreasing continuous from the right and such that

$$\lim_{\lambda \to -\infty} F(\lambda) = 0, \quad \lim_{\lambda \to +\infty} F(\lambda) = 1.$$

Also the converse is true: every function satisfying the enumerated conditions may be considered as a distribution function of some random quantity.

In the theory of probability it is conventional to denote a random quantity by one letter without indicating the argument.

Together with the concept of a random quantity we shall consider also the concept of a random vector or, as they say, a multidimensional random quantity.

The set of numbers $(x_1, x_2, ..., x_n)$ is called an n-dimensional random vector or an n-dimensional random quantity.

The function

$$F(\lambda_1, \lambda_2, ..., \lambda_n) = P \left\{ \begin{array}{l} x_1 \leq \lambda_1, \\ x_2 \leq \lambda_2, \\ \cdots\cdots \\ \cdots\cdots \\ x_n \leq \lambda_n, \end{array} \right\}$$

is called an n-dimensional distribution function of a random vector.

An n-dimensional distribution function has the following properties:

1) it is a nondecreasing function of every argument;

2) it is continuous from the right with respect to every argument;

3) it satisfies the relations:

$$F(+\infty, +\infty, ..., +\infty) = 1 ;$$
$$\lim_{\lambda k \to -\infty} F(\lambda_1, \lambda_2, ..., \lambda_n) = 0$$

for any $k = 1, 2, ..., n$;

4) it satisfies the symmetry condition, i.e. for every transposition $i_1, i_2, ..., i_n$ of the numbers $1, 2 ..., n$, the equality

$$F(\lambda_{i_1}, \lambda_{i_2}, ..., \lambda_{i_n}) = F(\lambda_1, \lambda_2, ..., \lambda_n)$$

has to be satisfied;

5) it satisfies the condition of coordination: if $m < n$, then for all λ_{m+1} $\lambda_{m+2}, ..., \lambda_{m+n}$

$$F(\lambda_1, \lambda_2, ..., \lambda_m, \infty, ..., \infty) = F(\lambda_1, \lambda_2, ..., \lambda_m).$$

Also the converse assertion holds: every function satisfying the enumerated conditions may be considered as a distribution function of some random vector.

Alongside one-dimensional and multidimensional quantities one also considers random functions. We shall call a random function over T the totality of random quantities corresponding to all elements t of the set T, i.e. with the point of view adopted, this will be the function $X(\omega, t)$ of two variables $t \in T$ and $\omega \in \Omega$.

In the classical problems of the theory of probability, as the region T of values of t one takes a finite set. However, one gets to consider processes which include infinitely many random quantities, and the term "probabilistic process" is usually applied only in that case. Most important are the following two cases:

1) T is an infinite sequence. This type of process is called a process with a finite parameter;

2) T is an interval. We have a family of random quantities dependent on a continuous parameter. This type of process is called a process with a continuous parameter.

If in a random function $X(\omega, t)$ one fixes $\omega \in \Omega$, and considers as variable only the parameter t, then the function which then arises is called a sample function of the process. Sometimes sample functions of the process are called realizations, trajectories, or observed values of a random process. If the set T is finite or denumerable, the sample function will be, of course, a sample sequence.

If in $X(\omega, t)$ we fix t, then we obtain the value of the process (at the instant t).

In what follows, we shall omit the argument ω in the function $X(\omega, t)$.

A random function $X(t)$ we shall consider as given, if for every t of T the distribution function of the quantity $X(t)$ is defined

$$F_t(\lambda) = P\{X(t) \leq \lambda\}; \tag{2}$$

for every pair of elements t_1, t_2 from the set T will be defined the distribution function of the two-dimensional random quantity

$$\{X(t_1), X(t_2)\};$$
$$F_{t_1, t_2}(\lambda_1, \lambda_2) = P\{X(t_1) \leq \lambda_1, X(t_2) \leq \lambda_2\}; \tag{3}$$

and in general for any n elements $t_1, t_2, ..., t_n$ from the set T there will be defined an n-dimensional distribution function

$$F_{t_1, t_2, ..., t_n}(\lambda_1, \lambda_2, ..., \lambda_n) = P\{X(t_1) \leq \lambda_1, X(t_2) \leq \lambda_2, ..., X(t_n) \leq \lambda_n\}. \tag{4}$$

These functions are called finite-dimensional distributions of the process $X(\omega, t)$. Conversely: if one is given a system of functions possessing the properties of finite-dimensional distributions, then one may construct a process for which the distribution functions will be the functions of that system.

As another characteristic of the process serve the correlation functions

$$M[X^{m_1}(t_1)X^{m_2}(t_2)...X^{m_n}(t_n)] = K_{t_1, t_2, ..., t_n}^{m_1, m_2, ..., m_n} =$$

$$= \underbrace{\int_{-\infty}^{\infty}\int_{-\infty}^{\infty} ... \int_{-\infty}^{\infty}}_{n} \lambda_1^{m_1}\lambda_2^{m_2} ... \lambda_n^{m_n} \, dF(\lambda_1, \lambda_2, ..., \lambda_n).$$

For practical applications finite-dimensional distribution functions are rather unwieldy, and therefore one makes use of the system of correlation functions.

The methods of finding families of approximate solutions, as developed in Appendix I, play a very important role in the study of stochastic processes defined by means of differential equations with random right-hand members.

Say one is given a system of differential equations

$$\frac{dy_s}{dt} = F_s(t, y_1, ..., y_n, a_1, ..., a_m) \tag{5}$$

whose right-hand members are given for $t \in [0, T]$, $-\infty < y_i < +\infty$; $-\infty < a_i < +\infty$; real, continuous, and dependent on random quantities $a_1, ..., a_m$.

If one gives the system P of realizations of these random quantities then, following the method indicated in §1 of Appendix I, one may construct a stochastic process

$$y_s^{(P)} = \sum_{k=1}^{P} y_s^{(k)} P_k, \tag{6}$$

all the realizations of which are continuous and differentiable. Therefore one can compute the error

$$z_s = \frac{dy_s^{(P)}}{dt} - F_s(t, y_1^{(P)}, \ldots, y_n^{(P)}, a_1, \ldots, a_m), \tag{7}$$

which is also a stochastic process.

As $y_s^{(P)}$ is a polynomial in random quantities, one may compute all the correlation functions of that process. Thus, for example,

$$M_{(vs)}^{(P)} = \sum_{k=1}^{P} y_s^k M(P_k);$$

the second moments may be found according to the formulae

$$M\left[y_s^{(P)}(t_1) y_\sigma^{(P)}(t_2)\right] = \sum_{k=1}^{P} \sum_{l=1}^{P} y_s^{(k)}(t_1) y_\sigma^{(l)}(t_2) M(P_k P_l).$$

By $K(N, \bar{T})$ we shall denote the correlation function

$$M\left\{\left[y_1^{(P)}(t_{11})\right]^{n_{11}} \ldots \left[y_1^{(P)}(t_{1k})\right]^{n_{1k}} \ldots \left[y_n^{(P)}(t_{n1})\right]^{n_{n1}} \ldots \left[y_n^{(P)}(t_{nk})\right]^{n_{nk}}\right\},$$

where N is a matrix whose elements are nonnegative numbers n_{ij}, and $\bar{T}$ is a matrix whose elements are real numbers t_{ij} from the interval $[0, T]$. It is clear that $K(N, \bar{T})$ may be calculated in the general form, but in view of the cumbersome formula then obtained, it is not given here.

In order to clarify with what precision the correlation functions found describe the stochastic process defined by system (5), one has to study the error $z_s^{(P)}$. This can be done, as it is given explicitly.

If the system of equations contains random functions of time, then the above-mentioned method we shall apply only in the case when the random functions entering into the system of equations admit of a canonical expansion by means of a finite number of random quantities.

The general case may be investigated by means of the method indicated in §2 of Appendix I.

Say one is given a system of differential equations

$$\frac{dy_s}{dt} = F_s(t, y_1, \ldots, y_n, x_1, \ldots, x_m) \quad (s = 1, \ldots, n) \tag{8}$$

312 MATHEMATICS OF AUTOMATIC-CONTROL SYSTEMS

whose right-hand members are real continuous functions of their arguments given for $t \in [0, T]$, $-\infty < y_i < +\infty$; $-\infty < x_i < +\infty$; we shall also consider that the right-hand members of system (8) may be expanded in series in powers of $y_1, ..., y_n, x_1, ..., x_m$, everywhere uniformly convergent with respect to t.

Let us assume that $x_1, ..., x_n$ are random functions. We shall give a method of finding the correlation functions of the stochastic process, defined by the system of equations (8). For this we shall consider the system of equations

$$\frac{dy_s}{dt} = F_s(t, y_1, ..., y_n, bx_1, ..., bx_m) \quad (s = 1, ..., n).\tag{9}$$

It is clear that for $b = 1$ the system of equations (9) transforms into system (8).

We shall seek solution of the system (9) in the form of series in powers of the parameters b,

$$y = \sum_{k=0}^{\infty} y^{(k)} b^k,\tag{10}$$

where the $y_s^{(k)}$ are functions of time to be determined.

We shall substitute series (10) in system (9) and equate on the right and on the left the coefficients of the same powers of b. Then we shall obtain a sequence of systems of equations

$$\dot{y}_s^{(k)} = \sum_{i=1}^{n} p_{si}(t) y_i^{(k)} + R^{(k)} \quad (s = 1, ..., n; \quad k = 0, ..., \infty),\tag{11}$$

where

$$p_{si}(t) = \frac{\partial F_s}{\partial y_i}(t, y_1^{(0)}, ..., y_n^{(0)}).\tag{12}$$

The functions $y_s^{(0)}$ satisfy the system

$$\frac{dy_s}{dt} = F_s(t, y_1, ..., y_n, 0, ..., 0).\tag{13}$$

Let us seek the solution in the form of series (10) with the condition $y_s^{(k)} = 0$ for $t = 0$. Then the functions $y_s^{(k)}$ are defined by the initial condition $y_s^{(k)} = 0$ for $t = 0$.

As has been shown in §2 of Appendix I, the functions are expressed by means of the formulae

$$y_s^{(k)} = \int_0^t \sum_{j=1}^{n} y_{sj}(t, \tau) R_j^{(k)} \, d\tau.\tag{14}$$

We shall now dwell on the structure of the functions $R_s^{(k)}$. We shall note that system (11) may be obtained from system (9) if both of its members are differentiated k times with respect to the parameter b and thereupon one sets $b = 0$, as $d^k y_s / db^k = y_s^{(k)}$ for $b = 0$.

From this remark it follows that the functions $R_s^{(k)}$ are polynomials in the random functions $x_1, \dots, x_m$ and in the functions $y_s^{(l)}$, $l < k$; $s = 1, \dots, n$, whose coefficients are known functions of time. For example,

$$R_s^{(1)} = \sum_{i=1}^{n} \phi_{si}(t) x_i,$$

where

$$\phi_{si}(t) = \frac{\partial F_s}{\partial (bx_i)} \bigg|_{b=0}.$$

We shall assume that the functions $y_s^{(0)}$ have been found (see § 2 of Appendix I). Then formula (14) allows us to find all the functions $y_s^{(k)}$ For example,

$$y_s^{(1)} = \int_0^t \sum_{j=1}^{n} y_{s,j}(t, \tau) \left(\sum_{i=1}^{n} \phi_{ij}(\tau) x_i \right) d\tau.$$

From the last expressions it follows that they may be transformed to multiple integrals of homogeneous forms, dependent on random functions $x_1, \dots, x_m$ computed at various points, where the coefficients of these forms are known functions. Indeed, $y_s^{(1)}$ has the form described above; $y_s^{(2)}$ may be transformed into the same form if one makes use, for example, of the identity

$$1 = \int_0^\tau \int_0^\tau \frac{d\tau_1 d\tau_2}{\tau^2}.$$

The method of calculating the functions $R_s^{(k)}$ shows that they may be represented as a multiple integral of homogeneous forms of the type indicated above. Consequently, the functions $y_s^{(k)}$ $(k = 1, \dots, \infty)$ may be represented by the formulae $y_s^{(k)} = L_k[q_k(x_1, \dots, x_m)]$, where the symbol L_k denotes a multiple integral of multiplicity $2k - 1$, and q_k is a homogeneous form of the k-th degree in the random functions $x_1, \dots, x_m$, computed at $2k - 1$ different points. Thus

$$y_s^{(k)} = \int_0^t \int_0^{t_1} \cdots \int_0^{t_{2k-2}} \sum q^{m_1, \dots, m_\mu}(t, \tau_0, \tau_1, \dots, \tau_{2k-2}) \times$$

$$\times \prod [x_i(\tau_j)]^{m_{ij}} d\tau_0 d\tau_1 \dots d\tau_{2k-2}. \tag{15}$$

The summation under the integral sign is carried out over all nonnegative integral values of the quantities, such that $m_1 + m_2 + \ldots + m_\mu = k(\mu) = (2k-1)m$. The multiplication under the integral sign is carried out over all integral negative values of the quantities m_{ij} ($i = 1, \ldots, n; \, j = 0, \ldots, 2k-2$), such that $\sum m_{ij} = k$.

Into the argument we shall introduce the functions

$$y_s(q) = \sum_{k=0}^{q} y_s^{(k)} ; \tag{16}$$

$$z_s(q) = \frac{dy_s(q)}{dt} - F_s[t_1, y_1(q), \ldots, y_n(q), x_1, \ldots, x_m]. \tag{17}$$

Functions (16) may be considered as the stochastic solution of the original system if the stochastic process $z_s(q)$ is in some sense small in comparison with the process $y_s(q)$.

The simplicity of construction of the random functions (16) allows us to compute various correlation functions. Thus, for example,

$$M[y_s(q)] = \sum_{k=0}^{q} L_k[M(q_k)]. \tag{18}$$

Formula (15) allows us to give a more concrete version of the mathematical expectations of the functions $y_s(q)$, and namely

$$M[y_s(q)] = \sum_{k=1}^{q} \int_0^t \int_0^{t_1} \cdots \int_0^{t_{2k-2}} \sum q^{m_1, \ldots, \, m_{2k-2}}(t, \tau_0, \tau_1, \ldots, \tau_{2k-2}) +$$

$$\times K(N_k, T_k)\, d\tau_0 d\tau_1 \ldots d\tau_{2k-2} + y_s^{(0)}, \tag{19}$$

where $K(N_k, T_k)$ is the correlation function of the process $x_1, x_2, \ldots, x_m$; N_k is a matrix having m rows and $2k-1$ columns, whose elements are nonnegative integers m_{ij}; T_k is a matrix having m rows and $2k-1$ columns, where in each of its rows there stand one and the same numbers $\tau_0, \tau_1, \ldots, \tau_{2k-2}$.

In calculating the successive correlation functions, one does not meet difficulties of principle. However, the volume of computational labour grows.

This is the state of affairs relating to the application of the methods of expansion in series in powers of the parameters.

For the construction of stochastic solutions of a system of differential equations, one may also make use of the considerations brought in § 3 of Appendix I. That method gives a good result in the case when in the right-hand member of the system only random quantities enter, or else functions admitting of a canonical representation by means of power series with random coefficients.

APPENDIX IV

DESCRIPTION OF THE PROGRAMME

THE PROGRAMME is designed to work with matrices up to the order 16 inclusive. Information on the order of the matrix was given in cell 00047 of the memory unit (ZU) of the machine, and then a resetting of the programme in all the blocks for order n was carried out by the block "Preparation of the programme for n".

The number m—the dimensionality of the parameter space—was given in cell 0020 of the memory unit. Since the result was delivered at the output for fixed $m-2$ parameters, one has to choose for the calculations two varying parameters r and s.

After choosing r and s, the matrix b was computed for the chosen r and s and the maximum values of the varied parameters λ_r and λ_s. The subsequent computations are distributed in the order corresponding to the method described, as can be clearly seen from the flow diagram. For this b the quantity $S_p B^2$ was delivered at the output for initial λ_r and λ_s independent of $S_p B^2$, and then the coordinates of λ_r and λ_s were delivered only in the case that $S_p B^2 = 0$. For every result of the calculation of $S_p B^2$, the programme led to the block for calculating the next point of the interval (the block for the step along the contour), the exit from which led to the block for checking for return to the initial angle.

In the case of termination of the circuit along the contour, there was a check for the choice of (r, s), and if all the (r, s) had been exhausted, the introduction of the next matrix. If not all the (r, s) had been exhausted, then the choice of a new pair and the calculation of $P(\lambda_r, \lambda_s)$ were carried out.

If the circuit along the contour is not completed, then from the block "Check for return to the initial angle" the exit leads to the input of the block for computing the new value of the matrix $P(\lambda_r, \lambda_s)$ at the new point λ_r, λ_s.

It should be noted that the construction of the programme and also the modification of the method proposed in § 30, as applicable to the machine "Strela", was carried out by S. Ya. Fetialov, B. I. Korobochkin, and V. M. Yesipov.

315

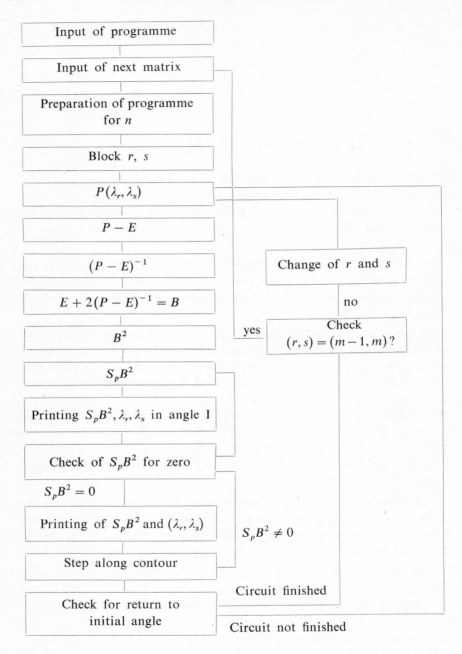

BLOCK DIAGRAM FOR THE PROGRAMME

APPENDIX V

SELF-OSCILLATIONS AND CONVERGENCE

§ 1. Self-oscillations of a general nature

LET US assume that the system of n differential equations

$$\dot{X} = F(X) \tag{1}$$

defines a dynamical system in E_n, having a bounded minimal set R. By $\rho(X)$ we shall denote the distance from the point X to the set R. The set R is called asymptotically stable if for an $\varepsilon > 0$ there exists a $\delta > 0$ such that if $\rho(X_0) < \delta$ then $\rho[X(t, X_0)] < \varepsilon$ for $t \geq 0$ and $\rho[X(t, X_0)] \to 0$ as $t \to +\infty$.

We shall say that the system has a *self-oscillatory trajectory* if it has an asymptotically stable bounded minimal set.

THEOREM 1. If the system (1) has a minimal bounded set R, then in order that it have a self-oscillatory trajectory, it is necessary and sufficient that there exist two functions V and W, real, continuous, given in $\rho(X) < r$, $r > 0$, and such that $V(X) = W(X) = 0$ for $x \in R$; $V(X) > 0$, $W(X) < 0$ for $\rho(X) > 0$ and $dV/dt = W$.

We shall say that a self-oscillatory trajectory in system (1) is stable under constantly acting perturbations if for an $\varepsilon > 0$ there exists a $\delta_1 > 0$ and $\delta_2 > 0$ such that if $|G(X_0)| < \delta_2$ and $\rho(X_0) < \delta_1$ then $\rho[X(t, X_0)] < \varepsilon$ for $t \geq 0$ where $X(t, X_0)$ is an integral curve of the system $\dot{X} = F(X) + G(X)$.

THEOREM 2. If $F(X)$ is differentiable and $G(X)$ is continuous in the neighbourhood of R, then the self-oscillatory trajectory in system (1) is stable under constantly acting perturbations.

The asymptotic stability of the set R is here defined from the geometric point of view. Therefore the trajectories entering in R may turn out to be unstable in the sense of Lyapunov and moreover: if, for example, a periodic self-oscillatory trajectory turns out to be asymptotically stable in the sense of Lyapunov then, in general, by an arbitrarily small change in the right-hand members of system (1) one may disturb that stability while retaining the property of self-oscillation.

The property of stability of the self-oscillation is sometimes called orbital stability.

§ 2. Almost-periodic oscillations under the action of an external perturbing force

In § 26 sufficient indications were given for the presence of periodic convergence based on the application of Theorem 54 from the work [63].

Here we carry out the study of the phenomenon of almost-periodic convergence. We shall consider the system

$$\dot{X} = F(X, t). \tag{2}$$

The vector function $F(X, t)$, given for all finite real values of its arguments, is real and continuous with coordinates which are almost-periodic functions in t for any fixed X and satisfies the Lipschitz condition with respect to X for a fixed constant.

THEOREM 3. In order that system (2) possess almost-periodic convergence, it is necessary and sufficient that the following conditions be fulfilled:

1) every solution of system (2) is bounded for $t \geq 0$;

2) for all $r > 0$ and $\varepsilon > 0$ there exists a $\delta > 0$ such that if $|X_0 - Y_0| < \delta$, then $|X(t, X_0, t_0) - X(t, Y_0, t_0)| < \varepsilon$ for $t \geq 0$ and $|X(t, X_0, t_0) - X(t, Y_0, t_0)| \to 0$ as $t \to +\infty$;

3) for a given X_0, for every $\varepsilon > 0$ there exist numbers l and T such that in every interval of length $l \in [\alpha, \alpha + l]$ there exists at least one number τ satisfying the conditions: $|X(t + \tau, X_0, t_0) - X(t, X_0, t_0)| < \varepsilon$ for $t \geq t_0 + T$ and $t + \tau \geq t_0 + T$.

If the X_0 are given, then the integral curve $X(t, X_0)$ is bounded for $t \geq t_0$ and, consequently, can be included in the sphere $|X| < r$. The numbers l and τ are the same as those which correspond to the right-hand members of system (2) according to the Definition of almost-periodicity [68].

THEOREM 4. Say

1) there exists a function $V(X, t)$ real, continuously differentiable on the set $|X| = r$ and $V(X, t) \leq V_0 < +\infty$ for $|X| = r$ and $t \in (-\infty, \infty)$; $V(X, t) \to +\infty$ as $|X| \to +\infty$ uniformly with respect to t;

2) for $|X| \geq r$ there holds the inequality

$$\frac{\partial V}{\partial t} + \sum_{s=1}^{\ } \frac{\partial V}{\partial x_s} F_s(x_1, \ldots, x_n, t) \leq 0;$$

3) there exists a real symmetric matrix A with positive characteristic values, such that the characteristic values of the matrix $G = B^*A + AB$ do not exceed $-\delta < 0$. The elements of the matrix B are defined by the equalities

$$b_{si} = \frac{\partial}{\partial x_i} F_s[x_i + \tau_s(y_i - x_i), t],$$

where τ_s are quantities determined from the formula for finite increments; — then system (2) possesses the property of almost-periodic convergence.

Let

$$F(X, t) = A(t)X + H(X, t) + P(t), \tag{3}$$

where $H(0, t) \equiv 0$ and $\left| H_s(X, t) - H_s(Y, t) \right| \leq \sum_{i=1}^{n} b_{si} \left| x_i - y_i \right|.$

By $Y(t, \tau)$ we shall denote the matrix of the fundamental system of solutions for the system $\dot{X} = A(t)X$, and we shall assume that

$$\left| y_{si}(t, \tau) \right| \leq e^{\lambda(t-\tau)} m_{si}, \quad \lambda < 0.$$

THEOREM 5. If the preceding conditions for the right-hand members of the system are satisfied and the characteristic values of the matrix $MB + \lambda E$ have negative real parts, then the system possesses the property of almost-periodic convergence. Here $M = \{m_{si}\}$, $B = \{b_{si}\}$.

We shall note that the phenomenon of almost-periodic convergence denotes the presence of a unique almost-periodic solution of system (2), uniform-asymptotically stable as a whole.

All the theorems formulated in this Appendix admit of certain generalizations, and their proofs may be carried out even with weaker conditions, for example, using approximately the same methods utilized in §§ 25 and 26.

1. I. G. PETROVSKIY, Lekhtsii po teorii obyknovennykh differntsialnykh uravneniy (Lectures on the Theory of Ordinary Differential Equations), *Gostekhteoretizdat*, 1952.

2. A. M. LYAPUNOV, Obshchaya zadacha ob ustoychivosti dvizheniya (The General Problem of Stability of Motion), *Gostekhteoretizdat*, 1950. [Available in French: "Problème général de la stabilité du mouvement", *Ann. Fac. Sci. Toulouse*, **9**, 1907. Reprinted in *Ann. Math. Study*, No. 17, 1949, *Princeton University Press*, Princeton, N. J.]

3. A. I. MAL'TSEV, Osnovy lineynoy algebry (Foundations of Linear Algebra), *Gostekhteoretizdat*, 1956.

4. F. RISS and B. SEKEFAL'VI-NAG', Lekhtsii po funktsional'nomu analizu (Lectures on Functional Analysis), *IL*, 1954. [Translated from Hungarian.]

5. K. P. PERSIDSKIY, "To the Theory of Stability of Solutions of Differential Equations", *Uspekhi matematicheskikh nauk* **I**, Nos. 5–6 (new series) *Ac. Sc. USSR*, 1946.

6. I. G. MALKIN, Teoriya ustoychivosti dvizheniya (Theory of Stability of Motion), *Gostekhteoretizdat*, 1952. [Available in English: AEC translation 3352, Dept. of Commerce U.S.A., 1958.]

7. JOSHIZAWA, "On the Stability of Solutions of the Differential Equation", *Mem. Col. Sci. Kyoto Univ.*, No. 1, 1955.

8. N. G. CHETAEV, Ustoychivost' dvizheniya (Stability of Motion), *Gostekhteoretizdat*, 1946.

9. V. I. ZUBOV, Metody A. M. Lyapunova i ikh primenenye (Methods of A. M. Lyapunov and their Application), *Izdatelstvo LGU*, 1957.

10. V. A. RUMYANTSEV, *Vestnik MGU*, No. 5, 1957.

11. N. P. ERUGIN, "On Some Questions of Stability of Motion and the Qualitative Theory of Differential Equations in the Large", *PMM* **XIV**, No. 5, 1950.

12. I. G. MALKIN, "To the Question of the Converse of Lyapunov's Theorem on Asymptotic Stability", *PMM* **XVIII**, No. 2, 1945.

13. A. I. LUR'YE, Nekotorye nelineynye zadachi teorii avtomaticheskogo regulirovaniya (Some Nonlinear Problems in the Theory of Automatic Control), *Gostekhizdat*, 1951. [English translation available: Her Majesty's Stationery Office, 1957.]

14. R. E. VINOGRADOV, "On a Criterion for Instability in the Sense of A. M. Lyapunov for Solutions of Linear Systems of Differential Equations", *DAN* **84,** No. 2, 1952.

15. TSZYAN' SYU-SEN', Tekhnicheskaya kibernetika (Engineering Cybernetics), *IL*, 1956.

16. N. P. ERUGIN, "Reducible Systems", *Trudy matem. inst. im. V. A. Steklova* **XIII,** 1946.

17. V. V. KHOROSHILOV, "On the Solution of Systems of Linear Differential Equations with a Regular Singularity", *Uchenye zapiski LGU*, No. 137, 1950.

18. L. I. DONSKAYA, "The Construction of a Solution of a Linear System in the Neighbourhood of a Singularity in Special Cases", *Vestnik LGU*, No. 6, 1952.

19. F. R. GANTMAKHER, Teoriya matrits (Theory of Matrices), *Gostekhteoretizdat*, 1954. [English translation available: Chelsey, New York, 1959; also Interscience, New York, 1959.]

20. I. M. RAPOPORT, O nekotorykh asymtoticheskikh metodakh v teorii differntsialnykh uravneniĭ (On Some Asymptotic Methods in the Theory of Differential Equations), *Izd. AN USSR*, Kiev, 1954.

21. G. N. DUBOSHIN, Osnovy teorii ustoĭchivosti dvizheniya (Foundations of the Theory of Stability of Motion), *Izdatel'stvo MGU*, 1952.

22. V. V.GOLUBEV, Lektsiya po analiticheskoĭ teorii differntsialnykh uravneniĭ (Lectures on the Analytic Theory of Differential Equations), *Gostekhteoretizdat*, 1950.

23. G. V. KAMENKOV, "On the Stability of Motion in a Finite Time-Interval", *PMM* **XVII**, No. 5, 1953.

24. A. A. LEBEDEV, "To the Problem of Stability of Motion in a Finite Time-Interval", *PMM* **XVIII**, No. 2, 1954.

25. V. V. STEPANOV, Kurs differentsialnykh uravneniĭ (Course in Differential Equations), *Gostekhteoretizdat*, 1953.

26. A. POINCARE, O krivykh opredelaemykh differntsialnymi uravneniyami (On Curves Defined by Differential Equations), *Gostekhizdat*, 1947. [Available in French.]

27. I. G. MALKIN, "Some Fundamental Problems in the Theory of Stability of Motion in Critical Cases", *PMM* **VI**, No. 6, 1942.

28. V. N. POSTNIKOV, K teorii ustoĭchivosti dvizheniya v kriticheskikh sluchayakh (To the Theory of Stability of Motion in the Critical Cases), Avtoreferat dissertatsii (Report on the Dissertation), 1942.

29. E. I. DIKHMAN, "On the Principle of Reduction", *Izvestiya AN Kazakhskoĭ SSR*, No. 97, 1950.

30. V. I. ZUBOV, "On a Method of Investigating the Stability of the Homogeneous Solution in Imaginary Cases", *PMM* **XXII**, No. 1, 1958.

31 V. I. ZUBOV, "On the Principle of Reduction", *DAN* **118**, No. 2, 1958.

32. G. V. KAMENKOV, "On the Stability of Motion", *Trudy Kazanskigo Aviatsionnogo Instituta*, No. 9, 1939.

33. E. A. BARBASHIN, "The Method of Intersections in the Theory of Dynamical Systems", *Matematicheskiĭ sbornik*, No. 29/2, 1951.

34. A. D. MYSHKIS, Lineĭnye differentsialnye uravneniya s zapazdyvayuschchim argumentom (Linear Differential Equations with a Lagging Argument), *Gostekhteoretizdat*, 1951.

35. L. E. EL'SGOL'TS, Kachestvennye metody v matematicheskom analize (Qualitative Methods in Mathematical Analysis), *Gostekhizdat*, 1955.

36. E. A. BARBASHIN, "On Two Methods of Proving Theorems on Stability in the First Approximation", *DAN* **111**, No. 1, 1957.

37. Yu. M. REPIN, "On the Stability of Solutions of Systems with a Lagging Argument" *PMM* **XXI**, No. 2, 1957.

38. N. N. KRASOVSKIY, "On the Application of the Second Method of Lyapunov to Equations with Lag", *PMM* **XX**, No. 3, 1956.

39. E. A. BARBASHIN and M. A. SKALKINA, "To the Problem of Stability in the First Approxi-mation", *PMM* **XIX**, No. 5, 1955.

40. E. A. BARBASHIN and N. N. KRASOVSKIY, "On the Existence of a Lyapunov Function in the Case of Asymptotic Stability in the Large", *PMM* **XVIII**, No. 3, 1954.

41. B. S. RAZUMIKHIN, "On the Stability of Systems with Lag", *PMM* **XX**, No. 4, 1956.

42. N. N. KRASOVSKIY, "On the Asymptotic Stability of Systems with Lag", *PMM* **XX**, No. 4, 1956.

43. N. N. KRASOVSKIY, "On the Stability of Quasilinear Systems with Lag", *DAN* **110**, No. 3, 1958.

44. H. POINCARE, "Sur les propriétés des fonctions définies par les équations differentielles", *J. Ecole Polytech.*, Cahier 45, 1878.

45. E. PICARD, Traité d'Analyse, **3**, 1898.

46. J. HORN, "Gewönliche Differentialgleichungen beliebiger ordnung", Leipzig, 1934.

47. N. I. BENDIKSON, "On Curves Defined by Differential Equations", *Uspekhi matematicheskikh nauk*, No. 9, 1941.

48. I. I. VOROVICH, "On Certain Cases of the Existence of Periodic Solutions", *DAN* **110**, No. 2, 1956.

49. V. V. NEMYTSKIY and V. V. STEPANOV, Kachestvennaya teoriya differntsialnykh uravneniï (Qualitative Theory of Differential Equations), *Gostekhteoretizdat*, 1949. [Available in English: translation of 2nd ed., *Princeton University Press*, Princeton, N. J., 1960.]

50. N. N. KRASOVSKIY, "On the Stability in the First Approximation", *PMM* **XIX**, No. 5, 1955.

51. A. D. GORBUNOV, "On Estimating the Coordinates of the Solutions of Systems of Ordinary Differential Equations", Vestnik *MGU*, No. 5, 1954.

52. E. P. POPOV, Dinamika sistem avtomaticheskogo regulirovaniya (Dynamics of Automatic Control Systems), *Gostekhizdat*, 1954.

53. V. S. PUGACHEV, Teoriya sluchaynykh funktsiy i ee primemenie k zadacham avtomaticheskogo upravleniya (Theory of Random Functions and its Application to Problems of Automatic Control), *Gostekhteoretizdat*, 1957.

54. V. L. GONCHAROV, Teoriya interpolirovaniya i priblizheniya funktsiy (Theory of Interpolation and Approximation of Functions), *Gostekhizdat*, 1954.

55. R. BELLMAN, "On the Existence and Boundedness of Solutions of Nonlinear Differential – Difference Equations", *Ann. of Math.* **50,** 1949.

56. E. M. WRIGHT, "The Linear Differential Equations", *Proc. Roy. Soc. Edinburgh* A **62,** I, 1949.

57. I. A. FRID, "On the Stability of Solutions of Linear Differential Equations with Lag in the Critical Case", *Uchenye zapiski MGU* **VIII,** No. 181, 1955.

58. A. I. MARKUSHEVICH, Teoriya analiticheskikh funktsiy (Theory of Analytic Functions), *Gostekhteoretizdat*, 1950.

59. M. A. LAVRENT'YEV and B. V. SHABAT, Metody teorii funkntsiy kompleksnogo peremennogo (Methods in the Theory of Functions of a Complex Variable), *Gostekhteoretizdat*, 1956.

60. A. I. KITOV, Elektronnye tsifrovye mashiny (Electronic Digital Machines), *Izdatel'stvo "Sovetskoe radio"*, 1956.

61. A. A. ANDRONOV, Sobranie trudov (Collected Works), *Izd. AN SSSR*, 1956.

62. I. G. MALKIN, Metody Lyapunova i Poincaré v teorii nelineïnykh kolebaniï (Methods of Lyapunov and Poincaré in the Theory of Nonlinear Oscillations), *Gostekhteoretizdat*, 1949.

63. ZLAMAL MILOS, "Über die Stabilität der nichtlinearen erzwungenen Schwingungen", *Chech. Mat. Jour.* **4,** No. 1, 1954.

64. A. A. FEL'DBAUM, "An Automatic Optimizer", Automatika i telemekhanika, **XIX,** No. 8, 1958.

65. J. B. PYNE, "Linear Programming on an Electronic Analogue Computer", *Communications and Electronics*, May 1956.

66. N. M. MATWEEV, Metody integrovaniya obyknovennykh differentsialnykh uravneniï (Methods of Integrating Ordinary Differential Equations), *Izd. LGU*, 1955.

67. N. YA. LYASHCHENKO, "To the Problem of Asymptotic Stability of Solutions of Nonlinear Systems of Differential Equations", *DAN* **104,** No. 2, 1955.

68. B. I. LEVITAN, Pochti-periodicheskie funktsii (Almost-Periodic Functions), *Gostekhteoretizdat*, 1936.

[The following short supplementary bibliography of related works in the English language was added by the translator.]

69. R. E. BELLMAN, "Stability Theory of Differential Equations", *McGraw-Hill*, New York, 1953.

70. I. FLÜGGE-LOTZ, "Discontinuous Automatic Control Systems", *Princeton University Press*, Princeton, N. J., 1953.

71. G. C. NEWTON, JR., L. A. GOULD, AND J. F. KAISER, "Analytical Design of Feedback Controls", *John Wiley*, New York, 1957.

72. A. S. HOUSEHOLDER, "The Approximate Solution of Matrix Problems", *J. Assoc. Comp. Machinery* **5,** 1958, pp. 205–243.

73. R. E. KALMAN, "On Physical and Mathematical Mechanisms of Instability in Nonlinear Automatic Control Systems", *Trans. ASME* **79,** 1957, pp. 553–556.

74. J. P. LASALLE, "The Time-Optimal Control Problem", "Contributions to Nonlinear Oscillations" V (book), *Annals of Mathematics Studies, Princeton University Press*, Princeton, N. J., 1959.

75. R. E. KALMAN AND J. E. BERTRAM, "Control System Analysis and Design Via the Second Method of Lyapunov", *National Automatic Control Conference*, Dallas, Texas, 1959.

INDEX